JOHN CATT'S

Which London School? & the South-East

2021/22

32nd Edition
Editor: Jonathan Barnes

Published in 2021 by
John Catt Educational Ltd,
15 Riduna Park,
Melton, Suffolk IP12 1QT UK
Tel: 01394 389850   Fax: 01394 386893
Email: enquiries@johncatt.com
Website: www.johncatt.com

Designed and typeset by John Catt Educational Limited

**A CIP catalogue record for this book is available from the
British Library.**

ISBN: 978 1 913622 59 6

Contacts
Editor
Jonathan Barnes

Advertising & School Profiles
Tel: +44 (0) 1394 389850
Email: sales@johncatt.com

Distribution/Book Sales
Tel: +44 (0) 1394 389863
Email: booksales@johncatt.com

Contents

GIVE THEM
THE PROTECTION
THEY DESERVE

Rest assured knowing your children are protected with
the same level of cover as you, at no extra cost*.

Just one way we're with you and your family.
Today, for the everyday and whatever's next.

Search **Bupa Global** or call **0333 355 7683**

COMMITTED TO YOUR
HEALTH AND WELLBEING

This pandemic has demonstrated the value and resilience of independent schools in London

Harriet Connor-Earl, Headmistress of St Mary's School Hampstead, looks at the lessons learned over the past year

Back in March 2020, no one could imagine the far-reaching repercussions that a national lockdown would have on the children of today. Nor could any educationalist predict the additional challenges that would be faced by all schools during this time.

Immediately, I set to work with my Senior Leadership Team to deliver an enriching distance learning programme, while still keeping the school open for children of key workers. But, this was just the first of many unforeseen tests.

At times, these tests seemed formidable, but never unmanageable. We put in place contingency plans to ensure that pupil numbers remained strong, staff morale stayed high, pupils were fully supported and an exciting curriculum was delivered that fully stretched the children academically. Alongside this, we successfully prepared our Year 6 girls for their 11+ exams.

As we reflect upon the last year, it has become clear that this period has amplified the indomitable spirit and determination of the pupils, staff and parents at St Mary's School. And, I know we're not alone.

Independent schools in London, and all over the country, rose to these complex and multifaceted demands swiftly and with professionalism. It's this rapid response and determination that our children's education and well-being would not be penalised that highlighted the inestimable value of independent education.

Before a global pandemic was even a possibility, many independent schools had implemented significant investment programmes to deliver the most up-to-date teaching for pupils. Tools such as Microsoft Teams and Google Classroom were being used, albeit on a smaller, ad-hoc scale.

As everyone was compelled to make the transition from the physical to the virtual world, it was this forward-thinking investment in technology that enabled entire schools to immediately pivot to accessing engaging lessons remotely. In turn, we must recognise that our school communities were incredibly fortunate to have ready access to computers, fast internet and the support of capable families who also adapted at pace.

Academic excellence is a key expectation of any independent school. But, it is the extra-curricular opportunities that play a crucial role in our children's development; helping them to discover their strengths and passions.

From the first day of lockdown learning, teachers delivered a full timetable across a wide-ranging curriculum. I was delighted that music, art and sports continued to be an essential part of online school life. In particular, pupils in Nursery and pre-prep years benefited from the routine and personalised learning that they received from their teachers.

Academic excellence is a key expectation of any independent school. But, it is the extra-curricular opportunities that play a crucial role in our children's development; helping them to discover their strengths and passions.

WWW.STORAGETRUNKS.CO.UK

**UK MANUFACTURER OF BOARDING, SHIPPING AND STORAGE TRUNKS
20 SIZES IN OVER 100 STYLES AND TRIMS**

LARGE BOARDING TRUNKS

MEDIUM BOARDING TRUNKS

SCHOOL TUCK BOXES

Info@storagetrunks.co.uk

Trunks direct from the factory with a lifetime guarantee

Sales office hours: 01702 216 222 - Outside office hours: 07768 364 726

Logicline Trunks Ltd, Unit 3 High House Farm, Barling Road, Barling, Essex SS3 0LZ

Online provision has helped pupils to increase their independence and take more ownership of their learning journey. This is a vital skill as they move through school and life more generally.

We've discovered other valuable lessons along the way.

In June 2020, when all schools were first allowed to re-open for specific years, but limited to bubbles of fifteen, the smaller class sizes enjoyed within the independent sector enabled us to welcome these age groups back straightaway. This meant we were able to work easily and safely within the guidelines and offer a continuous education for pupils.

The flexibility of the slightly longer school day in independent schools has meant that we have been able to modify our timetable for the benefit of the children, especially after we moved back to online learning in January 2021. Staff identified the impact of the shorter daylight hours on pupils. We responded by adding three sessions a week for well-being during the middle of the day. This allowed families to enjoy 90 minutes to come away from their computers to take part in fun and rewarding activities together.

Furthermore, by moving to interactive Virtual Visits, the admissions process has been enhanced for prospective parents at the start of their school search. Although online events are never able to truly convey the joy of walking through the doors of a school and meeting the wonderful pupils, the feedback received is overwhelmingly positive. The flexibility of the online approach means that more frequent and convenient events can be set up across lunchtimes, evenings and weekends to increase accessibility for working parents, especially those still overseas.

Outstanding independent schools will always endeavour to support pupils in all areas of their lives. We have the resources to care for and nurture them as unique individuals. Our overriding hope is that pupils will emerge from this time strengthened and having acquired new talents.

Nevertheless, independent schools are more than the teaching that happens within the building. A school is a community of people who come together to achieve a common goal and a shared interest in providing the very best opportunities for the children. The teachers at St Mary's School Hampstead and the pupils under their care have continued to thrive in these challenging circumstances by virtue of our resilience and commitment as a community.

The varied technology found in many independent schools has also proved instrumental in overcoming restrictions. Pupils normally enjoy a plethora of trips to London's museums and galleries to support our creative curriculum. Thanks to the VR headsets in the St Mary's STEAM Centre, our programme of trips has continued. Children can visit anywhere in the world, virtually, at the click of a button.

Far from technology replacing the skills of a teacher, this experience has highlighted how our talented and dedicated staff have enthusiastically deployed technologies. Feedback was transformed too. Written marking remained, but was enhanced by voice notes and video messages. The acceleration of digital learning will allow us to embrace a blended approach, such as setting stimulating work on Google Classroom when a teacher is away. The possibilities are seemingly endless, and certainly exciting.

Although online learning is no substitute for the classroom, the benefits for many pupils have been tangible. Not only have children increased their technological fluency, but it has also inspired creativity and collaboration.

St Mary's School Hampstead offers an outstanding and inspirational Catholic education for girls 2-11 years. Find out more about this remarkable school at: www.stmh.co.uk

You can also see the school's profile on page 78

How to use this guide

Are you looking for...

Help and advice?
If so, take a look at our editorial section (pages 5-48). Here you will find articles written by experts in their field covering issues you may well come across when choosing a school for your child.

A school or college in a certain geographical area?
Then you need to go to page D115 to find the directory page reference to a particular area. We suggest that you look first in the directory for basic information about all the schools in each region, complete with contact details, so that you will be better informed about the choices available to you. From this section you will be directed to more detailed information in the profile section, where this is available.

A certain type of school or college in a particular area?
Look in the directories for the area you want (again, you can find the directory page reference on D115). Underneath each school listed you will find icons that denote different types of schools or qualifications that they offer. You can find a key to these icons on the following page; this key is repeated at the front of each section of the directory.

Schools featured in this guidebook are also profiled on its accompanying website: www.whichlondonschool.co.uk and www.schoolsearch.co.uk

School profiles include embedded Twitter feed and YouTube/Vimeo video, direct links to email, website and social media. Users can search by region, county, or postcode; and by age, gender and day/boarding.

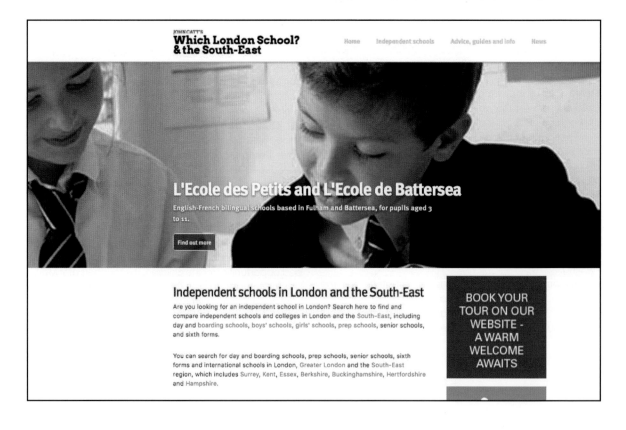

A specific school or college?

If you know the name of the school or college but are unsure of its location, simply go to the index at the back of the guide where you will find all the schools listed alphabetically. You will find that some page numbers are prefixed with the letter D, this denotes that the school appears in the directory section. Schools with page numbers not prefixed by the letter D are those that have chosen to include a fuller school profile, which will provide you with much more extensive information.

Maps?

See pp 50, 85 and 91 for maps of London, Greater London, and the South-East. There are also maps within the directory sections on D116 (Central London), D137 (Greater London) and D143 (South-East).

More information on relevant educational organisations and examinations?

Look in the examinations and qualifications section and the useful organisations section, both located towards the back of the guide.

Key to directory

County	**Wherefordshire**
Name of school or college	**College Academy**
Indicates that this school has a profile	*For further details see p. 12*
Address and contact number	Which Street, Whosville, Wherefordshire AB12 3CD
	Tel: 01000 000000
Head's name	**Head Master:** Dr A Person
School type	**Type:** Coeducational day & boarding
Age range	**Age range:** 11–18
Number of pupils. B = boys G = girls	**No. of pupils:** 660 B330 G330
Fees per annum. Day = fees for day pupils. WB = fees for weekly boarders. FB = fees for full boarders.	**Fees:** Day £11,000 WB £16,000 FB £20,000
	(ii) (A) (ii) (£) (/) (16)

Key to directory icons (abridged)

Key to symbols:
- (♦) Boys' school
- (ii) Coeducational school
- (♦) Girls' school
- (✦) International school

Schools offering:
- (A) A levels
- (♦) Boarding accommodation
- (£) Bursaries
- (16) Entrance at 16+

- (IB) International Baccalaureate
- (✐) Learning support
- (16) Tutorial/sixth form college
- (✿) Vocational qualifications

London is our classroom

How Fulham School makes full use of its prime city location

Situated in the heart of a bustling, culturally rich part of West London, Fulham School is an independent, co-educational through-school with three individual sections. Each section has its own building within close vicinity to each other. The fourth 'building' of this prestigious school is London itself – providing a wealth of uniquely exciting opportunities for children of all ages to make the most of.

Fulham Pre-Prep School for students in Reception to Year 2, rated Outstanding in 2020 by Ofsted for their Early Year provision, is situated on the south side of Fulham, close to the river. Fulham Prep School on Greyhound Road is just a 25-minute walk away.

. Fulham Senior School (with a brand new Sixth Form opening soon), for Years 9-13 is found on Chesilton Road close to the High Street and all central locations.

Chris Cockerill, Head of Fulham Senior, knows all too well how important it is for pupils to start immersing themselves in the opportunities both in and outside of

the school campus as soon as possible. He says, "From the first year in Senior School, pupils start making choices about what they study, with GCSE options considered in the Spring term of Year 9. By the end, they are making the momentous choice of what to study or do next as adults."

This is where the School's locations come into their own – allowing exposure to a multitude of different industries, facilities and resources so that pupils can choose their own path as soon as possible, helping them to stay connected and take ownership of their education from early on.

Immediately outside each campus, lies a set of opportunities that only the capital city can offer. Every subject group and choice of career is covered: from drop-in visits to the BBC or SKY studios to explore the world of journalism and media; access to world class rowing clubs on the River Thames; performing in high quality local theatre productions or sitting in on recording sessions as an introduction to the performance arts and the music industry; to showcasing art projects in famous art galleries or doing studio visits to begin life as an artist.

Despite its urban location, Fulham School is surrounded by green spaces where pupils can take their sport to a higher level. The famous Kings House Sports Grounds are just a short bus journey away in Barnes, where all pupils enjoy their games afternoons. There is also an abundance of parks nearby, such as Gilbert Common, Parsons Green, Bishops Park and Hurlingham Park, where pupils play and learn through teacher-led sessions. Fulham Football Club also brings a great deal of pride to the school, with pupils of all ages enjoying a fervent support for their local team.

Teachers can also make the most of opportunities as they arise: the Senior School Librarian arranged for pupils to study at the university library at Kings College London where she was doing her Masters; the Art Teacher has had exhibitions at Tate Modern and Saatchi galleries so she took pupils to see her work as well as exploring the rest of the galleries; the Drama Teacher took pupils to the Globe and local niche smaller theatres near to the School's grounds.

Seizing opportunities is very much a Fulham School trait instilled in all pupils. Speaking to local businesses and exploring all that local facilities have to offer helps pupils see the relevance of their education and how it can shape their careers and dreams – whether they're keen to be a chef or play music professionally.

All Fulham Schools from Pre-prep to Sixth Form organise experiential trips and visits to enhance the curriculum, such as annual visits to Bletchley Park for Computer Science pupils. While Pre-Prep, Prep and Senior trips are supervised, Sixth Form pupils are encouraged to make the most of elements around them, preparing them for university life, such as research and studying at Fulham Library which is just a three-minute walk away from the Senior School.

Even during lockdown, pupils have still been engaging, safely, with all that is on offer. Notably drama has successfully transferred to the virtual world, with most West End and National theatres putting on online performances. Pupils have been regularly engaging with online shows, which has helped keep a sense of normality.

To look after pupils' wellbeing during lockdown, an online timetable was delivered that perfectly matched their existing curriculum, so pupils could experience a full day as usual, keeping to their usual routine that started

at 8.30am and ended at 4.15pm. Extra-curricular clubs were run online so pupils could connect with their peers.

Being part of the Inspired Education group of schools also meant that Fulham School could benefit from best practices and shared learning from the Heads of over 60 international schools. Vietnam went into lockdown first, and much could be learned from seeing how they set assignments, marked and assessed work to the same high levels as normal.

To combat the effects of sitting at a screen all day, Inspired Education hosted an interschool physical challenge – a virtual 3K running event to get pupils, staff and families away from their screens and out in the fresh air. Fulham School were proud to come out on top and they used the competition to link sport and exercise to their mental and physical wellbeing.

As Neill Lunnon Head of Fulham Prep says, "Creating a happy school is the most important part, with happy pupils making the most of every opportunity, flourishing and thriving in and out of the classroom."

The new Sixth Form building is due to open after lockdown is lifted, with state of the art classrooms and science labs. Most of the Capital's favourite institutions and businesses will still remain, while new opportunities and ventures will arise – leaving Fulham School ready to pounce and enjoy London as their biggest classroom once again.

For more information about Fulham School see page 58

Supporting your child's mental health during the COVID-19 pandemic

Help and advice is available if your family is struggling

The past few months have been disorientating for children, with COVID-19 disrupting every aspect of normal life. For the second time, bedrooms have become classrooms, parents turned into teachers and packed after school schedules have been put on pause. And for many children, the pandemic has had a negative impact on their mental health.

According to a study of more than 10,000 parents and carers from the University of Oxford[1], children have experienced a range of emotional difficulties in lockdown, including feeling more unhappy and anxious.

This is corroborated by recent research[2] among high net worth parents from premium health insurer Bupa Global that found nearly one in five (18%) saw signs of anxiety in their families during lockdown.

But there are some steps that parents can follow to help their children cope with this challenging period.

Acknowledge their frustrations

Parents instinctively lean towards best-case-scenario responses when talking to their children. However, Bupa Global Lead Physician Dr Naveen Puri

---

1   According to research among 10,000 parents as part of the Co-SPACE (COVID-19 Supporting Parents, Adolescents, and Children in Epidemics) survey led by experts at the University of Oxford in 2020: https://www.ox.ac.uk/news/2020-06-16-children-show-increase-mental-health-difficulties-over-covid-19-lockdown

2   According to Bupa Global's Executive Wellbeing Index, conducted by Opinium Research in July and August 2020 among 100 high net worth individuals from the UK defined as those with over £1 million (or market currency equivalent) in annual salary and investable assets.

suggests that honest and open discussions are often more successful.

"Parents can't control what happens in the wider world, but they can control how they communicate with their children about any challenges they are facing. Though it may feel difficult at the time, children will benefit more from honest conversations in an understanding home environment."

Acknowledge that both homeschooling and coping with an eventual return to the classroom may be a struggle and chat through their frustrations (however minor) on a daily basis. Simply knowing they have your support and understanding can make a significant difference to their overall perspective on school.

Be mindful of your words

A 2019 study by charity Time to Change[3] found that the majority of young people (73%) want to talk about mental health but can't find the right words. This means it's important for parents to listen and respond to any school related concerns without judgement. Run through the conversation in your head, or with a friend beforehand, to ensure you feel comfortable with the topics you are tackling and to help avoid them closing down.

Have difficult conversations on neutral ground

If you recognise signs of stress and anxiety, then early intervention is key. Avoid their bedroom or the kitchen table and find a neutral space – such as an early evening walk – to open up the conversation.

"Be sure to let them properly process the chat," advises Dr Puri. "Let them know they can come back to you later on if needs be."

If your child boards, share your concerns with their Housemaster so they can monitor the situation until the next visit home and keep in regular contact via video calls.

Put the right support in place

Don't be afraid to get help if your family is struggling to cope. Bupa Global has multiple resources for those affected by mental health issues – including its Global Virtual Care service which provides confidential access to a global network of doctors available 24/7 in multiple languages – enabling you or your child to speak to a specialist at a time that suits you.

Bupa Global has a range of health insurance plans, whatever your needs. For families, the Elite Health Plan is ideal as it covers two children up to the age of 10 at no additional cost, subject to underwriting.

Seeking medical advice is necessary for a child who is suffering, but speaking to a professional yourself is also a great way to learn how to best support their condition, treatment and needs.

 **Global**

*For more information about Bupa Global premium health plans visit **bupaglobal.com/withyou** or talk to our Private Client team today on **0333 355 7683**.*

---

3   According to a survey of over 2,000 16 to 24-year-olds conducted for mental health campaign Time to Change in October 2019: https://www.time-to-change.org.uk/news/new-research-finds-nearly-1-5-young-people-experiencing-mental-health-problem-have-dropped-out

Bringing skills to the fore

Wendy Barrett, Headmistress of Cobham Hall School, considers how schools must become 'inspirational champions of lifelong learning'

Any school website will tell you that they equip their students for life beyond the school gates, but in 2021 what does that mean? Does that mean their students leave with a string of top grades, or with the ability to adapt to life's ever-evolving, ever-changing nature? Which is more essential for life in the 21st Century, where a report by the McKinsey Global Institute determined that "60% of employers said that new graduates were not adequately prepared for the world of work" and that "40% of employers have difficulty filling entry level vacancies because applicants lack soft skills"? 2020 certainly required us all to have the ability to adapt to remote working, remote teaching and learning, and limited social interaction. With the global pandemic descending with alarming speed and disrupting virtually every facet of life as we knew it, strong mental health, and character traits such as resilience, adaptability and kindness had never been more important.

The World Economic Forum stated as far back as 2015 that 'The gap between the skills people learn and the skills people need is becoming more obvious, as traditional learning falls short of equipping students with the knowledge they need to thrive. Good leadership skills as well as curiosity are also important for students to learn for their future jobs.' In 2020, they published the top ten skills required by 2025, and of these, just two link to specific curriculum-based skills (Technology use, design, programming and control) whilst the remainder are soft skills including active learning, complex problem-solving, creativity, resilience and leadership.

The pandemic created a multitude of problems for schools and their students. Not only having to adapt to a new way of educating, but with the cancellation of examinations both this year and last year, there was a heavy emotional toll for many students. What would happen with their university offers, conditional on

The last year has proven how critical both good mental health and polished life skills are; that they are essential and, it could be argued, proved to be much more irreplaceable than an examination outcome.

examination grades? What would happen to their future career plans without GCSE and A Level grades to fall back on? Yet perhaps, hidden with this gloomy forecast, was a nugget of potential. What if schools could become less examination-focused and more character-driven?

Elke Edwards, Founder and Creative Director, Ivy House London, believes it's time for this discussion, with COVID-19 being the catalyst for change. "One of the key changes," she states in Ivy House white paper 'It's Time', "has been an increased focus on the human side of education. A focus on resourcing students with the knowledge and skills to deal with change, navigate uncertainty and stay well; skills that are not only of critical importance right now but set students up for success in the future."

At Cobham Hall, we have always firmly believed that there is more to education than the confines of the classroom; that it is our role to support each student in the development of every facet of their character. As a result, character education is woven throughout our curriculum and co-curricular activities with students encouraged to step beyond their comfort zones, try new things and develop key skills – determination, perseverance, resilience and teamwork to name but a few. Equally, our pastoral provision provides students the tools and capability to take the gains of these skills and apply them to support, strengthen and maintain their mental health. Students are encouraged to be able to recognise both their own and their friends' mental health needs, with the understanding that by looking after our students' emotional, social and physical wellbeing, they feel happier and will thrive.

Yet there was one more step to take; it is one thing for students to be encouraged to use their initiative and take risks within the safety of a lesson, but quite another to apply those skills to 'real-life' situations. At what point does nurturing the development of soft skills become

something tangible? At what point do students have that 'Eureka!' moment when they realise there is more in them than they think, as Cobham Hall's motto declares?

This is why Cobham Hall introduced a 'Life Skills' curriculum, dedicated time within timetables to actively develop – and crucially, provide opportunities to hone – vital skills needed to compete and thrive in an ever-changing world. Mapped to our Personal Discovery Framework, modules have been designed to enhance social skills, such as teamwork, empathy, collaboration, and cultural awareness, as well as personal skills including problem-solving, presenting and public speaking, initiative, communication and resilience.

Within this practical-based 'Life Skills' curriculum, students will be working on exciting Dragons' Den-style projects, which will see them develop products and learn about market research, marketing, costing, presentation skills, financial capability, team work and leadership. There will also be competitive teamwork projects raising money for local charities; projects involving event organisation; learning sign language; and discovering local history. Risk taking and personal development are key to these projects, and we aim for the students to be as autonomous as possible. We also plan to develop students' social skills by enhancing links with, and providing opportunities to become an active member of, the local community. As part of this curriculum, we aim to embed aspirational thinking in our students and encourage them to break any remaining barriers imposed on them because of their gender and so will be inviting inspirational female speakers from a variety of fields to speak about their careers and experiences.

The last year has proven how critical both good mental health and polished life skills are; that they are essential and, it could be argued, proved to be much more irreplaceable than an examination outcome. Cobham Hall aims to provide a world-class education for students of all abilities, regardless of background, that enables them to be successful in a rapidly changing world.

It is by embracing students as individuals, and working to their strengths as well as supporting their weaknesses, that schools can become inspirational champions of lifelong learning. By providing as many varied and exciting opportunities as possible to sharpen crucial life skills, schools will have students that leave their settings with the grades they need to follow their chosen career paths, but importantly, also with the skills essential to adapt to and deal with situations and careers that no-one can currently prepare for or imagine. What a difference a year can make!

For more information about Cobham Hall School, see page 94

Boarding at school – the benefits for your family

Antonia Beary, Headmistress of Mayfield School, explains how there are many ways of boarding

Boarding encourages education in its widest sense, and complements what happens during the day and in the classroom. Moreover, it makes everything much more accessible: no travel to music lessons, ballet and dance rehearsals, drama or sports training. Still more valuable is the range of activities and excursions which take place. Teenagers' default can be to stay in their rooms, on their phones or computers, often until late at night. However, a boarding programme allows girls to be involved in activities that encourage them to be healthy, broaden their horizons and help them look out, beyond themselves. Weekend boarding provision provides the sort of events, activities and trips that you would like to provide for your daughter, but don't quite have the time, expertise or connections. You might rue the fact that she wouldn't be seen walking round an art gallery with her parents, but it tends to be true that she is happier to discuss the context of female impressionist artists with her friends. At the other end of the spectrum, nights round a campfire with marshmallows, after the challenges of an expedition, are where friendships are forged. That is what boarding can offer. Such a network of friends, often from differing backgrounds and cultures, is an advantage when you are performing on a global stage, but more so

when you need someone to celebrate or commiserate the inevitable joys and sorrows of adult life.

Mayfield, like many boarding schools, has a thriving sporting programme. All girls are encouraged to be involved in a wide range of sports and the skills they learn from winning and, just as importantly, from losing, provide important tools for negotiating life's inevitable challenges. Everyone plays, and so there are opportunities to be in a team to suit your proficiency and competitiveness. At Mayfield, staff very much encourage 'sport for life' so we want girls to enjoy being active and continue well after they have left school.

Providing a wider engagement with the society in which we live is another advantage of boarding. Whether it be listening to the reminiscing of older local villagers, as part of Mayfield's Life Stories Project, helping primary school children with their literacy and numeracy, or volunteering at the local hospice, the opportunities for young people to look beyond themselves and to give something of themselves back are just as valuable – if not more so – for them as for the individuals to whom they offer support. Our most recent initiative is the Lockdown Listening Programme in which the girls have been encouraged to reach out to members of their family or

Girls often comment, with a smile, that boarding helps them appreciate their parents just that little bit more!
Antonia Beary, Headmistress

local community who may be feeling isolated or lonely (after consultation with their parents or guardians), to see if they would welcome a regular chat on the phone. This has been a great success and I continue to be impressed by news of the girls proactively supporting friends and neighbours, and I hope everyone will gain something from the intergenerational friendships developed and perspectives broadened. For some, an ostensibly unimportant conversation can provide a lifeline, and I hope our girls realise the positive impact they can have.

Becoming self-sufficient is another value and girls often comment, with a smile, that boarding helps them appreciate their parents just that little bit more! An increasingly high drop-out rate from university means that admissions tutors are keen to offer places to those who are able to cope independently with managing the workload and the social pressures of university life. It's not just about being able to work the washing machine (although that it a distinct advantage), but about learning to balance your work commitments and, most importantly, learning to live with and appreciate, or at the least tolerate, those with different strengths and weaknesses. Such social skills (I feel 'soft skills' is something of a misnomer), and resilience, are part of the portfolio of skills that employers are increasingly prioritising as crucial for success in the modern workplace, and for society as a whole.

Underestimate a girl at your peril: girls can and do cope well with and enjoy boarding. While of course it is normal to get homesick initially – I would worry if they didn't – being able to cope with this sort of emotion is an important step towards maturity: it contributes to making you stronger and more resilient, and also strengthens bonds with your friends. Communication is now so much easier and many boarding parents find they have more meaningful conversations with their teenagers, who want to find the time to talk to them, than those who have their children at home all the time. Often it is parents, not children, who worry about boarding. While it may not work for every family, boarding can provide many opportunities during term time, especially for working parents for whom professional commitments mean they often only see their families at weekends anyway.

There are so many more ways of boarding now, that I am sure you can find one that works for you. If you want to be sure that your children are happy, safe and productive at the weekends as well as in the week, why not give boarding a try?

Antonia Beary MA MPhil (Cantab), PGCE is Headmistress of Mayfield School, a leading Catholic independent boarding and day school for girls aged 11 to 18 located in Sussex. Awarded the top rating of "excellent" by the Independent Schools Inspectorate and described by Country Life as "one of the finest schools in the land", a Mayfield education combines academic excellence, breadth of opportunity and exceptional pastoral care in a nurturing environment, which welcomes all.

For more information on Mayfield School, visit the School website at www.mayfieldgirls.org or see page 101

Lessons from lockdown

Claire Murdoch, Headteacher of Faraday Prep School, gives her top five tips for surviving lockdown, no matter which side of the Zoom call you're on.

I am constantly amazed by the ability of staff and children to adapt. From becoming unlikely YouTube stars to preforming drama online, competition in national sports challenges and dressing to express in celebration of Children's Mental Health, this has been a year that has tested, stretched and challenged us all and I couldn't be more proud of how my school has responded.

Whilst we are all delighted to be back in the classroom and exceptionally proud of our Year 6s and their excellent senior school results, there are a few takeaways from a period of remote learning that I think it is only fair to share…

Stay in control of the mute button

The highlight of our week whilst teaching remotely was the whole school Zoom assembly, where we had a chance to all be together and see what everyone has been learning throughout the week. These golden half hours never failed to amuse, delight and impress us, as children were able to show, share and discuss the week's topics. It was just one week when I'd decided everyone should be free to unmute themselves at will. Bad idea. It turns out, children in a lockdown are all very keen to

share and their enthusiasm can escalate when given the chance!

Unleash your inner YouTuber

Some of our younger members of staff, embraced the chance to make tutorial videos online and before we knew it we had weekly Italian, Musical Theatre, Sports and Arts to run alongside our usual lessons. We had inadvertently made YouTube stars of all of them and the online sessions by lesser known teachers, even celebrities like Joe Wicks, just weren't the same anymore. The children wanted to see their teachers lead these sessions and to continue with all their extra-curricular pursuits, and they were right to, so soon these Faraday Extras were a staple of our remote programme.

Close the door

When working from home, you never know who else is in the house and what might be going on around you as your concentrate on your live lesson. I think we all have a funny story or mishap we can recall and they do sum up the time we've been in lockdown. But having these common tales has also helped to tie the community together. We've all let learning into our households over this period, and as much as it has been a learning curve for the children, it's been equally ambitious a change for teachers and parents. We've built trust, understanding and respect through this testing time and that is something we will continue to value going forward.

I am not a cat

After the family Zoom quiz night, remember to change your settings before the next morning's history lesson. That Hawaiian background is less appropriate for the classroom and will only mean you have children joining you from weird and wonderful worlds for the remainder of the day. We've become pros at Zoom and all its many features. Some of which have been so fantastic – Break Out Rooms, for example, have been a wonderful way for the children to work in small groups, study together and collaborate on their work. Giving the children a chance to experiment and try things out, whilst keeping tight on the rules in the live lessons has helped us to channel the children's enthusiasm into their learning.

Community and creative collaborations

Here at Faraday, we have always placed great value on learning together, collaborating and working as a community. And for this reason I was sceptical about whether we could maintain our close-knit and Faraday Family ethos online. But as it turns out, you can. This year, we have dived further into our local area, working with artists and entrepreneurs on our doorstep to continue to

offer the children exciting, new and inspiring events and activities despite the restrictions.

The first exciting visitor to knock on our door was local poet, Hussain Manawer, with a film in support of Marcus Rashford's promotion of school breakfast clubs and his subsequent visit and talk at the school, judging and presenting our winning class with their award.

Next came, the wonderful animator, Tim Allen, making a lockdown film with faraday families and subsequent workshops at the school on how to create stop animation.

Another highlight was Kate Mason, Company Director of the Big Draw located across the wharf, She spoke with students about their ideas, work and accomplishments and oversaw the unrolling of our 10 metre artwork.

Most recently the wharf was used as the stunning location for the finals of Landscape Artist of the Year. Witnessing three spectacular painters interpret the intriguing view that we see each day from our roof-top playground was something magical. Of course, this inspired our children to create artworks of their own and draw the magnificent views on our doorstep.

We're lucky to be based at the hub of a vibrant, diverse and creative community filled with people only too excited to share their skills and knowledge with the generation of tomorrow. And while over the past year it's been easy to think that spirit may wane, at Faraday we have seen new bonds form and our strength as a community develop further.

*For more information about
Faraday School, see page 57*

Choosing a small, local school makes sense

Sarah Gillam, Headteacher of Maple Walk Prep School, considers the benefits

Maple Walk is a small school, with a big heart. It doesn't have a vast array of specialist rooms but it does have children who leave with a love of learning and a desire to pursue subject opportunities at their secondary schools. They also leave with an excellent work ethic and a strong sense of well-being and confidence and an understanding of the community within which they live.

As a small school, we are able to tailor instruction to meet the needs of individual pupils while also encouraging all pupils to meet higher expectations. When class sizes are small, teachers are able to better know the academic strengths and weaknesses of each of their pupils and tailor their instruction accordingly[1]. At the same time, because teachers are able to know their pupils better in small schools, they often have higher expectations for them.

Additionally, teachers are able to provide the support needed to meet those high expectations by collaborating with colleagues, maintaining consistent professional development and conversations, and having regular contact with parents[2].

There is much more freedom for pupils to work collaboratively and fun activities that bring learning to life. Our very strong pupil-teacher relationships help pupils feel comfortable taking risks both academically and socially. Researchers have found that "although a variety of factors affect pupil achievement, the greatest factor was the reduction of anonymity — going to a school where someone knows your name."[3]

Pupils at small schools develop life-long relationships with their peers and their teachers in an environment where they are known and appreciated as a whole person, not just a classmate or another pupil. These close peer relationships help pupils in small schools feel safe and included, regardless of their differences.[4]

Maple Walk has a small staff team who are connected with each other and collaborate all the time; they can easily share ideas, updates and research. It is known that, when a teacher is enthusiastic about teaching, "pupils are more likely to be interested, energetic, curious, and excited about learning."[5]

I believe that Maple Walk can foster citizenship, leadership, and social skills through increased pupil engagement. Pupils are more likely to be highly engaged in the school community, leading to a sense of personal responsibility for the community. Pupils generally have more opportunities to participate in clubs, athletics, and the arts, allowing them to develop leadership skills in a greater diversity of situations.

Maple Walk has a positive ethos that fosters a family atmosphere; the children have a strong sense of connection mixing with all year groups, encouraging kindness and care. Excellent standards of behaviour can be established within a small community and very strong and close links with parents and the community.

It's no surprise then that pupils enter their secondary school of choice, academically well prepared, self assured and equipped with excellent life skills reinforced by our recent ISI Inspection who judged us "Excellent in All Areas". However, for us internally, perhaps the fact that they frequently return to visit us is both rewarding and affirming that we have given them the best start on their learning journey.

References

1. Method Schools. What are the Advantages to Schools with Small Class Sizes? June 2015. http://www.methodschools.org/blog/what-are-the-advantages-to-schools-with-small-class-sizes
2. Dunne, Diane Weaver.
3. Dunne, Diane Weaver. Are Smaller Schools Better Schools? Education World. 2000. http://www.educationworld.com/a_issues/issues108.shtml
4. The Tenney School. 5 Social Advantages of Small Schools. http://www.tenneyschool.com/5-social-advantages-of-smallschools/
5. Patrick, Angela Scott. Examination of Teacher Workplace Satisfaction and Student Achievement. Georgia Southern University, Jack N. Averitt College of Graduate Studies. Fall 2007. http://digitalcommons.georgiasouthern.edu/cgi/viewcontent.cgi?article=1272&context=etd

For more information about Maple Walk School, see page 68

Apart, but together

How the power of community won the year and a Boarding Schools' Association Award for Reddam House Berkshire

In March 2020, it took just two days for Reddam House Berkshire to be emptied of pupils after the announcement that a UK lockdown was imminent. The campus felt like a ghost town as boarders scattered to their home countries, including Ukraine, Mexico, and Croatia, while day students remained at home. So how did this premium private school continue to provide excellence in learning, and keep students engaged during this fractured time?

Principal Tammy Howard believes the School's already close-knit community played a major part in the strength of their response to the crisis, and in the resilience of its pupils and staff. She says, "One of the most special things about Reddam House is our relationships with the students, so it was an extraordinary pleasure working with the teaching team to ensure a transition from live to virtual school in all its fullness."

The cohesion of these existing relationships enabled the community to remain engaged and feel connected, even with some pupils caught in hotels for quarantine measures or in transit staying with guardians. In fact, the move to virtual learning was so successful the School went on to win an award for technical innovation at the 2020 Boarding Schools' Association (BSA) Awards.

Head of Boarding, Andy Towse says, "It was a great honour for us to win this award and we owe a huge thank you to all of our teachers and tutors for their wonderful support to not only our boarders, but all of our pupils, during such a difficult period in lockdown. With the hard work and dedication of the staff, as well as with an excellent platform to learn on, our pupils were able to continue their learning seamlessly."

Right from the beginning of the crisis, the School felt it was paramount to keep school life as close as possible to what it would have been. Teachers, pupils, and parents all pulled together to look at innovative ways to keep timetables, coursework, and exam preparation on track. Thanks to an existing relationship with technology, Reddam's teachers were able to use software in new ways to seamlessly include pupils in the online experience. Live online classes followed the timetable and curriculum as closely as possible. Tutor groups ran as normal and daily Assembly was still observed. It was tricky with some students being in different time zones, so live lessons were recorded, and the video files and assignments were uploaded via chat functions, so that students could access later, or revisit them again for further comprehension.

All of this was delivered with the teacher on hand to answer questions and maintain contact throughout. This gave the flexibility to accommodate all students' situations and enable interaction with teachers and fellow classmates.

Practical lessons were harder to replicate online so some subjects moved towards theory-based learning, with additional PE classes instead of swimming, and individual music lessons if students had instruments with them. Sports days went ahead virtually, bringing everyone together in an experimental experience that kept physical health and morale high.

For Years 9, 10 and 11 keeping GSCE prep on track was key; not only did study continue, but Reddam House also extended past the Easter holidays to ensure students had finished their courses before moving onto challenging topics in preparation for the next steps of their journey. Reddam House firmly believes in the power of exams, to show students have fully understood and to highlight areas that need additional support.

Course content was also bolstered with innovative extension projects that encouraged deep-dives into different subjects. For example, Year 13 economic

students looked at the economic impact of the virus and lockdown, through a research-based approach, which continued to enrich their school life and dialogue with pupils and teachers.

For Early Learners there were more playful activities such as using pots and pans to create music. For older Year groups there were House competitions, with teachers joining in too – doing sit ups with the students and keeping their cameras on so they could share laughs and encouragement.

Cristina, a Reddam House student told us, "I felt like the world was going to stop when I realised I needed to leave school in March. As much as I love in-class learning, I admit the world did not stop as my education continued with the RHB online system. I thank my teachers for keeping us a close community during tough times. It was fun, it was different, we kept together!"

Tammy Howard adds, "Not only did we offer the full timetable live online but also continued with the excellent pastoral care, community time, whole school events and one to one mentoring meetings for our students."

Transforming the closeness of the School's community into a virtual world, was second nature; support for students and family members remained high. Staff helped students understand about wellbeing, their relationship with screen time and mental health. Students knew they could talk to someone they trusted about anything – from how they were feeling, to the WiFi signal being patchy.

Being part of the Inspired network of schools also meant that Reddam House could borrow good practise and innovations from Inspired schools around the world that were discussed in their weekly virtual conferences. Inspired schools in Spain and Italy shared their successes early on, while the group Reggio Emilio expert ran workshops for Early Years teachers focussing on ways to engage younger minds.

When pupils returned to their beloved Reddam House campus and boarding rooms, they returned fluent with technology, ready to keep the flexibility that tech had afforded them during the lockdown. Some students didn't return physically at all – a testament that Reddam's staff can present to a physical class and an online platform at the same time.

And when the next lockdown arrived, the school was readier than ever. Tammy Howard concludes, "We may be apart, but we feel very much together."

For more information about Reddam House Berkshire, see page 102

SMSC: Are schools keeping secrets?

Leighton Park School promotes a Spiritual, Moral, Social and Cultural model

What on earth is SMSC? You may have attended a dozen (virtual) open days and heard not one utterance of this particular acronym from staff or students, yet it underpins every aspect of school life. It is the foundation on which your child's education will be built and a powerful influence over their life choices well beyond Sixth Form. It will mould their character, shape their relationships and you will witness the success of its effect with a burst of parental pride. So why are schools not telling you anything about it? What is the secret they don't seem to want to share?

SMSC activities encompass everything taking place in a school which could, or should, have a Spiritual, Moral, Social and Cultural dimension. In practice, this involves everything from language lessons to hockey matches and even fills the spaces in the school day associated with downtime such as co-curricular programmes, evenings in the boarding houses and voluntary work undertaken in pupils' free time. According to SMS Quality Mark, an organisation offering independent accreditation to schools going above and beyond in their provision of

SMSC education, "Spiritual, Moral, Social and Cultural (SMSC) development is the over-arching umbrella that encompasses personal development across the whole curriculum". Ofsted see it the other way round and consider SMSC as a subset of personal development explaining in their inspection framework that 'This is a broad concept that can be seen across the school's activities, but draws together many of the areas covered by the personal development judgement." What they do both agree on is articulated by SMSC Quality Mark as the fact that successful SMSC provision "requires schools to think about the kind of people we aspire to be, the kind of world we aspire to create and the kind of education we aspire to provide."

If your school search is making you more familiar than you might like with the mission statements, strategic visions and inspirational straplines which are presented front and centre on so many schools' prospectuses and websites, the concept of SMSC will most likely be ringing some bells with all you have read about the importance of a schools' ethos. Ethos is a Greek word meaning 'character' and refers to the attitudes, behaviours and spirit that characterise a particular culture or community. Within a school context, character is built, attitudes shaped and behaviours modified by the intangible ethos of the school manifested through its commitment to a robust and much more tangible SMSC delivery.

Some schools have an advantage for the confused parent of being able to offer an ethos that can be evidenced through their historic traditions as much as through their current SMSC initiatives. Forces schools such as Pangbourne College with its naval heritage or The Duke of York's Royal Military School have a distinct ethos combining discipline and service which supports many of the SMSC values. Faith schools such as the Ampleforth College, where over 75% of pupils are catholic, the school is attached to an Abbey and the Housemasters are all priests, will find it easy to find examples of the spiritual and moral aspects of school life. Quaker schools such as Leighton Park School in Reading welcome all students with a humanist approach to faith embraces both diversity and faith through the Quaker testimonies of simplicity, truth, integrity, peace, equality, sustainability and respect. Its ethos can be evidenced through sustained periods of silent reflection, addressing all members of the community, even the Head, by their first names to promote equality, and adopting a dress code rather than school uniform to support individual choice.

Many schools however don't have a heritage which has such a strong influence on their ethos and even those that do, cannot afford to ignore the importance of their SMSC provision. Given that it is an inspection requirement, every school you consider should be more than well aware of their necessary commitment to robust SMSC provision, and this provides an invaluable opportunity for you to find out exactly how your offspring's educational establishment is going to deliver on their promises of turning out a well rounded individual, ready for life beyond school, by the end of the Upper Sixth.

In much the same way as SMSC appears to be the best kept secret of an open morning so it is the best kept secret in a student's experience of their school. No pupil will ever be told by their coach on the rugby pitch that the adrenaline of a close fought match, the camaraderie of their teammates and the acceptance of a narrow defeat in a gracious, sportsmanlike manner, has given them an experience building social, moral and cultural values. A group of boarding students who give up their weekends to help prepare over 100 Christmas stockings for families in need, as pupils in Leighton Park's Field House, did last December, do not realise that this is building their SMSC education as much as a discussion on transgender issues

in PSHE or an understanding of democracy in Politics.

So if the staff don't mention it and the students don't recognise it, how are you supposed to find out whether or not it's any good? The best approach is almost certainly to ask: but without mentioning the unmentionable acronym!

When you enquire about clubs does there seem to be a balance? Sport, Music, Art and Drama are likely a given but what about co-curricular activities with a spiritual, cultural or moral dimension? At Leighton Park there are after school activities for those interested in Chinese Culture, Amnesty International, Debating, LGBTQ+ and charity work. The hobbies should cater for a diversity of interests; Book Clubs, Baking Clubs, Chess, Lego: all these offer SMSC as much as team sports, orchestra and school productions. Socially are there opportunities for pupils to spend time together in engaging ways? Are there day trips, overseas trips, a prom, celebrations for special or silly occasions (pancake flipping challenge anyone)? Try to dig a bit deeper into what happens at the weekends and in the evenings for boarders: movie nights and board games are not enough! What are the lessons actually like; are pupils encouraged to debate ideas and explore around the topic? When this happens are discussions respectful and productive or confrontational arguments with a grudge born beyond the classroom? And if covid restrictions ever allow you to actually visit a school take the opportunity to witness the interactions between staff and students, between students of different year groups, between students and yourself. However lovely the buildings and the grounds might be, the heart of the school is in the community that inhabits it, and the life blood flowing through it will be a culture rich with SMSC experiences. Just don't tell anyone you've noticed!

For more information about Leighton Park School, see page 98

Becoming your best self

Victoria Mast, Director of College Counselling, describes Marymount London's bespoke approach

The Greek aphorism 'Know Thyself', inscribed in the forecourt of the Temple of Apollo at Delphi, is a key tenet that underpins the bespoke approach to College Counselling at Marymount. In Grade 11 PSHEE classes, or Peeshee as the students have dubbed it, we start the year by reflecting deeply on a big question: Who am I? The students are given the time and space to think about a number of important questions: What strengths do you have? What are your areas for improvement? Where do you get your energy from? What values do you hold dear? What do you enjoy doing and, equally important, what don't you enjoy doing? All of these questions need to be considered when applying to university. I don't expect the students to be able to answer the question 'Who am I?' (who can?), but answering the smaller questions helps them to hone in on a course that is right for them. Of

course, as individuals we are constantly evolving, so time for reflection on goals and development is factored in throughout the college counselling programme. The very wise man Leonardo da Vinci once said: "Study without the desire spoils the memory, and it retains nothing that it takes in". Reading widely around areas of interest is imperative. After all, course is key.

In the words of Frank Sachs, former NACAC President, 'College Admissions is a match to be made, not a prize to be won'. Helping each student to find the 'best fit' for them is at the heart of Marymount's College Counselling programme. When the girls pack their bags for university, open their book in their first lecture, and smile, then we can be happy at a job well done. And speaking of jobs, students at Marymount learn to distinguish between a course and a career through research, fun quizzes, career fairs, and alumnae speakers. As well as lessons with me and individual meetings, we run and facilitate workshops for students and their families, which are designed to highlight myriad options available to Marymount students, and demystify the application process. Visits from university admissions tutors from colleges all over the world help the students to make informed choices. It is a delight to see our girls blossoming in confidence while speaking to Admissions Tutors. Indeed, universities often comment to me that our students have 'great questions', something I attribute strongly to the inquiry-based learning embedded within the IB Diploma Programme, as well as to the ample opportunities our students have for public speaking. Given our diverse, international community, it is not unusual to support applications for up to (or sometimes more than) ten countries per cohort. Discovering more about the fantastic opportunities available globally is one of the highlights of my job, as is belonging to the warm, friendly, and open, college counselling community.

Another highlight is hearing from our alumnae about their experiences at university or on their gap year. One of our School goals is to instill 'A Lifelong Love of Learning', and our alumnae family is a shining example of this mission lived out. It is especially wonderful to hear how well they have been prepared for university life by the IB Diploma. An outstanding and rigorous academic programme, the curriculum offers both breadth and depth. The students'

qualities as IB Learners (open-minded, risk-takers, balanced, reflective, principled) make them excellent candidates for universities in the UK and across the world. The IB Diploma is the gold standard of education and is certainly recognised as such by universities (colleges in the USA offer IB DP students a significant amount of credits, for example). Theory of Knowledge lessons hone the students' critical thinking skills by challenging them to question how we know, or even how do we know we know (who knows?). The Creativity, Activity, Service programme is a core component of the IB Diploma programme. Through playing sport, learning a new skill, or service to others, the girls learn more about themselves, the world around them, and their place in it. The students are encouraged to see and to understand education more holistically.

Indeed, a holistic approach is fundamental to a successful college counselling programme. A great deal of reflection, wider reading, research and open communication is necessary if one is to achieve the deceptively simple and straightforward equation: best fit course + best fit institution = a student who is happy and who thrives in Higher Education and beyond.

If I was to condense the various tips and tricks that I offer to students throughout the application process, I would be left with these words:

'Do what you love and play to your strengths.' You can't go too far wrong with that.

For more information on Marymount London, see page 89

Real life is not about subjects – it's about learning how to make connections

Why thematic learning should be at the heart of a modern secondary education, writes Susan Brooks, Head of Northwood Senior

What is 'Thematic Learning' and how does it benefit children?

A thematic curriculum is one in which the skills and knowledge for each subject is acquired through the study of one central topic or theme; for example, 'All About Me', 'Childhood', or 'Myths and Legends: Ancient China'. To take Ancient China as an example, students would explore mythology and traditional stories for their English studies; investigate the innovations of Ancient China through analysing historical sources; learn about the varied geography of China and the role that rivers play in an environment; anf explore the origins, beliefs and practices of Buddhism in TPR.

Real rewards

Students reap huge benefits from this style of teaching and learning as they promote 'joined up' thinking: we interact with the world in a complex way; we don't see it through the lens of isolated subjects; in this style, learning becomes more meaningful. With one teacher planning so many subjects across the week, all skills are taught in the same way. For example, essay writing in history is the same as in English, consolidating learning and simplifying approaches.

It is exciting that the rhythm of the lessons change week on week, though students know that they will continue studying the current topic, subjects are not fixed to a particular lesson; thematic lessons can be

Quotes from some Year 7 students

- I like that we have enough time to understand the topic we're studying in really good detail.
- The reason I like Thematic is because is nice having a mix of subjects instead of doing one thing which can get quite boring.
- I find that it is a lot more fun that when I am learning about a new subject I can learn all about it and all the connections in one Thematic lesson instead of in English, Geography, History and Religious Studies. It is also fun that I don't know what is coming up next and it will be a surprise.
- I think Thematic is good because it's easier to make links between all the different subjects. I like coming to the lesson not knowing what we're going to do. When we learnt about the silk road we learned about the full picture which brought it to life. Now with WW2 our learning makes it easy to imagine what it was like.
- I think Thematic is fun as you can learn about history one day and then the next you would be doing some religious studies about the place you have just learnt so it all just makes sense in your mind.

- I like the Thematic learning because we do a huge variety of fun learning that's always different and changing.
- Thematic is great because when we learn we take on lots of different roles and we are actually just having lots of fun.
- Thematic is very fun because you do not know what subject you are going to focus in that lesson.
- Thematic is the best because we learn something new and different every day.
- It think that a benefit of Thematic learning is how we learn things in more depth and I feel like I'm learning much faster because of that. I'm amazed at how much we've done this term!
- Because Thematic learning is a variety of subjects all in one it makes us understand so much more in just in one lesson really quickly.
- It always feels like you've learned everything you would want to know about something.
- I like Thematic because when we go into the lesson, we have no idea what we'll learn about next which is exciting.

tailored to suit a student's engagement and need. While one subject usually takes a lead in a lesson, the skills and knowledge from other subjects can be reinforced throughout. This hugely benefits students through regular exposure to relevant skills, resulting in them being acquired more efficiently and embedded more deeply. Finally, the learning is highly attuned to students' interests. If they become absorbed in one aspect of the topic this can be explored further; as long as the skills are covered, the learning can be adapted to suit the needs of the students.

More active engagement
The best news is that this approach promotes more engagement and more active learning – which ultimately leads to more progress and some extraordinary results as it encourages higher order thinking.

Students enjoy making connections for themselves and are more engaged in the material and are more willing to engage and work hard in lessons. Their enthusiasm when they are in thematic lessons is palpable. Many Students who previously professed to dislike certain subjects, or tasks such as extended writing, willingly participate in all activities and have improved their marks in assessed pieces of work.

Demonstrable benefits – both now and for the future
Alongside more active engagement in lessons the development of higher-order thinking skills and active teamwork, this style of learning has real long-term benefits.

Students are more self-motivated and more able to develop the real-world analytical and problem solving skills that should not only pay dividends in examinations but stand them in good stead for the future.

For more information about Northwood Senior see page 72

Why the arts offer more than you might think

David Woodward, Head of Performing Arts at Dallington School in London, believes teachers can boost enthusiasm and engagement with an arts-focused approach

Music, and the Performing Arts, play such a vital role in the development of a well-rounded child. The very pulse and vitality of life keep us as human beings growing and moving and seeking. But for some children, music is not just an extra-curricular activity, it is an outlet for inspiration and creativity, which forms the basis for physical and emotional development. Any visitor to a primary school will tell you that it's not long division, equivalent fractions or fronted adverbials they are drawn to (though these skills are no less important) but the energy and pulse of singing and dancing echoing down the corridor, almost beckoning you to join in- Music is infectious and totally inclusive.

For me growing up and not being the greatest mathematician in my class, I was drawn to music and the joy of coming together on a weekly and/or daily basis to sing and play. It was the establishment of a carefully designed curriculum, interlaced with music that guided me on my quest for a lifetime of music making. In the playground, we sang repetitive rhymes with a clear beat while hopscotching our way up and down the asphalt. We learnt the pulse of the skipping rope and when to jump in, and you aligned your inner pulse with the timing of the rope- if you weren't too careful, you'd be hit by that rope. It only takes spending 30 seconds inside a Nursery classroom to understand the integral role that the elements of music play in so many facets of the learning journey. The development of sound and phonics training, listening and critiquing, and the development of memory and motor skills can all be enhanced by a curriculum that is woven through the Performing Arts. As an educator, on a daily basis I see the development of physical coordination (jumping, running, dancing, stepping and even walking) and listening through the use of the elements of music.

The development of a child through the arts can contribute immensely to their mental wellbeing (especially in a time where children are under such pressure to achieve results in examinations- music is such a great brain break for them). As individuals, we all have our own strengths, weaknesses and interests. But all children, no matter what background, love to sing. As an opera singer and now educator, the energy you receive standing in front of an audience or auditorium of children can be such a rush. Row after row of children singing their hearts out, beaming with energy and smiles. The incorporation of extra-curricular activities, be it whole school singing or orchestra practice or flute lessons, will bring joy to all children and might just give that one budding student the opportunity of a lifetime. I've seen children grow in confidence in such a short amount of time through engaging in music ensembles where they can bond with other like-minded children.

Having taught across a wide range of schools and sectors in Australia and the UK, I've found the most happiness in a setting where children are in charge of their own learning and are free to enjoy all subjects because they have been carefully designed by teachers who really know their children. I am very fortunate to now work in a school where the Performing Arts are now a vital ingredient for the development of the whole child. All subjects are interlaced with music and the greatest cross-curricular links are being implemented. In my capacity as Head of Performing Arts, I am constantly seeking ways to enhance the learning of all children, and discussing ways of differentiation to meet the needs of all students. It was only the other day that I wrote a Long Division jingle for a class to help them remember the order of doing things- and this worked such a treat!

So I put it to you, the next time you teach, how can you use music to increase enthusiasm and engagement in your class! Try it and see what happens!

For more information about Dallington School, see page 54

How to run an award-winning Early Years setting

Babington House School in Kent is where curious minds grow

90% of all brain development occurs by the age of five; in the Early Years we have the unique opportunity to affect eternity.

At Babington House School we strive to inspire curious minds with experiences that deepen the mastery of all curriculum areas. Here, children design woodwork masterpieces, learning new life-long skills and enthusing peers through their creations. Through Forest School adventures, where children source their own materials for their projects, they become resilient and open to all that is possible to make and achieve.

Weekly yoga sessions enable calm reflection as children deepen their understanding of their learning over time. We add to each child's 'cultural capital' building knowledge and expertise that contribute to lifelong success.

Children have been 'Chislehurst Society Environmental Art Competition' winners with their three-dimensional entry and show awe and wonder towards our natural world during our Early Years Eco Warrior classes; which help them understand that the future of our planet is in their hands.

Children are immersed in music through studying musicians from around the world to learning to read music by sight at Nursery level with beautiful notes being played collectively on the class hand bells. Regular Drama classes help add to their confidence and presence on the stage.

Children learn French and Spanish in real life scenarios and sample an adventurous menu reflective of our diverse society. During Diwali, Indian street food is offered alongside an Indian dancing experience.

Our award-winning chef provides imaginative and outstanding creations that further deepen the children's thirst for knowledge. It is not unusual to find a pot of George's Marvellous Soup during World Book Week or a new food tasting station which helps broaden the children's food repertoire.

Sporting achievement features highly in our Early Years environment with trained specialists delivering experiences ranging from speed stacking challenges to core strength gymnastics.

Children want to make a valuable contribution to society through their many charity events including our annual Pedal Push sponsored cycling event for Childline, Ramble for Children in Need and our Danceathon for the NSPCC.

The Early Years host many performances, perhaps most notably Grandparents Day extravaganza where loved ones are invited to celebrate the work of our youngest children and enjoy a concert to honour their special relationship.

Children are exposed to a wide range of cross curricular clubs ranging from taekwondo to rugby and ballet. Aspirations are high, and children can see that the climbing wall and abseiling tower will be available as they mature.

It is an extraordinary community where every individual can thrive pastorally and academically. Pupils' strengths, physical and emotional wellbeing, interests and cognitive development are planned for exceptionally well. Inspiring staff clearly foster their own lifelong love of learning and this is evident in their teaching styles.

These experiences have led to Babington House Early Years Department being top of the Bromley Borough league tables for three consecutive years. This extraordinary achievement is a testament to the positive partnership between our wonderful staff and our super-supportive parents who work in partnership to help curious minds grow.

"A teacher affects eternity; he can never tell where his influence stops." – Henry Adams

For more information about Babington House School, see page 86

Providing a bespoke education

Simon Collins, Headmaster, explains how Aberdour School developed its own personal learning system

Our world is changing fast and it is more unpredictable than ever. In the future, today's children will be competing for employment with both technology and Artificial Intelligence, as well as with bright, able and well-educated people from other countries and cultures. What we have traditionally regarded as essential knowledge is being augmented by the requirement for life skills, thinking skills, creative skills and people skills, all of which are becoming ever more important. Further to our vision that every childhood should be special and that education should touch the hearts and souls of all children, Aberdour developed our award-winning Personalised Achievement Learning® (P.A.L®) to provide a truly individualised education with breadth and flexibility.

We have supported P.A.L® with major investments in our staff, our systems, our buildings, our IT and our resources. This investment in technology proved

particularly invaluable when moving from face-to-face to remote teaching, with all children from Year 3 upwards having access to their own ipad.

Through P.A.L®, we believe that every child will fulfil their individual potential if we nurture the talent that is within them – whatever that talent may be. We aim to remove any uncertainties that a child might have about school; 'Night-time tummies' and the 'I'm fine' syndrome will become a thing of the past, as each child can look forward to his or her school day with enthusiasm. Within a safe environment, children are able to reach for the stars and chase their dreams, whilst realising their ambitions and goals through an education programme that is built around them and their individuality.

Uniquely, we provide dedicated, specialist staff to manage each child's progress and aspirational development – we call them 'PAL Tutors'. These are highly qualified and experienced teachers whose sole focus is to plan and holistically manage the children's progress. They build a long-term knowledge of each child over a period of several years and, from Year 3 through to Year 6, provide each pupil with an individual plan that covers all aspects of their aspirational development.

At Aberdour, we follow our own three elements of educational development – Academic, Pastoral and Aspirational. Aspirational Development also includes Star Goals, Stepping Stones, The Aberdour Challenge and Aberdour Active programmes. At Aberdour, the curriculum is divided into three areas:

Core: English; Maths; Reasoning; IT and STEAM; and 11+ preparation

Extension: Science; Communication and Languages; Humanities – History and Geography; Visual Arts; Sport; and PSHCEE

Lifelong Learning: Building an individual, questioning approach to four elements:

- Living – biology, geography and our environment
- Being – philosophy, culture, RS and history
- Create – enterprise, digital learning and producing
- Endeavour – challenge, performance and exploration

Within the P.A.L® curriculum, the Lifelong Learning programme gives the children even more opportunities to explore themes such as creativity and innovation, entrepreneurialism, technology and personal skills development.

Our Stepping Stones syllabus, together with the Aberdour Challenge, encourages all children from Years 2 to 6 to extend their horizons by facing new and exciting personal challenges, and through planning their own unique experience within the eight disciplines: The Arts, Fitness, Our Community, Budgeting, Current Affairs, Domestic Science, New Skills, and Outdoor Active. These programmes help each child to enjoy a healthy lifestyle, improve their confidence and self-esteem, and to think about the world in which they live by taking an active responsibility for their personal development.

A great education begins with a great start. Pre-Prep consists of Nursery, Reception and Year 1. Staff work extremely hard delivering a range of educational, fun and engaging experiences. The happy and nurturing style will continue to give the youngest children a safe and reassuring environment, while the staff will continue to help them to explore, to learn and to develop their social and practical skills. Incorporating the principles of P.A.L®, the focus on the individual allows children to develop an even greater love of learning, as well as excitement and pride in real achievements.

When we say that Aberdour provides a bespoke education, we mean exactly that. Aberdour children are self-motivated and feel encouraged and supported, while receiving teaching that matches their abilities and challenges them at every level. Through P.A.L®, children build skills, confidence and self-awareness and are excited about their learning.

To deal successfully with a future world, our young children will need resilience, courage, empathy and optimism – all of which may be learnt within the nurturing and supportive community that is Aberdour.

For more information about Aberdour School see page 92

Choosing a school – what to consider

However much a school may appeal at first sight, you still need sound information to form your judgement

Schools attract pupils by their reputations, so most go to considerable lengths to ensure that parents are presented with an attractive image. Modern marketing techniques try to promote good points and play down (without totally obscuring) bad ones. But every Head knows that, however good the school prospectus is, it only serves to attract parents through the school gates. Thereafter the decision depends on what they see and hear. Research we have carried out over the years suggests that in many cases the most important factor in choosing a school is the impression given by the Head. As well as finding out what goes on in a school, parents need to be reassured by the aura of confidence that they expect from a Head. How they judge the latter may help them form their opinion of the former. In other words, how a Head answers questions is important in itself and, to get you started, we have drawn up a list of

points that you may like to consider. Some can be posed as questions and some are points you'll only want to check in your mind. They are not listed in any particular order and their significance will vary from family to family, but they should be useful in helping you to form an opinion.

Before visiting and asking questions, **check the facts** – such as which association the school belongs to, how big it is, how many staff *etc*. Is there any form of financial pie chart showing how the school's resources are used? The answers to questions like these should be in the promotional material you've been sent. If they aren't, you've already got a good question to ask!

Check the website. Is it up-to-date? Look at the school's social media feeds and videos. What type of tone do they set? That first impression is very important.

When you get to the school you will want to judge the

Leighton Park School – see editorial on page 24

overall atmosphere and decide whether it will suit you and your child. Are any other members of the family going to help to pay the fees? If so, their views are important and the school's attitude towards them may be instructive.

When you make it to the inner sanctum, **what do you make of the Head as a person?** Age? Family? Staying? Moving on? Retiring? Busted flush? Accessible to children, parents and staff? If you never get to see the Head, but deal with an admissions person of some sort, it may not mean you should rule the school out, but it certainly tells you something about the school's view of pupil recruitment.

Academic priorities – attitude towards league tables? This is a forked question. If the answer is 'We're most concerned with doing the best for the child', you pitch them a late-developer; if the answer is, 'Well, frankly, we have a very high entry threshold', then you say 'So we have to give you a foolproof academic winner, do we?'

Supplementary questions:

- What is the ratio of teachers to pupils?
- What are the professional qualifications of the teaching staff?
- What is the school's retention rate? In prep schools this means how many pupils do they lose at 11 when the school goes on to 13.
- How long is the school day – and week?
- What are the school's exam results?
- What are the criteria for presenting them?
- Were they consistent over the years?
- Is progress accelerated for the academically bright?
- How does the school cope with pupils who do not work?
- Where do pupils go when they leave?
- How important and well resourced are sports, extra-curricular and after school activities, music and drama?
- What cultural or other visits are arranged away from the school?

Other topics to cover:

- What is the school's mission?
- What is its attitude to religion?
- How well is the school integrated into the local community?
- How have they responded to the Charities Act initiatives?
- What are the responsibilities and obligations at weekends for parents, pupils and the school?
- Does the school keep a watching brief or reserve the option to get involved after a weekend incident?
- What is the school's attitude to discipline?
- Have there been problems with drugs, drink or sex? How have they been dealt with?
- What is the school's policy on bullying?
- How does the school cope with pupils' problems?
- What sort of academic and pastoral advice is available?
- What positive steps are taken to encourage good manners, behaviour and sportsmanship?
- What is the uniform?
- What steps are taken to ensure that pupils take pride in their personal appearance?
- How often does the school communicate with parents through reports, parent/teacher meetings or other visits?
- What level of parental involvement is encouraged both in terms of keeping in touch with staff about your own child and more generally, eg a Parents' Association?

And finally – and perhaps most importantly – what does your child make of the school, the adults met, the other children met, pupils at the school in other contexts, and the website?

Initial advice

Educational institutions often belong to organisations that encourage high standards. Here we give a brief guide to what some of the initials mean.

BSA

The Boarding Schools' Association

Since its foundation in 1965-66, the Boarding Schools' Association (BSA) has had the twin objectives of promoting boarding education and the development of quality boarding through high standards of pastoral care and boarding accommodation. Parents and prospective pupils choosing a boarding school can be assured that the 600+ plus schools in the UK and internationally that make up the membership of the BSA are committed to providing the best possible boarding environment for their pupils.

A UK boarding school can only be a full member of the BSA if it is also a member of one of the Independent Schools Council (ISC) constituent associations, or in membership of the BSA State Boarding Forum (SBF). These two bodies require member schools to be regularly inspected by the Independent Schools' Inspectorate (ISI) or Ofsted. Other boarding schools which are not members of these organisations can apply to be affiliate members. Similar arrangements are in place for international members. Boarding inspection of ISC-accredited independent schools has been conducted by ISI since September 2012, while Ofsted inspects boarding in state schools and non-association independent schools. Boarding inspections must be conducted every three years. Boarding in England and Wales is judged against the National Minimum Standards for Boarding Schools which were last revised for primary and secondary schools in England in 2015 and are set to be updated again soon.

In 2020, the Boarding Schools' Association became part of the BSA Group. BSA Group comprises BSA (Boarding Schools' Association), SACPA (Safeguarding and Child Protection Association) and BAISIS (British Association of Independent Schools with International Students). BSA Group champions excellence in boarding and safeguarding and delivers services for more than 600 members in 35 countries.

Relationship with government

The BSA is in regular communication with several government departments, including the Department for Education (DfE), Home Office, Foreign and Commonwealth Office and Ministry of Defence. The Children Act (1989) and the Care Standards Act (2000) require boarding schools to conform to national legislation and the promotion of this legislation and the training required to carry it out are matters on which the BSA and the DfE work closely.

Boarding training

Through the BSA Academy (training school), the association maintains the high standards expected as a consequence of that support and from the BSA's Commitment to Care Charter – which all member schools must abide by. The BSA organises five three residential conferences, six one day conferences and more than 90 seminars and webinars a year for governors, Heads, deputies, housemasters and housemistresses, and matrons and medical staff where further training takes place in formal sessions and in sharing good practice. The BSA provides the following range of training and information:

- Professional qualifications for teaching and non-teaching staff in boarding schools. The BSA Academy has developed a host of courses including: Certificates of Professional Practice in Boarding Education, Certificate in International Boarding, Certificate in Professional Practice for Nurses and Matrons, and a Diploma for senior leaders. A rolling programme of day seminars and webinars on current boarding legislation and good practice.
- Bespoke training, INSET, and consultancy on best boarding practice, particularly with regard to safeguarding.
- The Accredited Boarding Practitioner scheme, where individuals working in boarding can have their service and experience accredited by BSA.

- Centre for Boarding Education Research (CEBER) which brings together a wide variety of articles and research on all matters related to boarding.

State Boarding Forum (SBF)

The BSA issues information regards its 40 state boarding school members and the BSA should be contacted for details of these schools. In these schools, parents pay for boarding but not for education tuition.

60 St Martin's Lane
London WC2N 4JS
Tel: 020 7798 1580
Email: bsa@boarding.org.uk
Website: www.boarding.org.uk

GSA

The Girls' Schools Association, to which Heads of independent girls' schools belong

The Girls' Schools Association helps girls and their teachers to flourish. It represents the Heads of a diverse range of independent UK girls' schools (day & boarding), among which are some of the top-performing schools in the country.

The GSA encourages high standards of education and promotes the benefits of being taught in a largely girls-only environment. GSA schools are internationally respected and have a global reputation for excellence. Their innovative practice and academic rigour attract pupils from around the world. Students at GSA schools enjoy abundant extra- and co-curricular opportunities. Academically, they thrive in the humanities and do disproportionately well in 'difficult' modern languages and STEM (science, technology, engineering, maths) subjects. A high percentage – 96% – progress to higher education.

GSA schools share experience, specialisms, opportunities and facilities with state sector schools in a wide range of partnerships. Many also provide means-tested bursaries for families of limited financial means.

Twenty first century girls' schools come in many different shapes and sizes. Some cater for 100% girls, others provide a predominantly girls-only environment with boys in the nursery and/or sixth form. Some follow a diamond model, with equal numbers of boys but separate classrooms between the ages of 11 to 16. Educational provision across the Association offers a choice of day, boarding, weekly, and flexi-boarding education. Schools range in type from large urban schools of 1000 pupils to small rural schools of around 200. Many schools have junior and pre-prep departments, and can offer a complete education from age 3/4 to 18. Some also have religious affiliations. Heads of schools in the Girls' Day School Trust (GDST) are members of the GSA.

The Association aims to inform and influence national educational debate and is a powerful and well-respected voice within the educational establishment, advising and lobbying educational policy makers on core education issues as well as those relating to girls' schools and the education of girls. The Association liaises with the Department for Education, the Office for Standards in Education, the Qualifications and Curriculum Authority and other bodies.

The GSA also provides its members and their staff with professional development courses, conferences, advice and opportunities to debate and share best practice, ensuring that they have every opportunity to remain fully up-to-date with all aspects of their profession.

As the GSA is one of the constituent bodies that make up the Independent Schools' Council (ISC), its schools are required to undergo a regular cycle of inspections to ensure that these rigorous standards are being maintained. GSA schools must also belong to the Association of Governing Bodies of Independent Schools, and Heads must be in membership of the Association of School and College Leaders (ASCL).

The Association's secretariat is based in Leicester.

Suite 105, 108 New Walk, Leicester LE1 7EA
Tel: 0116 254 1619
Email: office@gsa.uk.com
Website: www.gsa.uk.com
Twitter: @GSAUK

**President 2021: Samantha Price, Benenden School
Chief Executive: Donna Stevens (from January 2021)**

HMC

The Headmasters' and Headmistresses' Conference, to which the Heads of leading independent schools belong

Founded in 1869 the HMC exists to enable members to discuss matters of common interest and to influence important developments in education. It looks after the professional interests of members, central to which is their wish to provide the best possible educational opportunities for their pupils.

The Heads of some 296 leading independent schools are members of The Headmasters' and Headmistresses' Conference, whose membership now includes Heads of boys', girls' and coeducational schools. International membership includes the Heads of around 56 schools throughout the world.

The great variety of these schools is one of the strengths of HMC but all must exhibit high quality in the education provided. While day schools are the largest group, about a quarter of HMC schools consist mainly of boarders and others have a smaller boarding element including weekly and flexible boarders.

All schools are noted for their academic excellence and achieve good results, including those with pupils from a broad ability band. Members believe that good education consists of more than academic results and schools provide pupils with a wide range of educational co-curricular activities and with strong pastoral support.

Only those schools that meet with the rigorous membership criteria are admitted and this helps ensure that HMC is synonymous with high quality in education. There is a set of membership requirements and a Code of Practice to which members must subscribe. Those who want the intimate atmosphere of a small school will find some with around 350 pupils. Others who want a wide range of facilities and specialisations will find these offered in large day or boarding schools. Many have over 1000 pupils. 32 schools are for boys only, others are coeducational throughout or only in the sixth form. The first girls-only schools joined HMC in 2006. There are now 39 girls-only schools.

Within HMC there are schools with continuous histories as long as any in the world and many others trace their origins to Tudor times, but HMC continues to admit to membership recently-founded schools that have achieved great success. The facilities in all HMC schools will be good but some have magnificent buildings and grounds that are the result of the generosity of benefactors over many years. Some have attractive rural settings, others are sited in the centres of cities.

Pupils come from all sorts of backgrounds. Bursaries and scholarships provided by the schools give about a third of the 240,000 pupils in HMC schools help with their fees. These average about £35,000 per annum for boarding schools and £15,000 for day schools. About 190,000 are day pupils and 45,000 boarders.

Entry into some schools is highly selective but others are well-suited to a wide ability range. Senior boarding schools usually admit pupils after the Common Entrance examination taken when they are 13.

Most day schools select their pupils by 11+ examination. Many HMC schools have junior schools, some with nursery and pre-prep departments. The growing number of boarders from overseas is evidence of the high reputation of the schools worldwide.

The independent sector has always been fortunate in attracting very good teachers. Higher salary scales, excellent conditions of employment, exciting educational opportunities and good pupil/teacher ratios bring rewards commensurate with the demanding expectations. Schools expect teachers to have a good education culminating in a good honours degree and a professional qualification, though some do not insist on the latter especially if relevant experience is offered. Willingness to participate in the whole life of the school is essential.

Parents expect the school to provide not only good teaching that helps their children achieve the best possible examination results, but also the dedicated pastoral care and valuable educational experiences outside the classroom in music, drama, games, outdoor pursuits and community service. Over 89% of pupils go on to higher education, many of them winning places on the most highly-subscribed university courses.

All members attend the Annual Conference, usually held in a large conference centre in September/October. There are ten divisions covering England, Wales, Scotland and Ireland where members meet once a term on a

Leading Independent Schools

regional basis, and a distinctive international division.

The chair and committee, with the advice of the general secretary and membership secretary, make decisions on matters referred by membership-led sub-committees, steering groups and working parties. Close links are maintained with other professional associations in membership of the Independent Schools Council and with the Association of School and College Leaders.

Membership Secretary: Ian Power
Tel: 01858 465260

12 The Point
Rockingham Road
Market Harborough
Leicestershire LE16 7QU
Email: gensec@hmc.org.uk
Website: www.hmc.org.uk

IAPS

The Independent Association of Prep Schools (IAPS) is a membership association representing leading headteachers and their prep schools in the UK and overseas

With around 670 members, IAPS schools represent a multi-billion pound enterprise, educating more than 160,000 children and employing more than 20,000 staff. As the voice of independent prep school education, IAPS actively defends and promotes the interests of its members.

IAPS schools must reach a very high standard to be eligible for membership, with strict criteria on teaching a broad curriculum, maintain excellent standards of pastoral care and keeping staff members' professional development training up-to-date. The head must be suitably qualified and schools must be accredited through a satisfactory inspection. IAPS offers its members and their staff a comprehensive and up-to-date programme of professional development courses to ensure that these high professional standards are maintained.

Member schools offer an all-round, values-led broad education which produces confident, adaptable, motivated children with a passion for learning. The targets of the National Curriculum are regarded as a basic foundation which is greatly extended by the wider programmes of study offered. Specialist teaching begins at an early age and pupils are offered a range of cultural and sporting opportunities.

IAPS organises a successful sports programme where member schools compete against each other in a variety of sports. In 2019-20, over 17,000 competitors took part in 119 events across 7 sports.

Our schools are spread throughout cities, towns and the countryside and offer pupils the choice of day, boarding, weekly and flexible boarding, in both singe sex and co-educational schools. Most schools are charitable trusts, some are limited companies and a few are proprietary. There are also junior schools attached to senior schools, choir schools, those with a particular religious affiliation and those that offer specialist provision as well as some schools with an age range extending to age 16 or above.

Although each member school is independent and has its own ethos, they are all committed to delivering an excellent, well-rounded education to the pupils in their care, preparing them for their future.

IAPS
11 Waterloo Place
Leamington Spa
Warwickshire CV32 5LA
Tel: 01926 887833
Email: iaps@iaps.uk
Website: iaps.uk

Excellence in Education
The Independent Association
of Prep Schools

ISA

The Independent Schools Association, with membership across all types of school

The Independent Schools Association (ISA), established in 1879, is one of the oldest of the Headteachers' associations of independent schools that make up the Independent Schools' Council (ISC). It began life as the Association of Principals of Private Schools, which was created to encourage high standards and foster friendliness and cooperation among Heads who had previously worked in isolation. In 1895 it was incorporated as The Private Schools Association and in 1927 the word 'private' was replaced by 'independent'. The recently published history of the association, *Pro Liberis*, demonstrates the strong links ISA has with proprietorial schools, which is still the case today, even though boards of governors now run the majority of schools.

Membership is open to any Head or Proprietor, provided they meet the necessary accreditation criteria, including inspection of their school by a government-approved inspectorate. ISA's Executive Council is elected by members and supports all developments of the Association through its committee structure and the strong regional network of co-ordinators and area committees. Each of ISA's seven areas in turn supports members through regular training events and meetings.

ISA celebrates a wide-ranging membership, not confined to any one type of school, but including all: nursery, pre-preparatory, junior and senior, all-through schools, coeducational, single-sex, boarding, day and performing arts and special schools.

Promoting best practice and fellowship remains at the core of the ISA, as it did when it began 140 years ago. The association is growing, and its 541 members and their schools enjoy high quality national conferences and courses that foster excellence in independent education. ISA's central office also supports members and provides advice, and represents the views of its membership at national and governmental levels. Pupils in ISA schools enjoy a wide variety of competitions, in particular the wealth of sporting, artistic and academic activities at area and national level.

President: Lord Lexden
Chief Executive: Rudolf Eliott Lockhart

ISA House, 5-7 Great Chesterford Court, Great Chesterford, Essex CB10 1PF
Tel: 01799 523619
Email: isa@isaschools.org.uk
Website: www.isaschools.org.uk

The Society of Heads

The Society of Heads represents the interests of independent secondary schools

The Society of Heads represents the interests of independent, secondary schools. Established in 1961, The Society has as its members 125 Heads of well-established secondary schools, many with a boarding element, meeting a wide range of educational needs. All member schools provide education up to 18, with sixth forms offering both A and AS levels and/or the International Baccalaureate. Also some offer vocational courses. Many have junior schools attached to their foundation. A number cater for pupils with special educational needs, whilst others offer places to gifted dancers and musicians. All the schools provide education appropriate to their pupils' individual requirements together with the best in pastoral care.

The average size of the schools is about 350, and all aim to provide small classes ensuring favourable pupil:teacher ratios. The majority are coeducational and offer facilities for both boarding and day pupils. Many of the schools are non-denominational, whilst others have specific religious foundations.

The Society believes that independent schools are an important part of Britain's national education system. Given their independence, the schools can either introduce new developments ahead of the maintained sector or offer certain courses specifically appropriate to the pupils in their schools. They are able to respond quickly to the needs of parents and pupils alike.

Schools are admitted to membership of the Society only after a strict inspection procedure carried out by the Independent Schools Inspectorate. Regular inspection visits thereafter ensure that standards are maintained.

The Society is a constituent member of the Independent Schools Council and every full member in the Society has been accredited to it. All the Society's Heads belong to the Association of School and College Leaders (ASCL) (or another recognised union for school leaders) and their schools are members of AGBIS.

The Society's policy is: to maintain high standards of education, acting as a guarantee of quality to parents who choose a Society school for their children; to ensure the genuine independence of member schools; to provide an opportunity for Heads to share ideas and common concerns for the benefit of the children in their care; to provide training opportunities for Heads and staff in order to keep them abreast of new educational initiatives; to promote links with higher and further education and the professions, so that pupils leaving the Society's schools are given the best advice and opportunities for their future careers; and to help Heads strengthen relations with their local communities.

The Society of Heads Office,
12 The Point, Rockingham Road, Market Harborough,
Leicestershire LE16 7QU
Tel: 01858 433760
Email: info@thesocietyofheads.org.uk
Website: www.thesocietyofheads.org.uk

The Independent Schools Council

The Independent Schools Council (ISC) works with its members to promote and preserve the quality, diversity and excellence of UK independent education both at home and abroad

What is the ISC?

The ISC brings together seven associations of independent schools, their heads, bursars and governors. Through our member associations we represent more than 1,350 independent schools in the UK and overseas. These schools are among the best in the world and educate more than half a million children each year.

The ISC's work is carried out by a small team of dedicated professionals in an office in central London. We are assisted by contributions from expert advisory groups in specialist areas. Our priorities are set by the board of directors led by our chairman, Barnaby Lenon. We are tasked by our members to protect and promote the sector in everything we do.

ISC schools

Schools in UK membership of the ISC's constituent associations offer a high quality, rounded education. Whilst our schools are very academically successful, their strength also lies in the extra-curricular activities offered – helping to nurture pupils' soft skills and encourage them to be self-disciplined, ambitious and curious. There are independent schools to suit every need, whether you want a day or boarding school, single sex or co-education, a large or a small school, or schools offering specialisms, such as in the arts.

Our schools are very diverse: some are selective and highly academic, while others have very strong drama or music departments full of creative opportunities in plays, orchestras and choirs. For children with special needs such as dyslexia or autism there are many outstanding independent schools that offer some of the best provision in the country.

Academic results

Typically, the ISC publishes a sector-wide analysis of Year 11 and Year 13 exam results for independent schools every August. However, due to the coronavirus pandemic, there was no sector-wide publication of results in 2020 because exams were temporarily replaced by an assessment process that Ofqual had to create in response to the crisis. Schools provided students with their grades in August as normal and the Department for Education is expected to publish results for all schools (state and independent) in January 2021.

Looking back at exam results in 2019, 45.7% of Year 13 exam entries at independent schools were graded A*/A, compared to the national average of 25.5%. That year also saw 95.6% of Year 11 exams at independent schools graded C/4 or higher, compared to the national average of 67.3%. Figures recorded in 2019 also demonstrated more students are following different pathways post-GCSE.

Fee assistance

Schools take issues around affordability very seriously and are acutely aware of the sacrifices families make when choosing an independent education. Schools work hard to remain competitive whilst facing pressures on salaries, pensions and maintenance and utility costs. They are strongly committed to widening access and have made strenuous efforts to increase the amount they can offer in bursaries. This year, £440m was provided in means-tested fee assistance for pupils at ISC schools. Currently a third of pupils at our schools benefit from reduced fees.

School partnerships

Independent and state schools have been engaged in partnership activity for many years, with the majority of

Our schools are very diverse: some are selective and highly academic, while others have very strong drama or music departments full of creative opportunities in plays, orchestras and choirs.

Cobham Hall School – see editorial on page 14

ISC schools currently involved in important cross-sector initiatives. These collaborations involve the sharing of expertise, best practise and facilities, and unlock exciting new opportunities for all involved. To learn more about the partnership work taking place between state and independent schools, visit the Schools Together website: www.schoolstogether.org/

ISC Associations

There are seven member associations of the ISC, each with a distinctive ethos in their respective entrance criteria and quality assurance: Girls' Schools Association (GSA), Headmasters' and Headmistresses' Conference (HMC), Independent Association of Prep Schools (IAPS) Independent Schools Association (ISA), The Society of Heads, Association of Governing Bodies of Independent Schools (AGBIS), and the Independent Schools' Bursars Association (ISBA).

Further organisations who are affiliated to the ISC: Boarding Schools Association (BSA), Council of British International Schools (COBIS), Scottish Council of Independent Schools (SCIS) and Welsh Independent Schools Council (WISC).

The Independent Schools Council can be contacted at:
First Floor,
27 Queen Anne's Gate,
London,
SW1H 9BU
Telephone: 020 7766 7070
Website: www.isc.co.uk

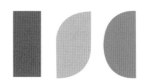

independent
schools
council

Help in finding the fees

Chris Procter, joint managing director of SFIA, outlines a planned approach to funding your child's school fees

Average school fee increases between the last year 2 school years, according to the ISC census, were 4.1%. This is lower than expected given the increased cost of Teachers Pension Scheme which came in last year. There appears to have been a conscious effort by schools over the last 10 years to control fees. Since 2010 fee increases have averaged 3.9%. Between 2000 and 2010 they averaged 6.6%.

The latest Independent Schools Council (ISC) survey, conducted in January 2020 and completed by all 1,374 schools in UK membership, indicate that there are now a record 537,315 pupils being educated privately, the highest number since records began in 1974, rising 0.22% since 2019.

Pupils registered to board stands at 13.0% with weekly and flexi boarding becoming increasingly popular. The percentage of pupils attending single sex schools stands at 24.5%, marginally lower than last year.

The overall average boarding fee is £11,763 per term and the overall average day fee is £4,980 per term.

However, fees charged by schools vary by region – for example, the average boarding fee ranges from £9,292 per term in the North East to £13,372 per term in Greater London; the average day fee ranges from £3,725 per term in the North West to £5,993 per term in Greater London.

The overall cost (including university fees) might seem daunting: the cost of educating one child privately could well be very similar to that of buying a house but, as with house buying, the school fees commitment for the majority of parents can be made possible by spreading it over a long period rather than funding it all from current resources.

It is vital that parents do their financial homework, plan ahead, start to save early and regularly.

Grandparents who have access to capital could help out; by contributing to school fees they could also help to reduce any potential future inheritance tax liability.

Parents would be well-advised to consult a specialist financial adviser as early as possible, since a long-term plan for the payment of fees – possibly university as well – can prove very advantageous from a financial point of view and offer greater peace of mind. Funding fees is neither science, nor magic, nor is there any panacea. It is quite simply a question of planning and using whatever resources are available, such as income, capital, or tax planning opportunities.

The fundamental point to recognise is that you, your circumstances and your wishes or ambitions, for your children, or grandchildren are unique. They might well appear similar to those of other people but they will still be uniquely different. There will be no single solution to your problem. In fact, after a review of all your circumstances, there might not be a problem at all.

So, what are the reasons for seeking advice about education expenses?
- To reduce the overall cost
- To get some tax benefit
- To reduce your cash outflow
- To invest capital to ensure that future fees are paid
- To set aside money now for future fees
- To provide protection for school fees
- Or just to make sure that, as well as educating your children, you can still have a life

Any, some, or all of the above – or others not listed – could be on your agenda, the important thing is to develop a strategy.

At this stage, it really does not help to get hung up on which financial 'product' is the most suitable. The composition of a school fees plan will differ for each family depending on a number of factors. That is why there is no one school fees plan on offer.

The simplest strategy but in most cases, the most expensive option, is to write out a cheque for the whole bill when it arrives and post it back to the school. Like most simple plans, that can work well, if you have the money. Even if you do have the money, is that really the best way of doing things? Do you know that to fund £1,000 of school fees as a higher rate taxpayer paying 40% income tax, you currently need to earn £1,667, this rises to £1,818 if you are an additional rate taxpayer where the rate is 45%.

How then do you start to develop your strategy? As with most things in life, if you can define your objective, then you will know what you are aiming at. Your objective in this case will be to determine how much money is needed and when.

You need to draw up a school fees schedule or what others may term a cash flow forecast. So, you need to identify:
- How many children?
- Which schools and therefore what are the fees? (or you could use an average school fee)
- When are they due?
- Any special educational needs?
- Inflation estimate?
- Include university costs?

With this basic information, the school fees schedule/ cash flow forecast can be prepared and you will have defined what it is you are trying to achieve.

Remember though, that senior school fees are typically more than prep school fees – this needs to be factored in. Also, be aware that the cost of university is not restricted to the fees alone; there are a lot of maintenance and other costs involved: accommodation, books, food, to name a few. Don't forget to build in inflation, I refer you back to the data at the beginning of this article.

You now have one element of the equation, the relatively simple element. The other side is the resources you have available to achieve the objective. This also needs to be identified, but this is a much more difficult exercise. The reason that it is more difficult, of course, is that school fees are not the only drain on your resources. You probably have a mortgage, you want to have holidays, you need to buy food and clothes, you may be concerned that you should be funding a pension.

This is a key area of expertise, since your financial commitments are unique. A specialist in the area of school fees planning can help identify these commitments, to record them and help you to distribute your resources according to your priorities.

The options open to you as parents depend completely upon your adviser's knowledge of these complex personal financial issues. (Did I forget to mention your tax position, capital gains tax allowance, other tax allowances, including those of your children and a lower or zero rate tax paying spouse or partner? These could well be used to your advantage.)

A typical school fees plan can incorporate many elements to fund short, medium and long-term fees.

Each plan is designed according to individual circumstances and usually there is a special emphasis on what parents are looking to achieve, for example, to maximise overall savings and to minimise the outflow of cash.

Additionally, it is possible to protect the payment of the fees in the event of unforeseen circumstances that could lead to a significant or total loss of earnings.

Short-term fees

Short-term fees are typically the termly amounts needed within five years: these are usually funded from such things as guaranteed investments, liquid capital, loan plans (if no savings are available) or maturing insurance policies, investments etc. Alternatively, they can be funded from disposable income.

Medium-term fees

Once the short-term plan expires, the medium-term funding is invoked to fund the education costs for a further five to ten years. Monthly amounts can be invested in a low-risk, regular premium investment ranging from a building society account to a friendly society savings plan to equity ISAs. It is important to understand the pattern of the future fees and to be aware of the timing of withdrawals.

Long-term fees

Longer term funding can incorporate a higher element of risk (as long as this is acceptable to the investor), which will offer higher potential returns. Investing in UK and overseas equities could be considered. Solutions may be the same as those for medium-term fees, but will have the flexibility to utilise investments that may have an increased 'equity based' content.

Finally, it is important to remember that most investments, or financial products either mature with a single payment or provide for regular withdrawals; rarely do they provide timed termly payments.

Additionally, the overall risk profile of the portfolio should lean towards the side of caution (for obvious reasons).

There are any number of advisers in the country, but few who specialise in the area of planning to meet school and university fees. SFIA is the largest organisation specialising in school fees planning in the UK.

This article has been contributed by SFIA and edited by Chris Procter, Managing Director.
Chris can be contacted at: SFIA, 29 High Street, Marlow, Buckinghamshire, SL7 1AU
Tel: 01628 566777
Fax: 0333 444 1550
Email: enquiries@sfia.co.uk
Web: www.schoolfeesadvice.org

Search for the UK's best schools

The online partner to John Catt guidebooks, including:

www.schoolsearch.co.uk
www.whichlondonschool.co.uk
www.prepschoolguide.co.uk

www.schoolsearch.co.uk features premium listings of schools profiled in our guidebooks. It has more than 170,000 users a year, viewing over 600,000 pages.

It features dedicated search pages for UK regions and counties, many of which feature on the first page of Google search results.

Our site has visitors from across the world looking for UK independent schools, as well as from across the UK. Families can find and compare their nearest schools with our postcode search.

In addition to school profile information and pictures, schools can feature open day information, news

stories and features, add links to their social media and embed a featured video.

www.schoolsearch.co.uk is in association with *John Catt's Which School?* guidebook, now in its 97th edition, *John Catt's Preparatory Schools* and *Which London School? & the South-East*.

Contact: enquiries@johncatt.com or call 01394 389850

Profiles

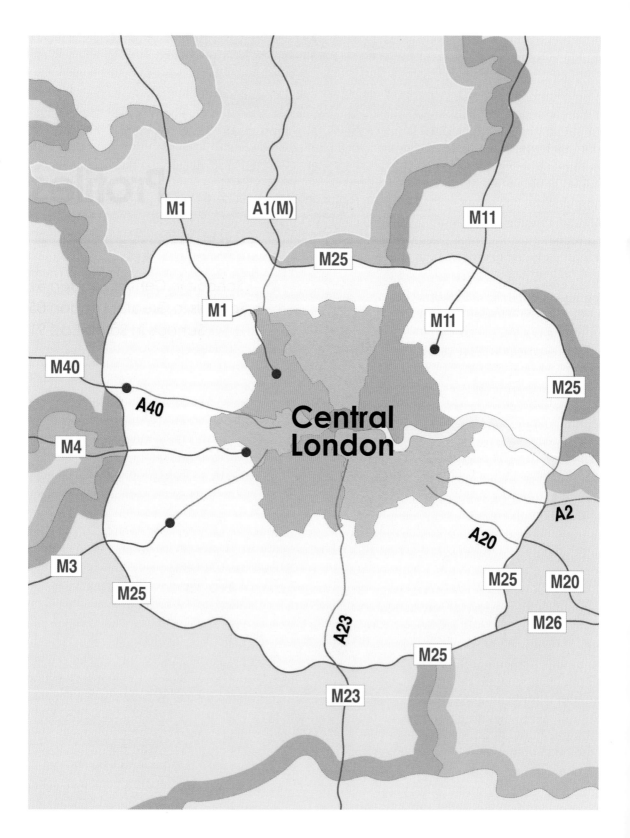

Schools in Central London

Broomwood Hall Lower School
Part of Northwood Schools

Reception & Year 1: The Vicarage, Ramsden Road, SW12 8QR

Tel: 020 8682 8820
Class 2 and Class 3: 50 Nightingale Lane, London, SW12 8TE
Tel: 020 8682 8840
Email: admissions@northwoodschools.com
Website: www.northwoodschools.com
Head: Miss Jo Townsend

School type: Co-educational Pre-Prep
Religious Denomination: Church of England, all denominations welcome
Age range of pupils: 4–8
No. of pupils enrolled as at 01/01/2021: 320
Fees per term as at 01/01/2021:
Day: £5,610
Average class size: Max 20

ABOUT US: Broomwood Hall Lower School is a co-educational pre-prep school for children aged 4-8 in Wandsworth, South West London offering an excellent and rounded education. We offer a broad, modern and innovative curriculum designed to provide mastery of the building blocks of education, delivered in an inclusive, exciting and enjoyable way, harnessing curiosity and creating a desire to learn. All children have specialist teaching in arts, sport, music and French. Maths mastery is a speciality.

MOTTO: 'To do your best, to be your best' exemplifies our ethos. We help each child develop to the best of their individual ability and believe that a supportive but focused environment, without undue stress or 'hot-housing', is the best way to enable them to fulfil their potential, both inside and outside the classroom.

GAMES & THE ARTS: All children take part in PE and Games for at least five periods per week and progress from learning basic skills to playing in competitive matches. Great emphasis on

building confidence through art, drama and musical performance. A multitude of clubs from Year 1 onwards include karate, coding, art and cookery. We hold a prestigious Gold Artsmark Award.

PASTORAL CARE: The school is split between two buildings a short walk from each other. Each site is small enough, and intimate enough, for all children to be well known to all staff. We have a strong pastoral team which includes learning support, a full time school nurse and a qualified school counsellor.

ADMISSIONS: Entry into our Reception classes is by random ballot which is designed to ensure an equal mix of boys and girls and a good spread of birthdays. Entry at other ages is subject to a satisfactory school report and a baseline assessment. Children from the Lower School progress automatically to either Northcote Lodge, (boys) or Broomwood Hall Upper School (girls) at the age of 8 providing these are the right schools for them. We also offer a limited intake at age 7 for children wishing to move on to either of these prep schools.

HEAD TEACHER'S PHILOSOPHY: We embrace the best of tradition with the best of modern innovative teaching to deliver an outstanding education that excites, stimulates and nurtures the whole child. Our five learning powers: Curiosity, Communication, Creativity, Independence and Resilience plus our Mastery and Thematic learning approach, are the bedrock for all we do and designed to equip children with the problem solving and analytical skills they need to succeed in the workplaces of the future.

Broomwood Hall Upper School
Part of Northwood Schools

68-74 Nightingale Lane, London, SW12 8NR
Tel: 020 8682 8810
Email:
admissions@northwoodschools.com
Website: www.northwoodschools.com
Head: Mrs Louisa McCafferty
School type: Girls' Preparatory

Religious Denomination: Church of England, all denominations welcome
Age range of girls: 8–13
No. of pupils enrolled as at 01/01/2021: 250
Fees per term as at 01/01/2021:
Day: £6,880
Average class size: Av 17

ABOUT US: Broomwood Hall Upper School is a girls' prep school in Wandsworth, SW London preparing for both 11+ & 13+ exits which offers an excellent and rounded education that nurtures and stretches in equal measure. Our winning combination of traditional values and innovative teaching coupled with an exciting enrichment programme challenges and stimulates both breadth and depth of learning. Broomwood girls are happy, confident, rounded individuals who are well prepared for future success.

THE CURRICULUM: A broad and stimulating mastery approach, with technology used at every level fosters a love of learning, bolsters self-confidence, creativity and critical thinking, helping girls to maximise their potential.

GAMES & THE ARTS: Sport and the arts are an important part of our curriculum and we offer a surprisingly wide variety. We place great value on creativity with exceptionally strong music, art and drama departments. New Art and DT block. Winners of prestigious Artsmark Gold Award. Leiths Cookery school on-site for Years 6 & 7.

PASTORAL CARE: We know that happy children thrive academically. With small class sizes, an excellent tutor system and mindfulness and wellbeing programmes built into the curriculum, we pride ourselves on nurturing the whole child and developing individual strengths so that when girls leave us at 11 or 13, they are confident, happy, well-rounded individuals with a strong sense of purpose.

ADMISSIONS & EXIT: Entry at ages 8 and 11 is automatic for girls coming from the Lower School. We take pride in the breadth of our curriculum and get wonderful results in all areas with girls regularly winning awards and scholarships at both 11 and 13, in all subjects, to some of the country's best schools, both day and boarding including Alleyn's, Benenden, Emanuel Marlborough, Bradfield, JAGS, Streatham & Clapham High, Woldingham, Wellington, Cranleigh and King's, Canterbury. From September 20, option to progress on to recently opened Northwood Senior. On average, around 25 per cent of leavers win awards across all areas: academic, art, music, drama and sport.

HEAD'S PHILOSOPHY: We prepare for life, not just the next school. Our focus on the essential skills of creativity, critical thinking, resilience, independence and confidence, provides girls with the benefits of a holistic education where everything is important, and each girl is supported and enabled to be and do her best and is prepared for an exciting future.

Dallington School

Dallington School

(Founded 1978)

8 Dallington Street, Islington,
London, EC1V 0BW
Tel: 020 7251 2284
Email: hercules@dallingtonschool.co.uk
Website: www.dallingtonschool.co.uk
Headteacher: Maria Blake
Appointed: 2019

School type: Co-educational Day and Nursery
Age range of pupils: 3–11
No. of pupils enrolled as at 01/01/2021: 103
Boys: 64 **Girls:** 39
Fees per annum as at 01/01/2021:
Day: £11,490–£14,490
Teacher/pupil ratio: 1:10 (with full time TA)

A family-run, independent, co-educational day school for children aged 3 to 11, in the heart of London

Dallington is a school that holds a unique place in the constellation of outstanding London schools – a vibrant oasis of creativity; proudly and fiercely independent. Established and led for over 40 years by Mogg Hercules MBE, a Dallington education continues to celebrate and embody her vision and ethos.

Dallington offers a rich and ambitious curriculum, with excellence in core skills as the foundation. In addition, the creative and performing arts are embedded in the Dallington experience from the very beginning. The Dallington child is defined by the attitudes that ensure their future success in a fast changing world – Curiosity, Courage, Compassion, Creativity and Collaboration.

We actively encourage our children to be informed, to find their voice, to develop opinions and to explore their place in the world; to see themselves as global citizens from the earliest age and to understand that they are never too young to be heard or to make a difference.

Our children learn in bright and airy open-plan classrooms spread over five floors. First names are used and we do not have a school uniform.

Personal tours each day of the week. Non-selective entry policy. Early registration advised.

Devonshire House Preparatory School

(Founded 1989)

2 Arkwright Road, Hampstead,
London, NW3 6AE
Tel: 020 7435 1916
Email: enquiries@dhprep.co.uk
Website: www.devonshirehouseschool.co.uk
Headmistress: Mrs S. Piper BA(Hons)
School type: Preparatory, Pre-preparatory & Nursery Day School

Religious Denomination:
Non-denominational
Age range of boys: 2½–13
Age range of girls: 2½–11
No. of pupils enrolled as at 01/01/2021: 650
Boys: 350 **Girls:** 300
Fees per annum as at 01/01/2021:
Day: £10,545–£19,470

Academic & leisure facilities

The school is situated in fine premises in the heart of Hampstead with its own walled grounds. The aim is to achieve high academic standards whilst developing enthusiasm and initiative throughout a wide range of interests. It is considered essential to encourage pupils to develop their own individual interests and a good sense of personal responsibility.

Curriculum

Early literacy and numeracy are very important and the traditional academic subjects form the core curriculum. The younger children all have a class teacher and classroom assistant and their day consists of a mixture of formal lessons and learning through play. Whilst children of all ages continue to have a form teacher, as they grow older an increasing part of the curriculum is delivered by subject specialists. The combined sciences form an increasingly important part of the timetable as the children mature. The use of computers is introduced from an early stage, both as its own skill and as an integrated part of the pupils' education.

Expression in all forms of communication is encouraged, with classes having lessons in art, music, drama and French. Physical exercise and games also play a key part of the curriculum. Much encouragement is given to pupils to help widen their horizons and broaden their interests. The school fosters a sense of responsibility amongst the pupils, and individuality and personal attention for each pupil is considered essential to make progress in the modern world.

The principal areas of the National Curriculum are covered, though subjects may be taken at a higher level, or at a quicker pace. For the girls approaching the 11+ senior schools' entry examinations, special emphasis is given to the requirements for these, and in the top two years for the boys, Common Entrance curriculum is taught. The pupils achieve great success in these examinations and a number also sit successfully for senior school scholarships.

The school has its own nursery, The Oak Tree Nursery, which takes children from two-and-a-half years of age.

Entry requirements

The Oak Tree Nursery: For children entering the Oak Tree Nursery, places are offered on the basis on an informal assessment made at the nursery. Children in The Oak Tree Nursery transfer directly to the Junior School.

The Junior School: For children entering the junior school from the ages of three to five, places are offered on the basis of assessment made at the school. From the age of six places are usually subject to a written test taken at school. At eight, children transfer directly into the upper school. Parents and their children are welcome to visit for interview and to see around the school.

The Upper School: Entry to the upper school is principally from the junior school. For pupils seeking to join the school from elsewhere places are normally subject to a written entrance test.

École Jeannine Manuel – London

ÉCOLE Jeannine Manuel
International understanding through a bilingual education

(Founded 2015)

43-45 Bedford Square, London, WC1B 3DN

Tel: 020 3829 5970

Email: admissions@jmanuel.uk.net

Website:
www.ecolejeanninemanuel.org.uk

Head of School: Pauline Prévot

School type: Coeducational Day

Age range of pupils: 3–18 years

No. of pupils enrolled as at 01/01/2021: 550

Fees per annum as at 01/01/2021:

Day: £19,590

Average class size: 16

Teacher/pupil ratio: 1:8

École Jeannine Manuel in London is a French, bilingual, international school which opened its doors in September 2015 in three contiguous mansions on Bedford Square, steps away from the British Museum. In 2019, the school opened additional premises on Russell Square, where it now houses its Upper School (Year 10 – Year 13).

Our school welcomes pupils from all nationalities and cultural backgrounds, from Nursery to Year 13. Sixth Formers take either the French Baccalaureate (with an international option) or the International Baccalaureate. Both diplomas are recognised by the most prestigious universities across the globe.

École Jeannine Manuel is the young sister school of its Paris namesake, a UNESCO associated school founded in 1954 and one of France's most prestigious schools, ranked first among French high schools (public and independent) for overall academic performance for the past eight years. As is the case in France, École Jeannine Manuel London's mission is "to promote international understanding through the bilingual education of a multicultural community of students, the fostering of pedagogical innovation, and the constant exploration of best practices in the context of an ever-changing global environment."

A bilingual education

École Jeannine Manuel offers an enriched, bilingual adaptation of the French national curriculum, including English, Science and Chinese programmes developed by its sister school in Paris. In History, the French national curriculum is complemented to help pupils gain coherent knowledge and understanding of Britain's past and that of the wider world. Extra-curricular activities include sports – with outdoor facilities within walking distance of the school – as well as a broad range of artistic and tech-based clubs.

English and French are spoken equally in class. Our aim is to bring pupils to a native proficiency – orally and in writing – in both languages. We welcome non French-speaking students at all levels and help them adapt to the demands of a bilingual curriculum. With respect to English, the school accommodates beginners up to Year 7. Experience shows that studying in French and in English yields a strong and mutually reinforced command of both languages as well as a deep understanding of the cultures they express. A bilingual education enhances pupils' capacity for abstract, conceptual thinking and develops a sense of nuance, nurtured by exposure to multiple perspectives.

A multicultural community of students

Looking beyond French and bi-national families, the school welcomes pupils from all nationalities, cultural traditions and native languages. École Jeannine Manuel in London is positioned, as is the case in Paris, as a unique, truly bicultural institution with a multicultural student body representing more than 45 nationalities. We attract international and internationally minded families deeply invested in the education and well being of their children. Living within this cultural melting pot every day yields a special consciousness of one's place in the world, an appreciation for the broad landscape of culture and civilizations that we learn to understand and value together.

The fostering of pedagogical innovation

The key drivers of our school's pedagogy are coherence and innovation. Whether inspired by current research in the cognitive sciences, by best practices from around the world or home-grown, our teaching methods are constantly evolving. Our international teams of teachers stimulate new ideas that lead to a creative, pioneering education. Hands-on manipulations in math, inquiry- based learning in the sciences, and teamwork are among the practices that foster pupil engagement and growth. Our aim is to have pupils think, do and share. The school's pedagogical principles are founded on four pillars: the early mastery of core academic skills; the development of autonomy; the encouragement of collaborative work; and the nurturing of curiosity, creativity and a lifelong appetite for culture.

© Paul Riddle

Faraday Prep School

Old Gate House, 7 Trinity Buoy Wharf,
London, E14 0JW
Tel: 020 8965 7374
Email: info@newmodelschool.co.uk
Website: www.faradayschool.co.uk
Head Teacher: Claire Murdoch

School type: Co-educational Day
Age range of pupils: 4–11
No. of pupils enrolled as at 01/01/2021: 100
Fees per term as at 01/01/2021:
Day: £3,686
Average class size: 15

Founded in 2009, Faraday Prep School offers inspirational learning in an inspirational setting. A happy, vibrant and diverse independent primary school in East London, the school's historic and artistic riverside location, provides a magical environment and access to a stimulating, creative community that offers exciting learning opportunities.

We give every child a first-class education rooted in a creative curriculum, with small classes, quality teaching and a personal approach in a caring and kind environment.

In these formative years our aim is to inspire a love of learning and that the desire to explore, grow and create will stay with our pupils for life. We place a strong focus on literacy and numeracy, with a targeted approach that enables each child to progress at their own level.

Our lessons stretch, challenge and engage pupils of all abilities and interests. We present children with the great literature, music and works of art to help them acquire an increased understanding of the world in which they live and build a thorough understanding of knowledge in each subject. As such, our curriculum is broad and stimulating, and includes specialist teaching in French, Music, Drama and Physical Education.

Children join our Reception class in their fifth year and leave for senior school at the age of eleven. The school day runs from 8.45 am until 3.30 pm, with our private buses running before and after school from a range of East London locations. We support busy parents by welcoming children from 8.15 am and by offering after-school care until 5.30 pm each day, with a wide range of extra-curricular activities on offer from gardening to robotics.

We were founded in 2009 and maintain strong links with our sister school, Maple Walk, in North West London. Our setting beside the River Thames, opposite the iconic O2 arena and beside the Trinity Lighthouse, gives our pupils an inspirational location in which to learn. We are fortunate enough to be surrounded by creative industries and we make the best of all that London has to offer, with regular trips to museums, historic attractions and galleries.

Entry into Reception is non-selective and based on the date the completed registration form is returned to our Registrar, with siblings given priority. Entry higher up the school is by interview and informal assessment in the classroom. We offer regular open days and welcome private tours.

Fulham School

(Founded 1996)
200 Greyhound Road, London, W14 9SD
Tel: 020 7386 2444

Email: admissions@fulham.school
Website: fulham.school
Pre-Prep Head: Di Steven
Prep Head: Neill Lunnon
Senior & Sixth Form Head: Chris Cockerill
School type: Co-educational Day

Religious Denomination:
Non-denominational
Age range of pupils: 4–18
No. of pupils enrolled as at 01/01/2021: 700
Fees per annum as at 01/01/2021:
Day: £18,420–£21,567
Average class size: 18

About Fulham School

Fulham School is independent and co-educational, providing a rich and diverse curriculum to boys and girls from Reception to age 18.

Founded in 1996, Fulham School believes in co-education in its broadest sense: not just girls and boys learning together, but learners of all abilities understanding that they have much to offer each other, and teachers as keen to learn and evolve as their students.

All situated in the heart of Fulham, the three school sites, Pre-Prep, Prep and Senior, are ideally located to take advantage of London and the endless opportunities it offers to enhance education. Specialist teachers and support staff inspire pupils to work to the limits of their potential, so they are prepared for the next steps in life while learning more about themselves and developing a broad range of interests.

Personalised Learning

Teachers work alongside pupils to support the discovery of personal interests, gifts, and talents and instil the confidence in pupils to embrace what they find most challenging and join in with everything. From the most academic to the most creative, the most driven to the most supportive, Fulham School wants each pupil to delight in what they do, not where it will get them, and to be driven on by that delight to achieve more than they ever expected.

Support

Fulham School supports the highest of academic high-flyers to achieve the scholarships and university places that will challenge them most alongside pupils whose chief passions and interests are expressed in practice and rehearsal rooms or on the sports field. All pupils are encouraged to make contributions where their strengths lie and recognise the contributions of others.

"We seek to provide life skills, the ability to make connections between and beyond subjects, the ability to work together to achieve more than any individual can alone." Chris Cockerill, Head of Fulham Senior & Sixth Form

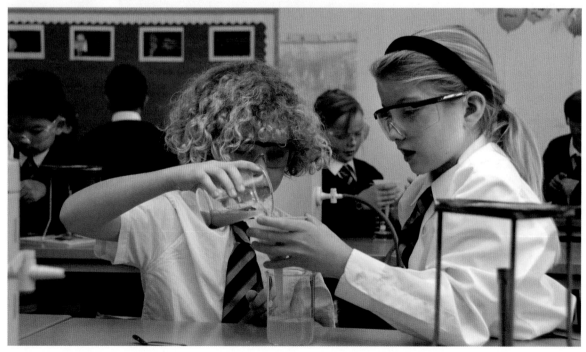

Hawkesdown House School Kensington

Hawkesdown House School
Endeavour • Courage • Truth

27 Edge Street, Kensington,
London, W8 7PN

Tel: 020 7727 9090
Email: admin@hawkesdown.co.uk
Website: www.hawkesdown.co.uk
Headmistress:
Mrs. J. A. K. Mackay B.Ed (Hons)
Appointed: April 2017
School type: Co-educational
Independent Preparatory Day

Religious Denomination:
Non-denominational
Age range of pupils: 2–11
No. of pupils enrolled as at 01/01/2021: 100
Fees per annum as at 01/01/2021:
Day: £13,800–£20,100
Average class size: 14
Teacher/pupil ratio: 1:9

Hawkesdown House is an independent prep school for boys and girls from the age of four to eleven, with two Nursery classes for children of two and three years of age. The Walnut Tree Nursery opened at Hawkesdown in April 2019. Both are housed in a fine building in Edge Street just off Kensington Church Street where bright and airy classrooms provide a creative and welcoming environment for the children.

Hawkesdown House is dedicated to providing an outstanding early education. The children are prepared for examinations at seven, eight and eleven years old to London's selective prep schools including King's College Jnr School, Latymer Prep, St Paul's Jnr School, Sussex House and Westminster Under, as well as for country boarding schools.

The excellence of the broad and creative educational provision enriches the children's lives across the curriculum and in all co-curricular and extracurricular activities, so fencing, judo, chess and coding, for example, are all included in the timetable.

Hawkesdown House pupils are actively encouraged to develop both their initiative and their intellectual curiosity.

The ethos and aims of the School embrace high academic standards and expectations, thoughtful teaching and individual attention and Hawkesdown House prides itself on its outstanding pastoral care. Right from the beginning, Hawkesdown House provides advice, support, reassurance and the preparation to give pupils and parents a very happy start at school.

Mrs Jenny Mackay, the Headmistress, has a deep commitment to pastoral care, academic excellence and the development of the individual. With a degree in Education from Oxford, she also has extensive experience of some of the best education in Britain, at some of London's most highly sought after and outstanding schools.

Hawkesdown House is a happy, nurturing and successful school. There is a fantastic, dedicated staff body and wonderful collaborative approach which ensures that the curriculum meets the needs of each and every child. The school exudes busyness and celebrate the excellence and achievements of all.

Hill House International Junior School

(Founded 1949)

17 Hans Place, Chelsea, London, SW1X 0EP

Tel: 020 7584 1331

Email: info@hillhouseschool.co.uk

Website: www.hillhouseschool.co.uk

Proprietors: Richard, Janet, William & Edmund Townend

Appointed: 2002

Founders: Lt Col Stuart Townend OBE & Mrs Beatrice Townend

School type: Coeducational Day

Age range of pupils: 4–13

No. of pupils enrolled as at 01/01/2021: 600

Boys: 350 **Girls:** 250

Fees per annum as at 01/01/2021:

Day: £15,000–£18,600

Average class size: 12-14

Teacher/pupil ratio: 1:7

'A child's mind is not a vessel to be filled, but a fire to be kindled.'

Hill House was founded in Switzerland in 1949 moving to La Tour-de-Peilz in 1951 when the building in Hans Place, London was opened. We hold fast to the guiding vision set by the founders that the modern child must be educated for a world community. He or she must be taught to understand that all nations depend on one another; learn to live with children of other nationalities; respect that which is unknown and often very foreign to them, and thus open the doors to a world which each day becomes smaller. Hill House became the first school to teach in two different countries at the same time with the same children. The purpose built house in Glion, 2,500 feet above Lac Leman, hosts specialist courses throughout the year for selected pupils from London, providing experience of a boarding school environment in the setting of a mountain village in the French speaking canton of Vaud.

Hill House is the oldest London school in which every aspect of the daily administration of the school remains in the care and control of the founding family. It is a school that enables children from all over the world to have the opportunity to follow an English curriculum while learning that every nation is equal but different and that peaceful co-existence comes from mutual respect, understanding and consideration for others from diverse backgrounds. A full academic programme, enriched by outstanding teaching in small classes, leads to pupils consistently going on to the leading day and boarding secondary schools of their choice with many scholarships awarded each year. We passionately believe in supporting and stretching all our pupils to seek the highest levels of academic achievement. There is a particular emphasis on Art, Drama, Music and Sport all of which are taught by over thirty specialist teachers. Throughout the year there are over seventy concerts, recitals and drama evenings in Founders' Hall where pupils can showcase their artistic talents and the school year ends with a celebratory Field Day culminating in the famous Gun Run.

Admissions

Children can enter Hill House at any age between four and eleven years old if places are available. There is no formal entry test at four years old. Older children will be assessed in English and Maths. Parents are invited to visit Hans Place any Monday, Tuesday, Thursday or Friday during term time at 8.30am for a tour of the school. Please telephone the registrar to arrange a time to visit. After the tour, if you wish, you may complete the simple admissions form. All forms must be completed by the parents, in person, at Hans Place. We will not send forms by post.

Contact

Miss Beryl Lang (Registrar)

Tel: 020 7584 1331,

registrar@hillhouseschool.co.uk

Lloyd Williamson Schools

LLOYD WILLIAMSON
—SCHOOLS—
Est 1999

12 Telford Road, London, W10 5SH
Tel: 020 8962 0345
Email: admin@lws.org.uk
Website: www.lloydwilliamson.co.uk
Co-Principals: Ms Lucy Meyer &
Mr Aaron Williams
Appointed: December 1999

School type: Coeducational Day
Age range of pupils: 4 months–16 years
Fees per annum as at 01/01/2021:
Day: £16,950
Nursery: £79–£99.50 per 10.5 hours day
Average class size: 12-16
Teacher/pupil ratio: 1:12

Over the past twenty-one years, Lloyd Williamson Schools have built an excellent reputation for being schools with high academic standards, personalised learning for individual children and a friendly, happy environment in which to learn. We foster initiative and a love for learning.

We are pleased to offer parents important extras:

- Breakfast and after-school club at no extra cost (the school and nurseries are open 7.30am – 6pm).
- Holiday clubs (we are open 50 weeks of the year).

- Small classes (max 16 to Year 6, max 18 in Secondary).
- Sensible fees.
- Home-cooked meals freshly prepared every day by our in-house chefs.

We boast an outstanding playground with excellent facilities, a homely atmosphere with school pets, and dedicated teachers who support the children to be focused, positive and enthusiastic. *"All staff are keen for pupils to be the best they can. The family ethos of the school promotes pupils' personal development very well. The working relationships pupils have with their teachers and other adults promote a*

harmonious environment." (Ofsted)

In the words of our children: *"I'm really happy here – the teachers really listen and if I get stuck they help!" "There is always someone who listens to me." "I like the way the big children look after the little children."*

And the parents: *"You always know a Lloyd Williamson child – they're so polite!" "I think the school is, beyond doubt, the best I could wish for." "The best-kept secret in London!"*

To visit the school or nurseries, please contact the school admin team on 020 8962 0345.

L'Ecole de Battersea

(Founded 2005)
Trott Street, Battersea, London, SW11 3DS

Tel: 020 7371 8350
Fax: 020 7801 3297
Email: admin@lecoledespetits.co.uk
Website: www.lecoledespetits.co.uk
Principal: Mrs F Brisset
Head: Mr L Balerdi
Founder: Mrs M Otten
School type: Independent Bilingual Pre-

Primary and Primary (Partenaire AEFE)
Religious Denomination: All
denominations welcome
Age range of pupils: 3–11
No. of pupils enrolled as at 01/01/2021: 260
Fees per annum as at 01/01/2021:
Day: £13,740
Average class size: 18 (max 21)

L'Ecole de Battersea opened in 2005 following on from the success of its sister school, L'Ecole des Petits.

The school is unique in that it offers a **continuous bilingual education from age three through until age eleven** at the end of primary, where both the French and English educational systems operate together.

The teaching emphasis throughout the school is fundamentally based on the French system, into which aspects of the English curriculum and methodology are integrated.

The highly motivated bilingual team of teachers are qualified in both the English and French educational systems.

This bilingual facility enables children and parents to choose to progress on to either the English private school system or on to the French Lycée system, and is also ideal for the increasingly popular International Baccalaureate.

The school welcomes bilingual pupils from a range of cultures, and so aims to generate a **truly international atmosphere**.

Partnership with the family is paramount in the school's ethos, and the school successfully seeks to **develop confident and balanced children** with experience of a wide range of activities, an appreciation of artistic and cultural heritage and a thoughtful and considerate attitude towards others.

We have installed high performance HyperHEPA air purification equipment (hospital standard) in all classrooms, gyms and canteens. These remove PM2.5 pollution particles, viruses (Covid) and bacteria from the air, reducing risk of infection.

The school is only **a five-minute drive from Chelsea** and operates a twice daily school bus service between South Kensington and Battersea, as well as a link to its sister school in Fulham, ten minutes distance.

The school is inspected by both the French Inspectorate and Ofsted and achieves excellent academic results.

OFSTED 2018 report said the school was "Outstanding in all categories" and it has been selected as one of the top 225 private schools in the country in *The Tatler Education Guides 2009-2021.*

L'Ecole des Petits

(Founded 1977)

2 Hazlebury Road, Fulham, London, SW6 2NB

Tel: 020 7371 8350

Fax: 020 7736 9522

Email: admin@lecoledespetits.co.uk

Website: www.lecoledespetits.co.uk

Principal: Mrs F Brisset

Deputy: Miss E Mesnage

Founder: Mrs M Otten

School type: Independent Bilingual Pre-Primary (Partenaire AEFE)

Religious Denomination:

All denominations welcome

Age range of pupils: 3–6

No. of pupils enrolled as at 01/01/2021: 125

Fees per annum as at 01/01/2021:

Day: £13,365

Average class size: 14 (max 18)

L'Ecole des Petits is a flourishing pre-primary school situated in Fulham, just **ten minutes from Chelsea**, with easy access by public transport. The school also runs its own daily morning and afternoon **bus service between South Kensington and Fulham**, and between its sister school in Battersea.

The school was founded in 1977 to cater for English and French families who want their children to **grow up in a bilingual environment**. By combining the Early Years curriculum with the French National curriculum, the school provides all aspects of education in both French and English, and today has a wonderfully **international flavour with children from more than 20 different countries** attending.

Children are taught by qualified and highly-motivated bilingual teachers. The school aims to provide **an education that enhances early learning skills in the controlled environment of small classes**.

The school has a warm and friendly atmosphere which encourages children to express themselves whilst following the structured bilingual curriculum. We consider maintaining **traditional family values** a very important aspect of our approach.

Our philosophy is to develop confident and happy children by providing **the best possible all-round education and care**, with an abundance of sports, drama, clubs, school outings and events as well as academic lessons.

We prepare our children to move onto both English and French schools, and many also continue their primary education at our sister school, L'Ecole de Battersea.

According to one of our parents, "This is an exceptional school that provides a nurturing environment, as well as good discipline and a wonderful education, and my child could not be happier and more confident about going to school."

OFSTED March 2020 report: "Outstanding in all categories".

Lyndhurst House Prep School

LYNDHURST HOUSE
PREPARATORY SCHOOL

(Founded 1952)

24 Lyndhurst Gardens, Hampstead,
London, NW3 5NW

Tel: 020 7435 4936

Email: office@lyndhursthouse.co.uk

Website: www.lyndhursthouse.co.uk

Head of School: Mr Andrew Reid MA
(Oxon)

Appointed: September 2008

School type: Boys' Day

Age range of boys: 4–13

No. of pupils enrolled as at 01/01/2021: 133

Fees per term as at 01/01/2021:

Day: £6,470–£7,245

Average class size: 15

Teacher/pupil ratio: 1:8

Lyndhurst House provides a structured but individually responsive education from Reception (4+) to Common Entrance and scholarship at 13, delivered by an experienced, well-qualified staff team. For 69 years Lyndhurst has been sending its 13-year-olds to the many renowned senior schools in London, and some to boarding schools further afield with an excellent record of academic success and achievement, balanced by strong participation in sports, music, art and drama.

Our pupils are lively, enthusiastic and engaged. We focus on providing a full-rounded education, by paying particular attention to the individual needs of every pupil. This is achieved by keeping class sizes small throughout the school. Staff are able to give boys the individual attention they need – whether that means pushing them on towards scholarship work or giving them extra support in areas where they may be struggling.

Reflecting its diverse north west London community, our school is non-denominational and welcomes families of all religions and cultures. Pupils from a wide range of cultural backgrounds work and play together harmoniously and are taught to be tolerant and respectful of the opinions of others. Put simply, they are taught to value the importance of kindness. Ask a Lyndhurst House boy what the most important thing about being at the school is and the most common answer will be to be kind to each other. Our 2019 ISI inspection report graded both pupils' achievements and personal development as "Excellent" and said: "Pupils are extremely considerate, caring and respectful of each other and all members of their school community. This is strongly encouraged by positive relationships with staff, firmly underpinned by strong values and well-established routines."

Maida Vale School

(Founded 2020)

18 Saltram Crescent, London, W9 3HR
Tel: 020 4511 6000
Email: admissions@maidavaleschool.com
Website: www.maidavaleschool.com
Headmaster: Steven Winter
School type: Co-educational

Age range of pupils: 11–18
No. of pupils enrolled as at 01/01/2021: 600
Fees per term as at 01/01/2021:
Day: £7,450

Maida Vale School is a co-educational, independent school in London for 11-18 year olds. Founded in 2020, it is the fourth school opened by the Gardener Schools Group, a family founded company celebrating 30 years this year.

Maida Vale School welcomes pupils with varying academic profiles, searching out and encouraging the individual abilities of each child, placing emphasis on confidence, self-esteem and creativity. We believe this approach produces high levels of achievement for each pupil.

We operate a true 'Open Door' policy, welcoming parents and members of the wider community to become a part of school life. Our school seeks to cultivate the feeling of a family and social hub that offers emotional support and security for all students and employees.

With a broad curriculum, a vast enrichment programme and an extended school day, Maida Vale School has the variety and flexibility to enable pupils to develop their individual talents and fulfil their potential. Our small teaching and tutor groups, combined with the importance we place on communication between home and school, allow us to provide the highest level of pastoral care.

Maida Vale School takes a fresh approach to all areas of school life and is not bound by current conventions and practices which no longer seem useful. Whilst retaining the core traditional values established in our schools, we will continue to make decisions about the curriculum, timetabling and the length and shape of the school day and term which reflect this.

Maida Vale School is a beautiful Victorian building that was once a former college. The Victorians believed in light-filled classrooms with high ceilings and large windows, and we have built on this, taking the school into the 21st Century by fitting it with cutting edge facilities and equipment.

Mander Portman Woodward – London

M|P|W

(Founded 1973)

90-92 Queen's Gate, London, SW7 5AB

Tel: 020 7835 1355
Fax: 020 7259 2705
Email: london@mpw.ac.uk
Website: www.mpw.ac.uk
Principal: Mr John Southworth BSc MSc
Appointed: August 2016
School type: Coeducational Day

Age range of pupils: 14–19
No. of pupils enrolled as at 01/01/2021: 600
Fees per term as at 01/01/2021:
Day: £9,905
Average class size: 6
Teacher/pupil ratio: 1:6

Tailored, not uniform: when it comes to a good education, one size does not necessarily fit all.

Founded in 1973, MPW London is one of the UK's leading Sixth Form colleges, offering a distinctive alternative to traditional schools. Situated in the heart of one of the capital's most exclusive and vibrant locations, the college offers a socially relaxed yet highly academically disciplined environment.

A bespoke approach

Our model is based around a strong focus on exam preparation and equipping students with the skills, attitude and confidence to succeed at the country's top universities.

Students choose their own unique paths with GCSEs and A levels offered in over 40 subjects and in any combination. Whichever combination they choose, each student has a Director of Studies, who provides them with tailored academic and pastoral support. The teaching method has been devised with a focus on individual attention too – teaching is in small Oxbridge-style tutorial groups, each with fewer than 10 students.

But it's not just in the academic realm where students can express themselves. Walk over the threshold of an MPW college and you will immediately sense the relaxed, yet focused atmosphere. Students are treated like the young adults that they are; there is no school uniform, they are on first-name terms with their tutors, they are not patronised by allowing low expectations of behaviour or attainment and they are encouraged to take responsibility for themselves.

Strong results and progression

Despite having a non-selective admissions policy and a wide variety of courses targeted at students of different academic abilities, our students achieve outstanding overall results year after year. In particular, our 'value-added' score (the progress students make from GCSE to A level) is exceptional.

In 2020, over 50% of A level grades were at A*/A. These results unlock the doors to some of the UK's best universities – in the same year, over 60% of our students progressed to top tier universities (Russell Group, University of London and specialist institutions).

Learning to secure those prestigious university places is also a key element of the MPW experience. Students are given unrivalled support in completing UCAS applications by the same experts who put together the renowned *Getting into* series of books, which offers invaluable advice and guidance on how to secure that coveted place at a first-choice university.

Stunning location

MPW London is located in South Kensington (Zone 1), one of the most exclusive and affluent parts of the capital. It is just a few minutes' walk from Hyde Park, Imperial College and many world-famous museums, including the Science Museum, the Natural History Museum and the Victoria & Albert Museum.

Rated Excellent by ISI

In our last Independent School Inspectorate (ISI) report, we received the highest rating of 'Excellent', prompting the inspectors to report, "The quality of the students' spiritual, moral, social and cultural development is excellent. In line with the aims of the college, students are encouraged to develop confidence, self-belief and self-discipline."

Maple Walk Prep School

MAPLE WALK
PREP SCHOOL

62A Crownhill Road, London, NW10 4EB

Tel: 020 8963 3890

Email: admin@maplewalkschool.co.uk
Website: www.maplewalkschool.co.uk
Head Teacher: Mrs S Gillam
School type: Coeducational Day
Age range of pupils: 4–11

No. of pupils enrolled as at 01/01/2021: 190
Fees per term as at 01/01/2021:
Day: £3,580
Average class size: 18

Maple Walk, judged excellent in all areas (ISI Inspection, March 2020), is a happy, vibrant, exceptional value prep school for boys and girls aged 4-11 in north west London, nurturing children's wellbeing and academic best through fun, kindness and respect for one another.

We provide a safe, supportive and stimulating environment with small class sizes for outstanding learning and personal development where children flourish, developing self-confidence, self-esteem and social awareness.

Cultivating a growth mindset, Maple Walk's innovative, creative curriculum underpinned by academic rigour instils a love of learning and resilience ensuring each child is well prepared for whatever the future holds. The numerous opportunities outside the classroom are fundamental to the school day. Through sporting activities, first class music, art and drama, we encourage every child to find their own particular strength with many gaining scholarships at top independent secondary schools. We are proud pupils receive secondary offers of their choice and often with multiple offers!

Our enriching selection of after school clubs allows pupils to explore a diverse range of activities beyond the school day including skateboarding, gymnastics, animation, robotics and plenty more.

Known as 'the small school with a big heart', we have a great school community and that strong community spirit goes beyond the school gates connecting and building relationships with the local community.

We are housed in purpose-built accommodation and comes with a host of eco credentials, including a ground source heat pump for our heating and hot water, solar PV panels for electricity and a growing sedum roof to attract local wildlife.

Entry into Reception is non-selective and based on the date the completed registration form is returned to our Registrar, with siblings given priority. Entry higher up the school is by interview and informal assessment in the classroom.

More House School

MORE HOUSE
SCHOOL
KNIGHTSBRIDGE

(Founded 1953)
22-24 Pont Street, Knightsbridge,
London, SW1X 0AA

Tel: 020 7235 2855
Fax: 020 7259 6782
Email: office@morehousemail.org.uk
Website: www.morehouse.org.uk
Head: Ms Faith Hagerty
Appointed: April 2021
School type: Independent Girls' Day

Age range of girls: 11–18
No. of pupils enrolled as at 01/01/2021: 200
Fees per term as at 01/01/2021:
Day: £6,950
Average class size: 16
Teacher/pupil ratio: 1:5

At More House, we provide a first-class education set in a nurturing environment that is high in challenge but low in stress. Our size means that we are small enough to meet the learning needs of each individual but large enough to challenge and provide a wealth of opportunities – academic, sporting, musical, artistic and more. We understand that each individual has something unique that only they can contribute to the growth and development of the school. We have outstanding pastoral support to enable our girls to flourish in a caring environment that recognises and cherishes each one as an individual.

We are not a 'hot house' but a 'green house'. Girls are encouraged to examine their religious, philosophical and ethical values, to prepare them for the changes they will face in the adult world. They are expected to be tolerant, thoughtful and good stewards of the life they have been given and to act with integrity, honesty and a sense of justice. At More House these values are evidenced in the way we treat one another, how we serve others and our responsibility for those less fortunate than ourselves.

Our School fosters an ethos of spiritual growth, not only for those within the Roman Catholic Church, but also for those who adhere to other Christian traditions and other faiths. Pupils of all faiths, or none, are welcome and the school has a broad cultural mix.

We believe that when your daughter leaves More House, she will not only have the qualifications she needs to pursue the courses and careers of her choice but also the self-confidence and composure to meet the challenges in an ever-changing world.

Everyone at More House is part of a community. We are not just a school; we are a family.

North Bridge House

North Bridge House

(Founded 1939)

65 Rosslyn Hill, London, NW3 5UD

Tel: 020 7428 1520

Email: admissionsenquiries@ northbridgehouse.com

Website: www.northbridgehouse.com

Head of Nursery & Pre-Prep Schools: Mrs Christine McLelland

Head of Prep School: Mr James Stenning

Head of Senior Schools: Mr Brendan Pavey

School type: Co-educational Day

Age range of pupils: 11–18 years

No. of pupils enrolled as at 01/01/2021: 430

Fees per annum as at 01/01/2021:

Nursery: £8,145 (half day) – £16,275 (full time)

Pre-Reception & Reception: £15,165 – £18,960

Pre-Prep: £19,665

Prep School: £20,520

Senior School: £20,520

Sixth Form: £21,735

Average class size: 20

Founded in 1939, North Bridge House shares a warm, family atmosphere across six prestigious sites in North London, providing a unique and personalised education for mixed ability pupils aged 2 to 18 years. In September 2020, the school extended its specialist expertise – from early childhood through to the teenage years – to families in West Hampstead, opening a new Nursery & Pre-Prep building which uses 3D technology and multi-sensory place space to deliver a rich and progressive curriculum.

At North Bridge House, we are on a constant journey of getting to know and understand every learner as a unique and rounded individual, fostering academic excellence while cultivating character and promoting wellbeing. As well as happy and understood, our pupils are notably high-achieving. Our Early Years and Key Stage 1 standards of English and maths score well above the national average, and pupils progress automatically to the Prep School which is renowned for first-

class results in both boys' and girls' senior school entrance examinations. NBH Senior Schools also celebrate outstanding exam results, with Sixth Form students gaining places at top Russell Group and Oxbridge destinations. 2020 saw an impressive 67% 7-9 grades at GCSE and 68% A*-A grades at A-Level.

We are committed to giving our pupils more than simply an academic education, continually building on our extra-curricular offering and providing outstanding pastoral support to ensure they find and realise their true personal potential. Everything from enrichment activities such as Forest School and the care of school pets, to residential and day trips, LAMDA, Duke of Edinburgh and our Inspiring Futures programme enhance the whole school experience – not forgetting our global school connections. Furthermore, North Bridge House provides 1-2-1 devices for all pupils in Year 3 and above, facilitating their learning both in school and at home.

Pupils also enjoy a wide range of sports during weekly PE and Games sessions, which make the most of both on site facilities and the school's prime north London location. From our Regent's Park home ground to Allianz Park, Hampstead Heath, Highbury Fields, Lee Valley White Water Centre and local leisure centres, students frequent the best facilities for track and field, outdoor adventure and water sports, as well as yoga, martial arts and fitness classes.

At the heart of the school is a highly qualified team of specialist teachers, dedicated to setting every child on their own individual path to success – so that they fulfil their time at North Bridge House and beyond. From the fundamental foundations that are established in the early years of education to the expert UCAS and careers advice that is provided at A-Level, North Bridge House prepares confident and determined boys and girls for the challenges and rewards of real life.

Our schools

North Bridge House Nursery Hampstead
33 Fitzjohn's Avenue, London NW3 5JY

North Bridge House Pre-Prep Hampstead
8 Netherhall Gardens, London NW3 5RR

North Bridge Nursery & Pre-Prep West Hampstead
85-87 Fordwych Road, London NW2 3TL

North Bridge House Prep Regent's Park
1 Gloucester Avenue, London NW1 7AB

North Bridge House Senior Hampstead
65 Rosslyn Hill, London NW3 5UD

North Bridge House Senior Canonbury
6-9 Canonbury Place, London N1 2NQ

Northcote Lodge
Part of Northwood Schools

26 Bolingbroke Grove, London, SW11 6EL
Tel: 020 8682 8888
Email: admissions@northwoodschools.com
Website: www.northwoodschools.com
Head: Mr Clive Smith-Langridge
School type: Boys' Preparatory

Religious Denomination: Church of England, all denominations welcome
Age range of boys: 8–13
No. of pupils enrolled as at 01/01/2021: 260
Fees per term as at 01/01/2021:
Day: £6,880
Average class size: Av 17

THE CURRICULUM: Boys thrive in our busy yet friendly school which provides outstanding teaching that stimulates, stretches, nurtures and develops individual strengths to prepare boys for entry to top secondary schools at 11 and 13 – both in and out of London.

GAMES & THE ARTS: Our sports team includes FA, RFU, and ECB qualified staff with a wealth of experience of playing sport to a high level who aim to inspire boys to enjoy and work hard in all sports, offering a high quality and wide varied sporting programme. All boys play matches in the major sports and teams are very competitive even against much bigger schools. A wide-ranging clubs programme includes karate, coding and spy-club. Thriving and vibrant music, drama and art departments with ambitious projects, multiple ensembles and exciting performances.

PASTORAL CARE: Our tutor system ensures that each boy has someone looking out for him over and above the care he receives from every staff member. The small and friendly community enables staff and boys to get to know each other well. Parent partnership is actively encouraged, and the Headmaster's door is always open.

ENTRANCE & EXIT: Automatic entry for boys from Broomwood Hall Lower School if it's the right school for them. Around 6-10 places a year for external candidate at 8 and some at 11 Exit to a broad mix of London day and out of town boarding at 11 & 13 including Bradfield, Dulwich, Harrow, Tonbridge, Marlborough, Wellington, Epsom, Emanuel, Trinity, Whitgift, Charterhouse, Sherborne, Cranleigh and Eton. Strong record in scholarships in all areas including academic, music, DT, drama and sport. From September 2020, opening of Northwood Senior provides an additional option.

HEAD TEACHER'S PHILOSOPHY: 'The whole child is the whole point': academic rigour, a focus on traditional manners, outstanding extra-curricular opportunities, holistic pastoral care and most importantly, running a school that allows the boys to be happy so that they fulfil their academic potential.

OUTSTANDING CHARACTERISTICS: Northcote Lodge really understands how to get the very best out of boys, giving them an outstanding all-round education in a stimulating yet nurturing learning environment and preparing them for exciting futures.

Northwood Senior
Part of Northwood Schools

3 Garrad's Road, London, SW16 1JZ
Tel: 020 8161 0301
Email:
NWSsenior@northwoodschools.com
Website: www.northwoodschools.com
Head: Mrs Susan Brooks
School type: Co-educational Secondary

Religious Denomination: Church of England, all denominations welcome
Age range of pupils: 11–16
Fees per term as at 01/01/2021:
Day: £6,880
Average class size: Av 15, Max 20

Northwood Senior opened in September 2020 as the fourth member of the Northwood Schools group. As a deliberately smaller school, it aims to offer an excellent secondary education in a more personal setting with an emphasis on equipping pupils with the skills and experiences they need to face their future with confidence. Alongside preparing for a wide range of GCCEs/IGCEs, we place great importance on well-being, community and social responsibility and in building and bolstering confidence within a friendly and supportive community.

THE CURRICULUM: Transformative teaching lies at the heart of our modern, stimulating curriculum which includes thematic studies, maths mastery and hands-on science, alongside well-being, community and life-skills. Our innovative approach leads to more active engagement in lessons, the development of higher-order thinking skills, strong teamwork, and motivated pupils who are better able to develop the real-world analytical and problem solving skills that pays dividends in examinations and stands them in good stead for the future.

GAMES & THE ARTS: As well as traditional sports such as football and netball, we are keen to explore alternative sports. We have our own sports court and located next to Tooting Common with the Lido and athletics track close by, and Streatham Leisure Centre and Ice Rink a short stroll away.

We strongly encourage creativity and have seen some great emerging talent in Art, DT, drama and film club.

PASTORAL CARE: We offer outstanding pastoral care to help each pupil develop the skills required for the challenges of modern life. Well-being is built into the weekly timetable and our tutorial system and thematic learning approach ensures that every pupil is well known, with all staff invested in the success and happiness of each pupil.

ENTRANCE AND EXIT: Main entrance in Year 7. Additional places in Year 9 with preferential entry for pupils from Northcote Lodge and Broomwood Hall Upper School. Assessment via digital testing data and Head's interview. All-Rounder Scholarships worth up to 20% of fees available at both Year 7 and Year 9 entry.

Exit to study A Levels, IB or Btec at sixth form at another school or sixth form college.

HEADTEACHER'S PHILOSOPHY: Education should be modern, relevant, and prepare children for the ever-changing world in which we live. In setting up a new school, I am in the fortunate position of being able to bring together the best, current practices in education with committed, innovative teachers who can transform the educational experience of our pupils so that they can move on to the next stage of their education with confidence.

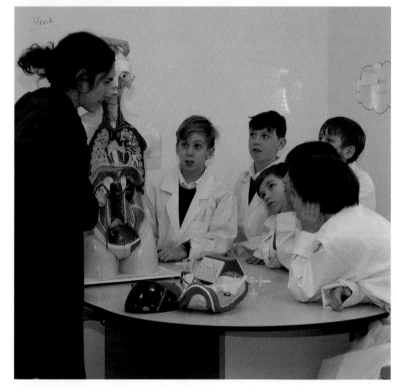

Ravenscourt Park Preparatory School

(Founded 1991)

16 Ravenscourt Avenue, London, W6 0SL
Tel: 020 8846 9153
Fax: 020 8846 9413
Email: admissions@rpps.co.uk
Website: www.rpps.co.uk
Headmaster:
Mr Carl Howes MA (Cantab), PGCE (Exeter)

Appointed: September 2015
School type: Co-educational
Age range of pupils: 4–11
No. of pupils enrolled as at 01/01/2021: 419
Fees per term as at 01/01/2021:
Day: £6,120
Average class size: 20

Ravenscourt Park Preparatory School (RPPS) is a lively, co-educational, independent school for children aged 4 to 11 in West London. Owned by the Gardener Schools Group, a family founded company set up in 1991 and celebrating 30 years this year, RPPS was the first of four schools to open, followed by Kew Green Preparatory School, Kew House Senior School and Maida Vale School.

There is a palpable sense of community at RPPS, and visitors often comment on the warm and happy atmosphere, and the family feel that they notice around the school.

Our school is situated next to Ravenscourt Park, a twenty-acre park which provides the setting for the majority of PE and Games lessons. RPPS has specialist on-site facilities such as a multi-purpose Auditorium, Library, Music Suite, Art Studio and Science Laboratory. Additional facilities include a designated gymnasium, ICT suite and large outdoor playground space.

RPPS provides an education of the highest quality with an engaging curriculum that is varied, exciting and forward-looking, whilst also preparing pupils for transfer at the end of Year 6 to London Day Schools and 11+ boarding schools.

Our pupils engage in the excitement of learning and develop the confidence to question, analyse and express their opinions. We encourage children to develop a Growth Mindset so that they become resourceful, resilient, reflective and enthusiastic learners who are able to learn from their mistakes and build on their successes.

We form strong and trusting partnerships with our parents and we operate an 'Open Door' policy, where parents' comments, views, contributions and suggestions are valued.

The Independent Schools Inspectorate (ISI) visited RPPS in 2016 and we were delighted to have received the judgement of 'excellent' in all areas.

Sarum Hall School

(Founded 1929)

15 Eton Avenue, London, NW3 3EL

Tel: 020 7794 2261

Email: admissions@sarumhallschool.co.uk

Website: www.sarumhallschool.co.uk

Headteacher: Victoria Savage

School type: Girls' Day

Age range of girls: 3–11

No. of pupils enrolled as at 01/01/2021: 184

Fees per term as at 01/09/2021:

£5,155 (Nursery)

£5,575 (Reception – Year 6)

Sarum Hall is a modern and successful school located in the heart of Belsize Park, in which pupils are motivated to learn, inspired to fulfil their potential, and encouraged to achieve excellence. Our motto of *spirit, happiness, success* underpins our philosophy of individuality, inclusivity and positivity. The Golden Values of kindness, courage, respect, honesty, fairness and resilience ensure that every girl develops as an individual with a strong sense of purpose and moral compass both in the school community and society beyond. We encourage children to engage with their future and understand their role in shaping the world in which they will live and work.

Our modern facilities were purpose built in 1995 and the girls benefit from spacious classrooms which promote creativity and curiosity in their learning. The girls have a wonderful variety of lessons with specialist teachers in which high standards are set and an emphasis on practical activities and the application of information is nurtured. We are proud of our outdoor space which boasts a floodlit netball court and 4 short tennis courts, garden, pond and our iconic treehouse and beach huts, which allow us to house a wealth of activities both in the curriculum and as part of our extensive clubs programme. In addition, our dedicated Science Lab, Art Room, Food Studio, Library, ICT suite and

separate Music and Drama classrooms provide cross-curricular learning opportunities and enable us to deliver a broad and engaging curriculum.

Our main entry point is at 3+ and we are non-selective as we advocate an individual approach to each child's educational journey; we feed to the most selective senior schools in the area and beyond. We believe in teaching the girls a set of transferrable skills, which they will use and apply in all aspects of life, establishing them as strong, confident and independent young women with a zest for life and a thirst for knowledge.

St John's Wood Pre-Preparatory School

(Founded 1982)
St Johns Hall, Lords Roundabout,
London, NW8 7NE
Tel: 020 7722 7149
Fax: 020 7586 6093
Email: info@sjwpre-prep.org.uk

Website: www.sjwpre-prep.org.uk
Principal: Adrian Ellis
School type: Coeducational Day
Age range of pupils: 3–7
Average class size: 16
Teacher/pupil ratio: 1:8

Happiness is at the heart of the philosophy at St Johns' Wood Pre-Prep School, and it works. This small school, described by owner and Principal, Adrian Ellis, as feeling more like a private members' club, is a 7+ specialist school. The School is immensely proud of the 2020/2021 Year 2 pupils for their outstanding entrance results. Places have been accepted at: Belmont; City of London School for Girls; Highgate; Pembridge Hall, Queen's College Prep, South Hampstead High School; St Paul's Juniors; UCS Junior School and Westminster Under School.

With a friendly and caring environment as its strength for three-to seven-year-old boys and girls, Mr Ellis believes that the excellent ratio of staff to pupils allows each child to reach their full potential. "*Of course, together with parents, we look to establish each child's unique qualities and particular talents and aim to develop them as fully as possible,*" said Mr Ellis.

Parents have high expectations of the school. Mr Ellis points out this is a two way street, "*Equally, we have high expectations of our parents. This combination is the recipe for success*".

Following this year's excellent results, St John's Wood Pre-Prep remains a recommended 'feeder' to many of London's top prep schools.

St Benedict's School

(Founded 1902)

54 Eaton Rise, Ealing, London, W5 2ES
Tel: 020 8862 2000
Email: admissions@stbenedicts.org.uk
Website: www.stbenedicts.org.uk
Headmaster: Mr A Johnson BA
Appointed: September 2016
School type: Co-educational Day
Age range of pupils: 3–18

No. of pupils enrolled as at 01/01/2021: 1073
Boys: 702 **Girls:** 371 **Sixth Form:** 203
Fees per annum as at 01/01/2021:
Day: £13,485–£17,655
Average class size: Junior School: 17;
Senior School: 18; Sixth Form: 7
Teacher/pupil ratio: 1:10

St Benedict's is London's leading independent Catholic coeducational school, in leafy Ealing. Within a caring, happy community, St Benedict's has strong academic standards. The Junior School and Nursery offer a holistic education for children aged 3 to 11, which continues through the Senior School and Sixth Form. St Benedict's, which welcomes children of other Christian denominations and faiths, is committed to supporting all children to develop their full potential.

Inspirational teaching and exceptional pastoral care are at the heart of the education we offer.

The Junior School and Nursery provide a supportive, friendly and vibrant co-educational environment in which to learn. In the Nursery a carefully planned and child-centred programme enables and extends learning and development. The Junior School provides a broad and balanced curriculum based on a rigorous academic core. Sharing excellent facilities with the Senior School, and participating in a programme of cross-curricular activities, helps ease the transition at 11+ to the Senior School, which is on the same site.

There are extensive opportunities in music, art, sport and drama. St Benedict's has a proud sporting tradition, which promotes the highest sporting aspirations while encouraging everyone to enjoy sport, fitness and teamwork. Music is excellent, with several choirs and many instrumental ensembles. A wide range of co-curricular activities is offered, and an after-school club is available at the Junior School.

There has been huge investment in building and facilities at St Benedict's. Having opened our new Sixth Form Centre and Art Department in 2015, a new Nursery and Pre-Prep Department opened in September 2017, providing our youngest pupils with a first-rate learning environment.

St Benedict's School is unique. Come and visit and see what we have to offer. You can be sure of a warm Benedictine welcome.

St Mary's School Hampstead

ST MARY'S SCHOOL HAMPSTEAD

(Founded 1871)

47 Fitzjohn's Avenue, Hampstead, London, NW3 6PG
Tel: 020 7435 1868
Fax: 020 7794 7922
Email: office@stmh.co.uk
Website: www.stmh.co.uk
Head Teacher: Mrs Harriet Connor-Earl
Appointed: September 2016

School type: Girls' Day
Religious Denomination: CISC
Age range of girls: 2 years 9 months–11 years
No. of pupils enrolled as at 01/01/2021: 300
Fees per annum as at 01/01/2021:
Day: £8,625–£15,945
Average class size: Max 20
Teacher/pupil ratio: 1:9.5

St Mary's School Hampstead provides an outstanding and inspirational Catholic education to girls from 3-11 years.

St Mary's School celebrates the uniqueness of every pupil and their achievements. The rigorous, challenging curriculum places a strong emphasis on high academic achievement within a culture of care and support.

The School aims to instil four key habits

of learning in their pupils. The children are encouraged to be risk takers, not only in their play, but also in their learning. They are also taught to be resilient and not to fall at the first hurdle. Staff ask the children to make mistakes because in the process of challenging themselves, they make more academic progress and in turn excel not only in the classroom, but in their own self confidence. The girls at St Mary's School are respectful, not just of each other, but of themselves. Finally, pupils are encouraged to be reflective, on their faith, their behaviour and their academic work.

Computer Science and digital literacy skills are integrated superbly within the classroom. Technology is used to support and enhance all curriculum areas and learning every day from Nursery to Year 6.

Music, drama, art and sports are also an essential part of life at St Mary's School and involve everyone. Children demonstrate great enthusiasm and build valuable skills that last a lifetime.

St Mary's School is an unexpected oasis amidst the bustle and activity of Hampstead. The outdoor space at St Mary's School is extensive, and the leafy playground makes it easy to forget you are in London. The children in Nursery have their own dedicated garden, aptly named 'The Secret Garden', where they can dig in the mud, play at the water tables, dress up and spend time in the sensory room.

Leavers achieve impressive results, gaining offers and Academic Scholarships from the best schools in the country, including City of London School for Girls, Francis Holland School, Highgate School, North London Collegiate, South Hampstead High School, St Mary's Ascot and St Paul's Girls' School.

St Paul's Cathedral School

**S⸈ PAUL'S
CATHEDRAL
SCHOOL**

(Founded 12th Century or earlier)

2 New Change, London, EC4M 9AD

Tel: 020 7248 5156

Fax: 020 7329 6568

Email: admissions@spcs.london.sch.uk

Website: www.spcslondon.com

Headmaster:

Simon Larter-Evans BA (Hons), PGCE, FRSA

Appointed: September 2016

School type: Co-educational Pre-Prep, Day Prep & Boarding Choir School

Religious Denomination: Church of England, admits pupils of all faiths

Age range of pupils: 4–13

No. of pupils enrolled as at 01/01/2021: 260

Boys: 147 **Girls:** 113

No. of borders: 31

Fees per annum as at 01/01/2021:

Day: £14,733–£15,861

Full Boarding: £8,911

Average class size: 15-20

Teacher/pupil ratio: 1:10

Curriculum

A broad curriculum, including the International Primary Curriculum, prepares all pupils for 11+, 13+, scholarship and Common Entrance examinations. There is a strong musical tradition and choristers' Cathedral choral training is outstanding. A wide variety of games and other activities is offered. At the latest ISI inspection in May 2017, the school was rated 'Excellent'.

Entry requirements

Entry at 4+, 7+ and 11+ years: Pre-prep and day pupils interview and short test; Choristers voice trials and tests held throughout the year for boys between 6 -8 years. Scholarships available at 11+ years.

St Paul's Cathedral School is a registered charity (No. 312718), which exists to provide education for the choristers of St Paul's Cathedral and for children living in the local area.

Sydenham High School GDST

Sydenham
High School

GDST
GIRLS' DAY SCHOOL TRUST

(Founded 1887)

15 & 19 Westwood Hill, London, SE26 6BL
Tel: 020 8557 7004
Email: admissions@syd.gdst.net
Website:
www.sydenhamhighschool.gdst.net
Headmistress: Mrs Katharine Woodcock

Appointed: April 2017
School type: Girls' Day
Age range of girls: 4–18
No. of pupils enrolled as at 01/01/2021: 665
Fees per annum as at 01/01/2021:
Prep: £13,623 **Senior:** £17,325

We are a high achieving school on a smaller scale. What makes us distinctly different is the value we place on the individual and our motto, Fear Nothing, underpins all that we do. Our pupils are ambitious and resilient with independence of mind, the courage to take risks, a strong moral compass and global perspective, accepting and respectful of themselves and others. Our pupils have been described as having 'self-confidence without arrogance' which is a perfect description of a Sydenham High girl.

Our school is cosy and welcoming though it is not an environment that cossets pupils to protect them from the realities of the outside world, but a place where resilience and independence are fostered, encouraged and developed over the years, allowing every girl to develop academic enthusiasm, an enquiring and discriminating mind and the ability to stand up for what is right.

Our pupils make us incredibly proud every day. They are kind, considerate, bright, articulate and courageous. Our pupils achieve across a broad range of areas, from having artwork selected for the Royal Drawing School's Summer Exhibition, gold medals at the National Junior Indoor Rowing Championships, Armada Cup diving competition, Beckenham Performing Arts Festival, a third place position in the British BMX Championships in the U16 Cruiser category for a year 8, selection for our Prep netball team to represent the London Borough of Lewisham at the London Youth Games and bronze medals in the Newham Junior Fencing Series to our year 10 Geography pupils passing the United Nations Qualification on Climate Change

(developed for post A Level graduates and for teachers) after our Head of Geography became the first teacher in London to become an accredited UN Climate Change teacher.

We are passionate about offering a plethora of enrichment opportunities for pupils, such as our Lecture Series which has seen girls at Senior School hear from, and quiz, fascinating speakers such as Dr Shola Mos-Shogbamimu, lawyer and human rights activist, and alumna and former GB fencer, Claire Bennett, whilst Prep School pupils engage with topics such as artificial intelligence, industrial product design, transport planning and Science workshops by the Royal Institution. Our bespoke Socrates Programme gives pupils the opportunity to develop the confidence to think for themselves and plan their own independent research, as

they hear from speakers across industries and create a final piece and written rationale - perhaps making a costume for a character in A Midsummer Night's Dream, developing an app to help donate money to the homeless or an exhibition of animals created using foraged plastic pollution. Each spring we challenge pupils aged 11-18 from schools across London to write an article on a topic of interest within the four STEM categories, which is then judged by experts in the field including pilots, journalists, mathematicians and surgeons. As well as academic enrichment there are many opportunities for cultural development such as our year 10 exchange programme with St Hilda's Anglican School for Girls, Perth, a biannual trip to Nepal to support our sister school, Shree Jugal, and World Challenge. Our broad co-curricular programme; Body, Mind and Soul, encourages all students to access clubs and societies ranging from ultimate frisbee to game design, bookworms and robotics, expanding and enhancing all three of these areas.

Our Eco commitment is bolstered by passionate Eco Councils at Prep and Senior School, who ensured that we achieve our Silver Eco Schools Award and are on our way to achieving the Green Flag Award. Community outreach and volunteering are integral parts of school life, from Prep through to Sixth Form, pupils are community spirited and globally conscious, welcoming the opportunity to give back in whatever way they can, be that through foodbank donations, charity fundraising and local community projects.

Our pupils leave with a real sense of purpose, confident and assured, and equipped to cope with life beyond school. As parents readily point out, our pupils are not 'spoon fed' but are curious, ambitious and have the ability to bounce back.

The Mulberry House School

THE MULBERRY HOUSE SCHOOL

(Founded 1989)
7 Minster Road, West Hampstead,
London, NW2 3SD
Tel: 020 8452 7340
Email:
admissions@mulberryhouseschool.com

Website: www.mulberryhouseschool.com
Headteacher:
Ms Victoria Playford BA Hons, QTS
School type: Co-educational Day
Age range of pupils: 2–7 years
No. of pupils enrolled as at 01/01/2021: 223

The Mulberry House School is a Nursery and Pre-Prep school in North London and was established to provide children between the ages of 2 and 7+ years with the highest standard of education and care. At our school, we regard all children as special, different and as having individual needs. We work in partnership with parents to ensure that each child's first important experience of school will be a secure and happy one, and that school is a place where children come eagerly each day and depart with a sense of achievement and pleasure.

The School Buildings
The school has two buildings less than 100 metres apart. The First School is for the children between the ages of 2 and 3 years. The Second School is for children between the ages of 3 and 7+ years. Both buildings have been designed to provide spacious indoor and outdoor environments.

The Learning Experience
We believe in a well-rounded education that nurtures the individual and offers an environment in which pupils learn without limits. Learning at The Mulberry House School is just as much about developing curiosity, resilience and a love of learning as it is about achieving academically.

We offer a broad and balanced curriculum in line with the Early Years Foundation Stage and the National Curriculum. We have the highest expectations of the children in our care. We strive to ensure that each child's full academic potential is realised while individuals' talents are encouraged and nurtured.

With us, children develop confidence and self-esteem through drama, dance, visual arts and music. Our aim is to inspire and stimulate the children's creativity and imagination through a wealth of Arts based experiences. Annual highlights include an art exhibition, LAMDA examinations, Mulberry's Got Talent, choir, termly concerts and Glee. To further enrich the curriculum, each class has a specialist teacher for Art, Music and Drama across the school.

The children are given the opportunity to learn through play, practical experiences, exploration and enquiry, to reflect on and discuss their learning, investigate new ideas, make choices and solve problems. During activities, the children work individually, collaboratively as a group and as a whole class. The curriculum is enriched and supported through educational visits, visitors and extracurricular activities. These activities form an integral part of the curriculum.

Beyond The Classroom
At The Mulberry House School, we constantly strive to produce well-rounded children capable of communicating effectively with confidence and eloquence. With this in mind, we provide children with a wide range of experiences to develop their interests and enrich their learning opportunities through first hand experiences.

Visits to the local park, Whipsnade Zoo, museums, galleries, wildlife centres and theatres are organised alongside topics and the children's interests. Visitors to the school also provide interesting specialist knowledge to extend their learning further. We offer a diverse range of clubs throughout the school and these have included, Spanish, Ball Skills, Debating, Engineering and Coding clubs.

Our outdoor classroom at Westbere Copse (a local nature reserve) has enabled the children to explore the natural environment first hand; building on their resilience, confidence and self-esteem. Each class visits the Copse weekly and this enables them to develop problem solving skills, giving them the ability to risk assess, enhancing creativity and encouraging a connection with nature. Outdoor sessions have included; pond dipping, minibeast hunts, creating bird feeders, den building, nature presses and creating clay sculptures. The children have the opportunity to build relationships and use teamwork outside. These are vital life skills, essential in them becoming independent learners.

Leavers

As a school we believe in finding the right school for your child. We want children to leave us developing a love of learning and for this to be continued into the next stage of their education. If you would like to see some of the schools we feed into at 4+ and 7+, please visit our website. We are immensely proud of the achievements of all of our pupils across the 4+ and 7+ classes. Following this year's excellent results, we remain a recommended 'feeder' into London's top Prep schools.

Admissions

Children usually join us on the Monday after their second birthday. Places are offered on a first come, first served basis and there is a high demand for places. Due to this, there can often be a waiting list for places so early registration is strongly advisable.

Inspection

The Mulberry House School was inspected in March 2020 by the Independent Schools Inspectorate. Following on from our 'Excellent' rating in every category in 2017, the school has achieved the highest possible standard in the Regulatory Compliance Inspection and has 'met' every category.

The Roche School

(Founded 1988)
11 Frogmore, London, SW18 1HW

Tel: 020 8877 0823
Email: office@therocheschool.com
Website: www.therocheschool.com
Headmistress:
Mrs Vania Adams BA(Hons), PGCE, MA
Appointed: September 2010
School type: Co-educational Day
Religious Denomination: Non-denominational

Age range of pupils: 2–11 years
No. of pupils enrolled as at 01/01/2021: 302
Boys: 156 **Girls:** 146
Fees per annum as at 01/01/2021:
Day: £14,970–£15,690
Average class size: 18
Teacher/pupil ratio: 1:9

The Roche School is a vibrant, aspirational family-run school in South West London committed to developing pupils intellectually, creatively and in sporting terms within the context of a warm, inclusive and friendly culture.

Core subjects are grouped according to focus so that pupils are challenged appropriately and everyone receives a high level of attention. The school seeks continually to build on its fine academic reputation which sees children placed at a wide range of London Day Schools after the 11+ examinations.

There is a strong focus on personal happiness and respect for oneself and others. The school is values-based, using The Roche Approach as a cohesive strategy in this respect. There is also a strong commitment to diversity and a strong understanding of Equal Opportunities is embedded with pupils accessing non-gender bias initiatives in sport, growth mindset programmes and Philosophy 4 Children. Expressive Arts are strong and the emphasis on holistic development reaps dividends in terms of confidence and individuality.

Schools in Greater London

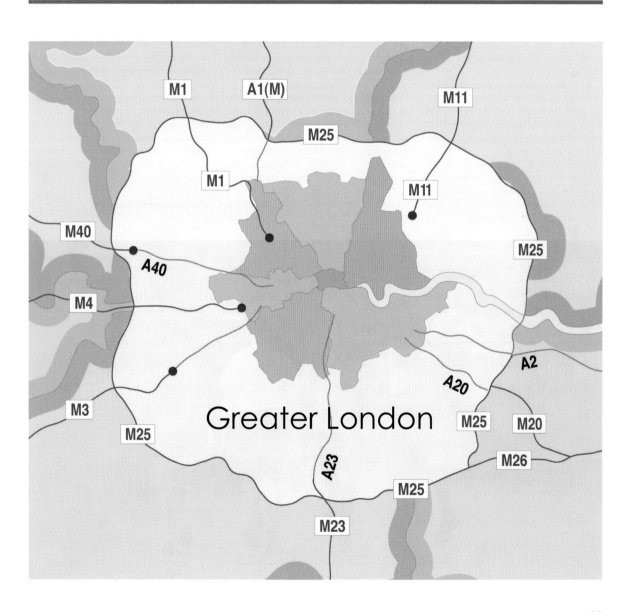

Babington House School

(Founded 1887)

Grange Drive, Chislehurst, Kent BR7 5ES

Tel: 020 8467 5537

Fax: 020 8295 1175

Email: enquiries@babingtonhouse.com

Website: www.babingtonhouse.com

Headmaster: Mr Tim Lello MA, FRSA, NPQH

Appointed: 2013

School type: Coeducational Day

Age range of pupils: 3–18

No. of pupils enrolled as at 01/01/2021: 432

Fees per term as at 01/01/2021:

Nursery: £3,950 (inclusive of lunches) based on 12 week term

Preparatory (Reception to Year 6): £4,460 (inclusive of lunches)

Seniors (11 to 18): £5,555 (inclusive of lunches)

Teacher/pupil ratio: 1:20

Inspiring Teachers, Inspiring Children

Over the past three years, Babington pupils have achieved 80% A* to B grades at A Level.

It is an excellent school achieving amazing results and inspiring pupils from the Sixth Form right down to the Nursery. Babington's Early Years provision has been top of the Bromley Borough league tables for three years running.

The school is an independent co-educational day school, situated in a beautiful group of buildings on Grange Drive in Chislehurst, near Bromley. It has just over 430 pupils from age 3 to 18.

Being a small school has BIG advantages. It has high standards of behaviour, dress and conduct, benefiting from no more than 20 pupils in a class and a strong sense of community.

Babington is an academic school. The School is committed to outstanding music, drama, sport and the arts in their broadest sense and offers a wealth of extra-curricular opportunities. Our academic, social and sporting endeavours are underpinned by core Christian values.

The co-educational Senior School is academically selective with an Entrance Examination for Year 7 entry. In Sixth Form, the focus is very much on A-level study in small sets with the opportunity for work experience, which helps university applications stand out and provides great self-confidence.

Headmaster, Tim Lello comments *"Our commitment to provide an academic and well-rounded education with small class sizes, tailored to the needs of our pupils is really paying off, our pupils and parents are happy and we are achieving excellent results."*

See for yourself –

www.babingtonhouse.com

Kew Green Preparatory School

(Founded 2004)

Layton House, Ferry Lane, Kew Green,
Richmond, Surrey TW9 3AF
Tel: 020 8948 5999
Fax: 020 8948 4774
Email: admissions@kgps.co.uk
Website: www.kgps.co.uk
Headmaster: Mr J Peck
Appointed: September 2011

School type: Co-educational
Age range of pupils: 4–11
No. of pupils enrolled as at 01/01/2021: 280
Fees per term as at 01/01/2021:
Day: £6,120
Average class size: 20
Teacher/pupil ratio: 1:6.4

Kew Green Preparatory School (KGPS) is a lively, co-educational, independent school for children aged 4 to 11 near Kew Gardens in Richmond. Owned by the Gardener Schools Group, a family founded company celebrating 30 years this year, KGPS is the sister school to Ravenscourt Park Preparatory School, Kew House Senior School and Maida Vale Senior School.

KGPS is housed in an attractive building, surrounded by mature trees and nestled in a peaceful corner of Kew Green. It is flanked by the Royal Botanical Gardens and the River Thames and we use these regularly along with the green itself.

We offer our children the opportunity to succeed, be recognised and be valued. Our pupils grow with the faculties required to tackle the many challenges that life may have to offer. We instil tolerance and respect for others and the capacity to celebrate diversity, embrace change and understand the importance of contributing to society. Above all, we believe that children need to be nurtured, guided, motivated and inspired to allow them to blossom.

We believe children thrive in an environment that is loving and supportive. Physically, socially, emotionally and intellectually – our pupils develop and

constantly achieve during their time with us. Our aim is that they leave as skilled and adaptable young citizens who will grow to meet the challenges of the 21st century. We believe in a broad and balanced curriculum, nurturing creativity and collaboration, resilience and determination whilst developing a strong self-esteem in each individual child. We enthusiastically share our pupil's education with their parents through our 'Open Door' policy.

KGPS is a thriving school community where laughter and enjoyment go hand-in-hand with the process of delivering a first-rate education.

Kew House School

Kew House, 6 Capital Interchange Way,
London, Middlesex TW8 0EX

Tel: 0208 742 2038
Email: admissions@kewhouseschool.com
Website: www.kewhouseschool.com
Headmaster: Mr Will Williams
School type: Co-educational

Age range of pupils: 11–18
No. of pupils enrolled as at 01/01/2021: 550
Fees per term as at 01/01/2021:
Day: £7,450
Average class size: 22

Located in West London, Kew House School is a co-educational, independent senior school for pupils aged 11-18 years. Owned by the Gardener Schools Group, a family founded company set up in 1991 and celebrating 30 years this year, Kew House is the sister school to Ravenscourt Park Preparatory School, Kew Green Preparatory School and Maida Vale Senior School.

Kew House School takes a modern and pioneering approach to every aspect of school life. The school recognises and enhances the individual abilities of each child, welcoming pupils with varying academic profiles and placing emphasis on confidence, self-esteem and creativity.

By operating a true 'Open Door' policy that welcomes parents and members of the wider community to become a part of school life, Kew House has developed the feeling of a family and social hub that provides emotional support and security for all pupils and employees.

Sport is an important part of the curriculum and Kew House pupils achieve national and regional championship. Pupils benefit from using state of the art facilities at sporting locations just a stone's throw away from the school, including professional tennis courts and cricket grounds. Just a short walk from the River Thames, rowing is also part of the curriculum.

In September 2017, Kew House opened a brand new Sixth Form Centre which benefits from a beautifully designed independent learning centre on the ground floor. Facilities include a Sixth Form Cafe, library, roof terrace, audio-visual suite, recording studio and Sixth Form seminar rooms.

Following an inspection of the school in February 2018 by the Independent Schools Inspectorate (ISI), Kew House was particularly delighted to learn from the lead inspector that the results of the student and parent questionnaires were the most positive they had ever seen.

Marymount London

George Road, Kingston upon Thames,
Surrey KT2 7PE

Tel: +44 (0)20 8949 0571
Email:
admissions@marymountlondon.com
Website: www.marymountlondon.com
Headmistress: Mrs Margaret Giblin
School type: Girls' Day & Boarding
Age range of girls: 11–18

No. of pupils enrolled as at 01/01/2021: 255
Fees per annum as at 01/01/2021:
Day: £25,985
Weekly Boarding: £42,135
Full Boarding: £44,000
Average class size: 12
Teacher/pupil ratio: 1:6

Marymount London is an independent, day and boarding school for girls which nurtures the limitless potential of curious, motivated students (ages 11 to 18) of diverse faiths and backgrounds. Founded in 1955 through the charism of the Religious of the Sacred Heart of Mary (RSHM), we proudly stand as the first all-girls' school in the United Kingdom to adopt the International Baccalaureate curriculum (IB MYP and Diploma), where girls are inspired to learn in a creative, collaborative, interdisciplinary, and exploratory environment.

Students are empowered to build their confidence, leadership skills, and sense of self on a seven-acre garden campus conveniently located just twelve miles from Central London. The campus offers outstanding facilities, including a STEAM Hub, sports hall, dance studio, modern dining hall, tennis courts and an All-Weather Pitch. The School's challenging academic program is based on the International Baccalaureate curricula:

- The Middle Years Programme (MYP), offered in Grades 6 to 10, encourages students to draw meaningful connections between eight broad and varied subject groups. With a central focus on the development of conceptual understanding and effective approaches to learning (ATL) skills, the MYP is a student-centered, inquiry-based programme rooted in interdisciplinary learning.
- The International Baccalaureate Diploma Programme (DP) for Grades 11 and 12 builds on the strong foundation of the MYP, leading to independent research opportunities as well as exceptional university placement within the UK and around the world.
- Our 2020 results are outstanding: 100% pass rate and an average of 38 points.

Marymount's bespoke, student-centred College Counselling Programme leads to successful placements at top universities in the UK and around the world.

Marymount's holistic approach to learning delivers a well-rounded education that encourages critical thinking, intercultural understanding, and participation in a wide array of interesting extracurricular offerings. Robust transport service from London/surrounding areas and boarding options (full, weekly, and flexi) are available.

Marymount offers year-round rolling admission as space allows. The admissions section of the website, featuring an online application portal, provides all of the information necessary to get started. Applicant families are encouraged to learn more about the School's strong tradition of excellence by exploring the website, making contact by phone/email, and scheduling a campus/virtual tour.

Radnor House

Pope's Villa, Cross Deep, Twickenham,
Middlesex TW1 4QG
Tel: 020 8891 6264
Email: admissions@radnorhouse.org
Website: www.radnor-twickenham.org

Head:
Mr Darryl Wideman MA Oxon, PGCE
School type: Co-educational Day
Age range of pupils: 9–18

Radnor House Twickenham is a selective coeducational day school of 440 pupils aged 9 to 18 that enjoys a stunning location on the banks of the River Thames, providing the ideal educational environment. It is easy to reach by public transport and offers three school coach routes. All pupils have access to first-rate sporting facilities nearby at Teddington Cricket Club and St Mary's University. As part of the Dukes Education family, we enjoy the benefits of close links to several schools in the area and the opportunities of being part of a forward-thinking and dynamic group. The school was judged as 'Excellent' in all categories in its latest ISI inspection in February 2020, with the inspectors commenting on…

"The quality of the pupils' academic and other achievements, and the quality of their personal development, is excellent."

"Pupils' attitudes to learning are outstanding and they are highly productive in individual, group and whole class activities, within an inclusive and supportive environment."

Our pupils thrive in small classes with a strong focus on individual attention. We prefer encouragement to pressure. We stretch, challenge, and support every child through inspirational teaching, proactive pastoral care, and a wide range of co-curricular activities, including a dynamic and exciting performing arts programme. A top-quality education and

a friendly atmosphere combine to create an exceptional environment with proven outcomes of success, where happy children enjoy a busy, enriched school life supported by an actively involved parent community. Our core values of courage, excellence, perseverance, and respect permeate everything we do. We create every opportunity for the children to develop teamwork, co-operation, and diplomacy, to fine-tune their emotional intelligence, both in the classroom and beyond. Visit us on one of our open days, held on Saturdays in May, October and November each year. Booking is available via our website.

Schools in the South-East

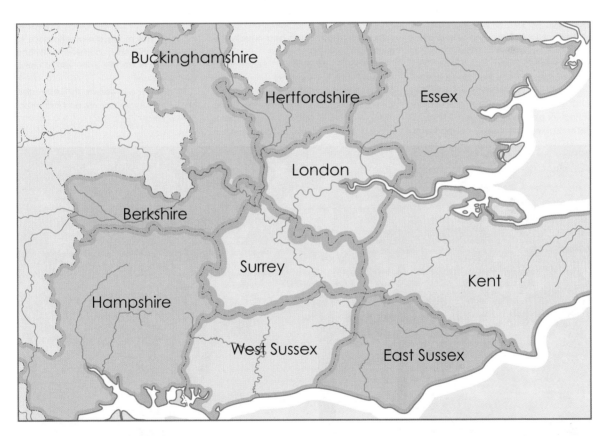

The following unitary authorities are also within the councils listed

Berkshire
Bracknell Forest, Reading, Slough, Windsor & Maidenhead and Wokingham

Brighton & Hove

Buckinghamshire

East Sussex

Essex

Hampshire

Kent

Medway

Milton Keynes

Peterborough

Portsmouth & Southampton

Thurrock and Southend-on-Sea

Aberdour School

Aberdour
floret qui laborat

(Founded 1928)

Brighton Road, Burgh Heath, Tadworth, Surrey KT20 6AJ

Tel: +44 (0)1737 354119
Email: enquiries@aberdourschool.co.uk
Website: www.aberdourschool.co.uk
Headmaster: Mr S. D. Collins
School type: Independent
Co-educational Day

Age range of pupils: 2–11 years
No. of pupils enrolled as at 01/01/2021: 344
Fees per annum as at 01/01/2021:
Day: £4,575–£15,270

**Finding the brilliance in every child
Enquire now for September 2021
Independent day school for girls and boys aged 2-11 years**

Every child has the potential to shine. At Aberdour, we aim to find the brilliance in every child, by providing an individual tailored education that identifies their potential and maximises their opportunities to learn, grow and succeed.

Founded in 1928 Aberdour is a thriving and extremely successful preparatory school for girls and boys aged 2-11 years. Set in 12 acres of beautiful Surrey parkland,

Aberdour is truly a hidden gem, providing a safe and happy haven for your child. With our many purpose-built facilities for learning, sport and play, your child can develop his or her talents and skills whilst experiencing an exceptional breadth of opportunity both inside and outside the classroom.

Aberdour developed Personalised Achievement Learning® in 2007, providing a truly personalised education with breadth and flexibility. We have supported P.A.L® with major investments in our staff, our systems, our buildings, our

IT and our resources, and the combination of a child-focused education. Through P.A.L®, we believe that every child will fulfil their individual potential if we nurture the talent that is within them, whatever that talent may be. Genuinely innovative teaching has made a real difference to the children's skills, achievements and enjoyment of life. We invite you to come see for yourself.

Please visit our website for information on our Admissions process and to contact our Registrar.

Berkhamsted School

(Founded 1541)
Overton House, 131 High Street,
Berkhamsted, Hertfordshire HP4 2DJ

Tel: 01442 358001
Email: admissions@berkhamsted.com
Website: www.berkhamsted.com
Principal:
Mr Richard Backhouse MA(Cantab)
Appointed: January 2016
School type: Co-educational &
single-sex, day & boarding
Age range of pupils: 3–18

No. of pupils enrolled as at 01/01/2021: 1852
Sixth Form: 406
Pre-Prep/Prep: 554
Senior Boys: 719 **Senior Girls:** 579
Fees per annum as at 01/01/2021:
Day: £10,725–£21,636
Weekly Boarding: £29,061
Full Boarding: £34,620
Average class size: 20

With a history dating back to 1541, an excellent reputation and an accessible location, Berkhamsted School offers much to make it worthy of consideration by parents across London and the South East. Our patron, who visited in 2016 to mark the School's 475th anniversary, is Her Majesty The Queen. Located in the historic market town of Berkhamsted, the School is a 30 minute train journey from Euston Station, and a short drive from Junction 20 of the M25. Full, weekly and flexi boarding, as well as term-time and holiday wraparound care for younger pupils, are on offer to support working parents. Berkhamsted is one of only a small number of schools in the country to offer a 'diamond' structure that combines both single-sex and co-educational teaching. Boys and girls are taught together until the age of 11, separately from 11-16, before coming back together again in a joint Sixth Form. In senior school, boys and girls are taught separately on different sites, but share in academic trips and visits and in some co-curricular activities, such as drama productions, orchestras, Duke of Edinburgh's Award and the Combined Cadet Force.

Academic results are consistently strong with around 80% A*- B grades at A Level over the last five years. In 2020, GCSE students achieved 75% of grades 7 and above. Berkhamsted offers all the key components of a traditional independent school education: small class sizes, specialist staff and excellent standards of teaching throughout the school. Alongside this, an outstanding cocurricular programme seeks to foster and develop a wide range of interests and hobbies – music, sport, drama, public speaking, and a vibrant outdoor education programme. The school timetable is structured to accommodate a wide selection of clubs and societies within core school hours. Berkhamsted also has a strong tradition of undertaking service within the local community from Year 9 (13+) onwards.

Pupils across the School enjoy the benefits of being part of a small, supportive community based in an environment appropriate to their specific educational needs, yet with access to the state-of-the art facilities of a large school; a 500-seat theatre, a six-lane 25m swimming pool and sports centre, 40 acres of playing fields, a High Ropes Course and a large art department.

The School prides itself on offering outstanding levels of pastoral care and, in an echo of its boarding roots, the House system is a key feature of Berkhamsted. Senior School pupils are allocated to Houses and the Head of House, supported by House Tutors, has the primary responsibility for the academic and pastoral progress of each student in their House. Over and above the close academic supervision and support, this structure provides an excellent social base for pupils, allowing them to mix and get to know others across the year groups. Berkhamsted offers scholarships – academic, art, drama, music and sport – and means-tested bursaries to talented pupils on entry to the school.

Unfortunately, we are unable to book tours to our School site at present due to Novel Coronavirus (Covid-19). However, please call us on 01442 358001 or complete our online form (www.berkhamsted.com/admissions-form) with your details and our Admissions team will be in touch to make arrangements for our virtual options and also to remain in contact with you so when we are able to welcome you into the School, we can make arrangements for your tour.

Cobham Hall School

(Founded 1962)
Brewers Road, Cobham, Kent DA12 3BL

Tel: 01474 823371
Email: enquiries@cobhamhall.com
Website: www.cobhamhall.com
Headteacher: Mrs Wendy Barrett
School type: Girls' Boarding & Day

Age range of girls: 11–18
No. of pupils enrolled as at 01/01/2021: 150
Fees per term as at 01/01/2021:
Day: £6,548–£7,936
Full Boarding: £9,893–£12,349

Dive into an education at Cobham Hall, where we aim for each student to discover there is more in her than she thought. Cobham Hall is an independent Round Square Boarding and Day School for girls, with approximately 150 students representing some 25 nationalities. Offering full, weekly and flexi-boarding, Cobham Hall provides ultimate flexibility for families.

Nestled in 150 acres of stunning historic parkland, the School is housed in a 16th Century Manor House; an idyllic rural setting, yet close to A2/M2, A20/M20 and M25 and Ebbsfleet International Station. For Day Girls and Weekly Boarders, local daily minibus transport is available, serving areas including Greenwich, Blackheath, Chislehurst and Sidcup.

At the heart of Cobham Hall lie our core values: Trust, Respect, Honesty, Kindness and Tolerance. These, alongside the Round Square IDEALS, provide the foundation for our Personal Discovery Framework, which encourages our students to explore and discover their talents, attributes and strengths.

We know brilliance lies within each of our students. We provide the academic knowledge for them to flourish and inspire each student to discover their future path. We encourage each student to develop the confidence to pursue goals and chase aspirations. A wide range of subject options are offered at GCSE and A Level, with small class sizes ensuring students have the attention they need academically. Cobham Hall encourages

students to achieve their fullest all-round potential, supplementing an integrated academic programme with a wide range of co-curricular activities. Furthermore, Wellbeing is at the core of all we do, with the knowledge that by looking after our students' emotional and physical wellbeing, they feel happier and will thrive. Alongside this strong academic and pastoral support, Cobham Hall actively promotes the development of Life Skills, ensuring all students leave the School capable of adapting to life's challenges.

Cobham Hall is part of the Mill Hill School Foundation. Currently a girls' school for ages 11 to 18, Cobham Hall is hoping to become co-educational in the Sixth Form from September 2022.

Davenies School

DAVENIES
Day Preparatory School for boys aged 4 to 13 years

(Founded 1940)
Station Road, Beaconsfield,
Buckinghamshire HP9 1AA

Tel: 01494 685400
Fax: 01494 685408
Email: office@davenies.co.uk
Website: www.davenies.co.uk
Headmaster: Mr Carl Rycroft BEd (Hons)
Appointed: September 2015

School type: Boys' Day
Age range of boys: 4–13
No. of pupils enrolled as at 01/01/2021: 343
Fees per annum as at 01/01/2021:
Day: £11,985–£17,985
Average class size: Max 20

Davenies is a thriving IAPS day school for boys aged 4-13. Our ethos and philosophy enable the boys to make the most of their preparatory years, supported by high-quality pastoral care, a broad and stimulating curriculum and numerous extra-curricular opportunities.

Davenies has its own distinct character and from their earliest years children are encouraged to relish the learning experience.

We are committed to an education both in and out of the classroom, thereby enabling the academic, artistic, musical, creative and physical potential of each child to flourish. This school is a warm, caring and happy one, where self-esteem is nurtured and grown; we believe that by fostering a wide range of interests and passions we provide the boys with every opportunity to develop in confidence. Our high-quality teachers have an excellent track record of preparing children for life at the country's leading senior schools and beyond.

Enterprises such as the unique Davenies Award Scheme and the permeation of technology in our teaching and learning ensure we offer a truly independent educational experience.

At Davenies, our outstanding facilities support us in providing a positive learning experience with our own language of learning that nurtures each boy's understanding of how he learns. Davenies' boys are polite and friendly with their own individual characters, personalities, passions and interests.

The School is owned by Beaconsfield Educational Trust Limited, a company limited by guarantee, whose registered office is at 73 Station Road, Beaconsfield, Bucks HP9 1AA. Registration No. 717500 Registered Charity No. 313120.

King Edward's Witley

King Edward's

WITLEY

(Founded 1553)

Petworth Road, Godalming,
Surrey GU8 5SG
Tel: 01428 686735
Email: admissions@kesw.org
Website: www.kesw.org
Head: Mrs Joanna Wright
School type: Co-educational Day & Boarding

Religious Denomination: Christian
Age range of pupils: 11–18 years
No. of pupils enrolled as at 01/01/2021: 400
Fees per term as at 01/01/2021:
£5,325–£11,350
Average class size: 15

Pupils thrive at King Edward's. We encourage them to be the best versions of themselves because individual achievement and personal growth count for more than league tables. Our unique heritage and place among British co-educational independent schools means that we can provide the best preparation for adult life to a wider range of young people than almost any other institution.

King Edward's offers your son or daughter a school that can feel as warm and welcoming as home. A springboard to a lifelong love of learning which can nurture confidence, foster collaboration and prepare them for life in a multicultural world. Most of all it can help them discover who they are. This is a school shaped by generosity of spirit, not by background.

Academic focus

A King Edward's education is a rounded education. All academic staff are subject specialists, GCSE/IGCSE in Year 11 followed by a choice of A-level courses or the IB Diploma programme in the Sixth Form. Young people discover skills, talents and enthusiasms they never knew they had and are encouraged to set their sights high and be ambitious in their learning. Our rich co-curricular programme broadens their horizons.

Pastoral

All our pupils benefit from small class sizes and our House system with its supportive pastoral networks at the heart of school life. Each House is committed to strong connections uniting and blending boarders and day pupils into a single team. Diversity has been a strength since our foundation in 1553 and while most of our 400 pupils are local, we attract international pupils from more than 40 countries. They help teach us what it means to be part of the wider human family.

Boarding

King Edward's is a thriving community with four senior boys and two senior girls Houses for day, weekly and flexi boarders. Lower School pupils in Years 7 and 8 reside in Queen Mary House, an impressive family-oriented building steeped in history. Each House has a pastoral team consisting of a House parent and assistant House parent, Matron and an academic tutor. Additionally, there is a 24-hour Medical Centre and an on-site chaplain. Each House has its own pupil team of House Prefects and Head of House who are another body of people to listen, support and represent the pupil voice in daily school life. The core focus of each pastoral team is pupil welfare, whatever their need may be. Every House parent's aim is to make their House a home during term time and to ensure that opportunities are provided for all our pupils to blossom.

Hobbies and activities

On our leafy, 100-acre site amid the Surrey Hills we have space for all the sport, drama, music, hobbies, and intellectual pursuits a young mind can take. King

Edward's is a wonderfully safe place for youthful adventure and curiosity.

The School creates a foundation for life both now and for the future. Our timeless education reaches far beyond the exciting and challenging academic curriculum and the broad range of opportunities in all areas of school life – sporting, artistic, social and cultural.

Pupils leave as independent free-thinkers – agile, motivated, and self-disciplined. The creative, entrepreneurial thinking they develop here gives the next generation of inventors, designers and problem-solvers the ability to grasp life with both hands.

Sport

Our ethos ensures there is ample choice for boys and girls to enjoy a wide variety of sports. Our sports programme is built on the latest research with activities that blend breadth with specific development, hence offering a vast array of Physical Education programmes.

Weekly sports matches – Saturdays and mid-week, and in recent years the School is proud to have achieved regional and national success in football, tennis, basketball, table tennis, fencing, climbing and athletics. If a pupil asks to participate in a particular sport, we will find an opportunity for them to do so. If a girl or boy has an aptitude for a sport, we support them in obtaining specialist and expert coaching, join programmes and local clubs to develop their skills and

compete. We help plan the pursuit of coaching qualifications for our pupils.

Music

Music flourishes inside and outside the classroom with some twenty choirs, orchestras and specialist instrumental ensembles from chamber music to rock bands. A carefully structured programme enables pupils of all abilities and aspirations to perform from informal showcase concerts and workshops to masterclasses and large-scale concerts. Annual instrumental and vocal competitions are held for soloists and ensembles. Annual

House Music competitions, 'Battle of the Bands' and 'Musician of the Year' all bring the school community together. The Music and Drama Departments regularly collaborate in school productions and, thanks to our strong link to the City of London, pupils often perform at events in the City.

We aim to inspire a love of independent learning, a wealth of lasting friendships, Christian values and hopeful vision. King Edward's is an extraordinary, distinctive, forward-thinking and global minded community. It is a wonderful place to be.

Leighton Park School

LEIGHTON PARK
FOUNDED 1890

Shinfield Road, Reading, Berkshire RG2 7ED

Tel: 0118 987 9600
Email: admissions@leightonpark.com
Website: www.leightonpark.com
Head: Mr Matthew L S Judd BA, PGCE
Appointed: September 2018
School type:
Co-educational Day & Boarding

Religious Denomination: Quaker
Age range of pupils: 11–18
No. of pupils enrolled as at 01/01/2021: 520
Fees per term as at 01/01/2021:
£6,425–£12,730 per term
Average class size: 16
Teacher/pupil ratio: 1:8

Introduction

A vibrant learning community, our values-based education focuses on each individual – with impressive results.

At its core, a Leighton Park education offers achievement with values, character and community.

The success of our academic approach is demonstrated by the latest UK Government analysis, which recognised Leighton Park as the best performing school in Berkshire and 27th in England for the academic progress of its Leavers. Leighton Park added an extra 0.6 of a grade on average to its students' achievements. The School's value-add contribution has secured a ranking of 8th in England when looking at schools with a cohort of at least 50.

Academic focus

An IB World School, our emphasis on problem-solving, critical thinking and intercultural skills ensures that every student can succeed in an ever-changing, globalised world. Central to the school's approach, we have particular strengths in Science, Technology, Engineering and Maths (STEM) as well as the Creative Arts (Music, Drama, Art and Dance). Combining these strengths, our students benefit from an interdisciplinary approach, fusing analytical skills from STEM with creative and interpersonal soft skills.

Particular examples, include the school's status as a Yamaha Flagship Music Education Partner, with excellent music and media teaching and a new Music and Media Centre. The School is a Lead School for the Network of Excellence in Computer Science, the only school in Berkshire to hold this accreditation. Our interdisciplinary iSTEM+ programme was awarded first place among secondary schools at the national STEM Innovation Awards.

Music is another particular strength of the School with a brand new Music and Media Centre providing students with exceptional facilities, including a Yamaha Live Lounge recording studio. Our Music department is accredited as a Flagship Music Education Partner, the only school in Europe to hold this status, with 50% of students studying an instrument and 27 music teachers on staff.

In Sixth Form, students can choose between the International Baccalaureate Diploma Programme (IB) or A Levels, and are offered an extensive selection of subject options, including Psychology, Politics, Economics/Business Studies, Dance and a BTEC in Music Technology.

Pastoral

All our students benefit from small class sizes. The average is 16 students per class, going down to 7 students in Sixth Form. Our dedicated teachers are able to cater lessons to each student and ensure they are kept on track both inside and out of lessons. This allows an unparalleled level of support and also a relationship between students and teachers that allows students to feel that they can speak honestly and openly to teachers about any problems they may be facing.

Boarding

Leighton Park has a thriving boarding community, offering full, weekly and flexible options for students. With co-educational communal spaces for day and boarding students there is a thriving House community downstairs in each House. The single-sex accommodation is arranged for Senior students in 2 boarding Houses for boys and 1 for girls. The Lower School (Years 7 and 8) offers co-educational boarding in a House with separate wings for accommodation by gender. Students represent 32 countries, with strong UK representation. The four houses mix boarding and day students, creating vibrant communities, with day students welcome to stay until 9pm to

spend time with friends or have time and space to focus on their prep.

House parents create homely environments supported by tutors and matrons, ensuring each student feels relaxed and comfortable. With a dedicated staff and plenty of opportunity to socialise with other students, each House is very much its own community.

Hobbies and other activities

Our wrap-around provision, which welcomes day students from 7.15am to 9pm, offers all our pupils the time to discover and develop their greatest talents. Students can choose from 90 different co-curricular activities to extend their learning, increase confidence, try new things and make new friends.

Sports

Sport plays an important role in life at Leighton Park with many individual performers and teams reaching county and regional level in sports. The school's Advanced Performer Programme supports elite athletes. While the school does very well in traditional sports such as rugby, netball, boys' cricket and hockey it also has strong teams in football and girls' cricket. The school is very supportive of individual talents and interests from rowing to gymnastics.

Music

Music and creative media is a particular strength at Leighton Park, reflected by the school's status as a Yamaha Flagship Music Education Partner. Students have so many opportunities to play or perform at Leighton Park, with the Music Department being one of the busiest places in school, catering for all musical tastes from classical to jazz, indie to rock. Opportunities to perform include regular concerts and tours abroad.

Facilities

Leighton Park has the facilities you would expect of a leading independent school, including a new Music and Media centre, an impressive library, swimming pool and a combination of high tech and historic buildings. The school's innovative use of the latest teaching and learning technologies is supported by continuous investment in technology, including Google Classroom, CleverTouch screens in classrooms and personal ChromeBook laptops for students.

School life

The quiet moments and the calm atmosphere of our 65 acre park, encourage students to collect their thoughts and reflect within a caring community, providing high academic standards, excellent pastoral care and a rich and diverse co-curricular programme of activities. All of this, and the focus on mutual respect, create a stable, unique and sustainable environment where children can live, learn and grow.

LVS Ascot

(Founded 1803)
London Road, Ascot, Berkshire SL5 8DR

Tel: 01344 882770
Email: enquiries@lvs.ascot.sch.uk
Website: www.lvs.ascot.sch.uk
Principal: Mrs Christine Cunniffe BA (Hons), MMus, MBA
Appointed: September 2010
School type:
Coeducational Day & Boarding

Religious Denomination:
Non-denominational
Age range of pupils: 4–18
No. of pupils enrolled as at 01/01/2021: 800
Fees per annum as at 01/01/2021:
Day: £10,785–£19,335
Full Boarding: £27,585–£33,975
Average class size: 18

LVS Ascot is an all-ability, independent day and boarding school that inspires boys and girls from 4 to 18 to exceed their expectations and become independent adults, through a rounded education that delivers academic rigor alongside sporting, performing and creative opportunities.

The campus includes all Infant & Junior School, Senior School and Sixth Form facilities as well as four Boarding houses within a spacious 26 acre site. LVS Ascot facilities include: infant & junior school environmental garden, indoor swimming pool, fully equipped 250 seater theatre with state of the art light and sound, learning resource centre, astro pitch and fitness centre.

LVS Ascot has been successfully inspiring independence in students for over 200 years. Founded in 1803, the School acquired the royal charter in 1836 and is proud to have Her Majesty the Queen as Patron to this day. As a vibrant hub with close proximity to the town of Windsor, the centre of London, Heathrow and Gatwick airports, the school welcomes families from a range of backgrounds both in the UK and abroad.

Proud of its excellent academic & pastoral care, staff across the school work together to ensure that every student's personal development is nurtured, believing that encouragement and support are essential to help young people become caring, confident citizens for the future.

Being one of three schools owned and managed by the Licensed Trade Charity, income generated by the School is re-invested in the site, to offer the highest standard of educational and co-curricular facilities and is also used to fund the work of the Charity.

Academic Scholarships and Bursaries are available, special discounts offered to HM Forces, Diplomats, those who work in the licensed trade and senior local academic staff.

Mayfield School

Mayfield

(Founded 1872)

The Old Palace, Mayfield, East Sussex
TN20 6PH
Tel: 01435 874642
Email: registrar@mayfieldgirls.org
Website: www.mayfieldgirls.org
Head: Ms Antonia Beary MA, MPhil
(Cantab), PGCE
School type: Girls' Boarding & Day

Religious Denomination: Catholic (we
accept all faiths and none)
Age range of girls: 11–18
No. of pupils enrolled as at 01/01/2021: 385
Fees per term as at 01/01/2021:
Day: from £7,280
Full Boarding: from £11,750
Flexi Boarding: from £60 per night
Average class size: 15-17

Mayfield is a leading independent boarding and day school for girls aged 11 to 18. Founded in 1872, a Mayfield education combines academic rigour, breadth of opportunity and a strong sense of community.

Set within the beautiful Sussex Countryside, conveniently located within an hour of central London and with easy access to Gatwick and Heathrow airports, the School has an excellent academic record, exceptional pastoral care and an extensive co-curricular programme. Every girl is encouraged and supported to find her strengths and develop them in an inspiring learning environment, which encourages independent critical thinking, determination and resilience. Mayfield

girls develop a lifelong love of learning, a range of transferable skills that will prepare them for their futures and friendships that will last a lifetime.

Mayfield's ethos reflects its Catholic foundation and encourages integrity, initiative, respect and a desire to be the best you can be within a vibrant and inclusive community. One of the School's greatest strengths is its proven ability to unlock and develop the unique potential and talent of each girl in an inspiring learning environment. Small classes, exemplary pastoral care, and a happy and vibrant community, ensure girls thrive and challenge themselves both inside and outside the classroom.

Mayfield's innovative curriculum

encourages questioning, reflection, creativity and the freedom to learn from mistakes. Pupils progress to prestigious universities, including Oxford and Cambridge, and increasingly to the US and Europe to study a wide range of subjects, with a regular stream of engineers, medics, vets, lawyers, economists, designers and architects.

For the past 150 years, Mayfield has nurtured generations of enterprising, purposeful young women with the skills and confidence to make a positive difference in the world. The skills, values, aspiration and resilience instilled in the girls prepares them to respond to the opportunities and challenges of the 21st century, whatever path they choose.

Reddam House Berkshire

REDDAM
HOUSE
BERKSHIRE

(Founded 2015)

Bearwood Road, Sindlesham,
Wokingham, Berkshire RG41 5BG
Tel: 0118 467 8731
Email: registrar@reddamhouse.org.uk
Website: reddamhouse.org.uk
Principal: Mrs Tammy Howard
School type:
Coeducational Boarding & Day

Religious Denomination:
Non-denominational
Age range of pupils: 3 months–18 years
No. of pupils enrolled as at 01/01/2021: 650
Fees per annum as at 01/01/2021:
Day: £11,490–£18,330
Weekly Boarding: £27,981–£32,244
Full Boarding: £29,526–£33,789

Introduction

This truly majestic school, in a beautiful parkland setting, is conveniently located near Wokingham in the English county of Berkshire, a vibrant hub with easy access to the M3, M4, Heathrow and London. A strong Reddam House culture is prevalent in which students are acknowledged and nurtured as individuals. Reddam House Berkshire offers a world renowned education within an inspirational setting, giving every student the best possible educational foundation.

About us

Reddam House Berkshire is led by an experienced and dynamic team. The through school structure constitutes an Early Learning School, Junior School, Middle School, Senior School and Sixth Form. This allows each year group to receive guidance from dedicated teachers and facilitates an easy transition.

"Students show excellent personal development. As they progress through the school they build confidence, develop independence and have a mature attitude to responsibility" – ISI Inspection Report

Abundant opportunities

The holistic curriculum integrates innovative academic, arts and sports programmes to enable the exploration of a range of interests. Students are encouraged to develop new competencies in preparation for an increasingly challenging future that may require resilience and numerous skills.

To complement the curriculum, Reddam House offers an extensive programme of expressive and performing arts subjects, supported by a unique collaboration 'Inspired by Berklee'. Visiting artists provide engaging workshops and share their passion for innovative education.

Further enrichment is offered outside of the curriculum through an extensive

array of sporting, academic, performing and visual art clubs. Reddam House is also the proud home to their own unit of the Combined Cadet Force (CCF), where students are introduced to activities such as leadership training, first aid, map reading, expedition training and survival skills.

Boarding facilities

The school offers full-time, weekly and flexible boarding for students between the age of 10 and 18. The dedicated boarding staff create a supportive environment that allows students to develop confidence and independence. A wide variety of extra-curricular activities are arranged for students, including sport, the arts and entertainment.

Academics and exam results

The secondary schools' curriculum is dynamic and flexible. It provides a rigorous academic, creative, and sporting education that aims to challenge and engage, offering students a secure foundation for continuing into Higher Education or a chosen career path.

Consistently improving exam results support this approach to learning, and the graduating cohort of 2020 achieved the best GSCE and A level results in the school's history.

GCSE results: A* 34% / A – A* 56%
A level results: A* 37% / A – A* 67%

Academic support and encouragement at every stage ensures that students perform to their strengths and achieve the best results possible.

Why choose RHB?

- Small class sizes and personal attention
- Bespoke curriculum at each educational stage
- Focus on facilitating subjects, university entrance and pastoral care
- Strong, welcoming community
- Extensive guidance for senior students
- Broad range of extra-curricular options
- Exceptional support for 6th form study, exams and university applications
- World-class facilities set within a mansion house and exceptional 125-acre estate
- Consistently high and improving exam results

Roedean School

ROEDEAN

(Founded 1885)
Roedean Way, Brighton,
East Sussex BN2 5RQ

Tel: 01273 667500
Email: info@roedean.co.uk
Website: www.roedean.co.uk
Headmaster:
Mr. Oliver Bond BA(Essex), PGCE, NPQH
Appointed: 2013
School type: Girls' Boarding & Day
Age range of girls: 11–18

No. of pupils enrolled as at 01/01/2021: 630
Sixth Form: 155
Fees per term as at 01/01/2021:
Day: £5,670–£7,415
Weekly Boarding: £10,030–£11,185
Full Boarding: £10,990–£13,305
Average class size: 18
Teacher/pupil ratio: 1:7

A Roedean education is unique. The School's genuinely holistic ethos brings together excellent academic results, a wide range of activities, outstanding facilities, and the space for every girl to forge her own path. Academic results are consistently strong: in 2020, at A Level, nearly 80% of all grades were A*-A, and 40% were A* grades; at GCSE, the majority of all grades, 71%, were at Grade 9-8, and over one third, 43%, were awarded Grade 9.

Roedean is a wonderful school, now numbering 630 girls, up from 360 on roll in 2014. The School enjoys very strong interest, both from local families and from those in London and the South-East who often become weekly and flexi-boarders; they come to the school for its fantastic grounds and facilities, and also

for a school that focuses on developing academic strengths without losing the enjoyment and delight that must be part of an all-round education. The girls grow up at their own pace, not constrained by finite external expectations, and they have the freedom to develop their talents and passions.

Roedean's ethos is focused on the remarkable benefits of a holistic approach to education, in which academic pursuits are complemented by a wide range of co-curricular activities. With well over 100 activities on offer every week, the girls enjoy sea swimming (we are entering the 2020 Cross-Channel relay race), international travel awards, pygmy goats on our Farm, House competitions, and our flood-lit all-weather pitch. Roedean girls excel in a range of sports, many musicians

play beyond Grade 8 level, and girls achieve at the very highest level in ballet. It is precisely this rounded education which produces independent and creative young women who will make their mark in the world.

Roedean is an extraordinary school – the girls play cricket and hockey with the sea's blue in front of them and the green of the South Downs behind them, the Maths and Humanities classrooms have perhaps the best views of any in the country, and which other boarding houses have been likened to a boutique hotel? But it is not just the location, but the strong academic focus with a genuine belief in the importance of creativity and an all-round education that makes Roedean unique.

St Hilda's School

St Hilda's School
HARPENDEN
Caring, Curious & Confident

28 Douglas Road, Harpenden,
Hertfordshire AL5 2ES
Tel: 01582 712307
Headmaster: Mr Dan Sayers
School type: Coeducational Nursery,
Girls' Day 4–11

Age range of girls: 2½–11 years
No. of pupils enrolled as at 01/01/2021: 150
Fees per term as at 01/01/2021:
Day: £3,154–£4,115

Prospective parents often ask us for a definition of the St Hilda's USP. This is summed up in our strapline 'Caring, Curious and Confident' which is quantified in our daily aim to ensure that our pupils can access as broad a range of learning experiences as possible whilst developing resilience for our fast-changing world is achieved within a safe, caring and family atmosphere where the needs of each and every pupil are attended to.

St Hilda's has been part of the Harpenden community for 130 years and our pupils receive a first-class education in a family atmosphere where every day provides rigour, breadth and fun. In a world where relentless pressure can cause huge anxiety for the rising generation of our society, our mission at St Hilda's is to ensure that our pupils can develop self-confidence and self-worth as paramount

aims. This is summed up by these spontaneous comments of appreciation from parents whose pupils are at the beginning, middle and end of their St Hilda's careers:

'If the pursuit of happiness is a life ideal, one only has to witness the arrival of the children each morning to see that you have achieved that so brilliantly. You have opened the door to the world of education and have shown your pupils what an amazing and exciting place that can be.'

'Your amazing staff have encouraged and inspired our child into a confident spirited individual once more. I cannot thank you enough.'

Early Years, where pupils can start from two and a half, provides a fabulous learning environment – including specialist sport, music, phonics and French - and a

terrific grounding, building confidence and inspiring our pupils to develop a 'can do' attitude, whilst giving them an academically stimulating experience that links seamlessly into the rest of the School.

At the other end of their St Hilda's journey, our girls advance to Senior School well-prepared for the next stage of their education and life beyond. This year all pupils have gained a place at their first choice of school and amassed a range of scholarships. Whether pursuing academic excellence or encouraging blossoming creativity inside and outside through the creative arts, aiming for your zenith in sporting endeavour or increasing your confidence amongst a caring, family atmosphere, St Hilda's has something for everyone.

Come and see for yourself what this outstanding School can give your child.

St Edmund's School

ST EDMUND'S SCHOOL
CANTERBURY

(Founded 1749)

St Thomas Hill, Canterbury, Kent CT2 8HU

Tel: 01227 475601
Email: admissions@stedmunds.org.uk
Website: www.stedmunds.org.uk
Head: Mr Edward O'Connor MA (Cantab), MPhil (Oxon), MEd (Cantab)
Appointed: September 2018
School type:
Co-educational Day & Boarding

Age range of pupils: 3–18
No. of pupils enrolled as at 01/01/2021: 558
Fees per term as at 01/01/2021:
Nursery & Pre-Prep from: £2,698
Prep from: £5,325 (day)–£8,697 (boarding)
Senior from: £7,220 (day)–£11,682 (boarding)
Average class size: 7-20
Teacher/pupil ratio: 1:7

St Edmund's School Canterbury is a dynamic co-educational 3-18 day and boarding school. Our pupils benefit from a caring and supportive environment, high-calibre teaching and a holistic educational approach that seeks to develop creativity, leadership qualities and original thinking. A broad academic curriculum and extraordinarily diverse co-curricular programme enable pupils to find their path and grow to 'be all they can be'. Our small class sizes enable the personalisation of learning so that pupils receive the attention and academic challenge they need to excel, and every pupil here is known and understood. The fact that we educate children from the age of 3 to 18 underpins the strong family atmosphere and sense of community that pervade the school.

Established in 1749, St Edmund's combines respect for tradition and history with a fresh, engaging and forward-thinking attitude to the education of young people. Our approach is focused on the unique abilities and needs of individual pupils. All our pupils are valued for their contribution to the school and we take great pride in their successes. Creativity flourishes here. Our Drama, Music and Art departments are renowned for their outstanding achievements. However, creativity is celebrated across the whole curriculum, as innovative teaching and small classes encourage pupils to think independently and express themselves with confidence and originality.

The school has a long-established reputation for outstanding pastoral care. This is our starting point. We believe if pupils feel happy, secure and supported at school they will naturally benefit from our outstanding educational opportunities and enjoy the wealth of stimulating extra-curricular activities on offer.

We also look to develop the whole person. Our dynamic sports provision, extensive activities programme and exciting range of outdoor education opportunities enable pupils to develop vital qualities such as leadership experience, inter-personal communication, the ability to work in teams and empathy for others. As a result, our school produces remarkable young people. Pupils leave St Edmund's as assured, articulate, thoughtful individuals who possess a strong social conscience.

Academic Ethos

St Edmund's is proud of its pupil-centred and ambitious academic ethos. We seek to foster original thinkers with the intellectual and personal skills to be leaders and decision makers in future.

We offer a variety of challenging and exciting I/GCSE and A-level courses which appeal to young people whatever their strengths and interests. Highly-qualified teachers and small class sizes mean that young people receive inspirational instruction, with vibrant debate and individual attention colouring every classroom. Pupils develop learning skills through project work and research opportunities such as the Extended Project Qualification and the Durrell Essay. We encourage cross-curricular work to promote original ideas and multi-dimensional thinking.

Essentially, our pupils are encouraged throughout their time at St Edmund's to aim for and achieve the very highest academic standards of which they are capable.

Pastoral Care & Wellbeing

At St Edmund's, great emphasis is placed upon the importance of supporting young people and recognising the individual. We understand that our pupils come to us with different experiences and aspirations. This diversity makes our community stronger and richer. The pastoral team comprises the Deputy Head Pastoral, Director of Safeguarding, Chaplain, Director of Boarding, housemasters, deputy housemasters, tutors, resident boarding staff, Director of Wellbeing, matrons, Medical Centre staff and Counsellor. Each of them works closely with pupils and parents, and understands that they are trusted to offer good, salient advice. We are confident that our pupils feel able to approach these adults should they want to discuss anything of concern to them.

Choristerships

St Edmund's School is proud to educate and care for the choristers of Canterbury Cathedral. They are a very special part of our school and benefit from all the same teaching and resources as our other pupils. The opportunity to be a chorister is something truly unique, given the international profile and prestige of Canterbury Cathedral. Choristership is a life-changing experience that creates a great sense of pride and personal fulfilment. Some choristers go on to distinguished musical careers, and for all the leadership, team work and organisational skills they learn are extremely useful in their lives at the school, at university and beyond. The Canterbury Cathedral Girls' Choir was founded in 2014: girls in Year 8 can audition, and a number of St Edmund's girls are currently in the choir.

I hope that you will be able to visit St Edmund's in the near future and experience for yourself the great strengths of our unique school.

St John's Beaumont Preparatory School

ST JOHN'S
BEAUMONT

(Founded 1888)

Priest Hill, Old Windsor, Berkshire SL4 2JN
Tel: 01784 432428
Email: abarker@sjb.email
Website: www.sjbwindsor.uk
Headmaster:
Mr G E F Delaney BA(Hons), PGCE, MSc
Appointed: 2006

School type: Boys' Day & Boarding
Age range of boys: 3–13
No. of pupils enrolled as at 01/01/2021: 250
Fees per term as at 01/01/2021:
Day: £3,410–£6,525
Full Boarding: £7,647–£10,005

Introduction
St John's Beaumont is a Roman Catholic preparatory boarding and day school for boys aged 3-13 years. Set in a rural location, adjacent to Windsor Great Park, St John's was founded in 1888 and is the oldest purpose-built preparatory school in the country. We combine the rich traditions of Jesuit education with the very best that modern teaching techniques and technology can offer.

Facilities
The school is set within 70 acres of established woodland, playing fields and enjoys excellent sporting facilities. There is plenty of space for cross-country, rugby, football, cricket and more. A 25m indoor swimming pool, a rowing suite and a climbing wall are also highlights of our facilities. Of equal importance to Sport is Music, Drama and the Arts, with the majority of boys learning an instrument and outstanding LAMDA results as well as a much-acclaimed annual drama production in the outdoor theatre.

Philosophy
We pursue excellence in teaching and learning through the development and care of the whole child. At our core is the principle of cura personalis – care for each person, so that boys may flourish academically, emotionally, socially, physically and spiritually.

Leavers
Our boys leave St John's aged 13 and move to some of the country's finest schools, but more importantly do so as confident, aspirational and resilient young men, aware of their own potential and their ability to leave a positive impression on the lives of others.

Boarding
Our vibrant boarding community, comprising of tailored (2 or 3 nights/ week), weekly and full boarders, enjoys a full evening & weekend program. The boys are making the most of the school's facilities as well as the proximity to Windsor and London for regular trips. Special activities for the boarders include a Diving (PADI) course, polo lessons and trips to Thorpe Park.

St Neot's School

ST NEOT'S
PREPARATORY SCHOOL

(Founded 1888)

St Neot's Road, Eversley,
Hampshire RG27 0PN
Tel: 0118 9739650
Email: admissions@stneotsprep.co.uk
Website: www.stneotsprep.co.uk
Head of School: Deborah Henderson
Appointed: September 2015

School type: Co-educational Day,
Preparatory
Age range of pupils: 2–13 years
No. of pupils enrolled as at 01/01/2021: 248
Fees per term as at 01/01/2021:
Day: £3,931–£5,624
Average class size: 18
Teacher/pupil ratio: 1:8

St Neot's, founded in 1888 is a coeducational day school for children aged 2-13 years, where the number one priority is to prepare children for successful, happy and purposeful lives. The school is situated on the border of Hampshire and Berkshire and is set in 70 acres of beautiful grounds and woodland.

Staff are inspired to awaken intellectual curiosity and encourage children to challenge themselves in a supportive and happy environment. Each individual is motivated to achieve their full academic potential, to discover their talents and to develop the passion to pursue them. They are given the tools to embrace opportunities, think creatively, develop self-confidence and foster empathy towards others, preparing them both intellectually and emotionally for success in the 21st Century.

We aim to provide the highest standards in teaching and learning within a well rounded educational experience and St Neot's has a very strong record of success

in achieving Scholarships and Awards to numerous Senior Schools.

St Neot's is committed to providing a World of Opportunity in every aspect of school life. Stimulating learning environments ensure that engaged pupils work towards the highest academic standards, whilst also enjoying a holistic education, pursuing sport, music, art, drama and dance.

Forest School, Outdoor Learning and Leadership Days encourage the children to venture outside their comfort zones, to take risks and develop the purpose and drive to make the most of their talents in life beyond school. The St Neot's journey culminates in the Years 7 and 8 leadership programme, which draws together a mix of skills developed through the school's commitment to the Pre Senior Baccalaureate (PSB).

Physical Education is a strength of the school and our sports complex, comprising sports hall, 25m indoor swimming pool, all-weather astro, cricket nets, hard

tennis and netball courts, significantly supplement our extensive playing fields. There is also an on-site mountain bike track and a traversing wall. Judo, dance, tennis and swimming are taught by specialist coaches and there are many after school clubs and activities covering a wide range of interests. Holiday Clubs run in all school breaks and offer a wealth of opportunities, both sporting and creative.

St Neot's holds a Gold Artsmark award, giving recognition to achievements in art, music, drama and dance. A number of plays, concerts and recitals take place throughout the school year for all age groups, either in the school grounds or the Performing Arts Centre.

Open Mornings take place termly and details of these can be found on the school website – www.stneotsprep.co.uk. We would also be delighted to arrange an individual tour and a meeting with the Head. Please contact Admissions on 0118 9739650 – e-mail – admissions@stneotsprep.co.uk

Tonbridge School

TONBRIDGE SCHOOL

(Founded 1553)
High Street, Tonbridge, Kent TN9 1JP

Tel: 01732 304297
Fax: 01732 363424
Email: admissions@tonbridge-school.org
Website: www.tonbridge-school.co.uk
Headmaster: Mr James Priory MA (Oxon)
Appointed: August 2018
School type: Boys' Boarding & Day

Age range of boys: 13–18
No. of pupils enrolled as at 01/01/2021: 802
Fees per annum as at 01/01/2021:
Day: £31,587
Full Boarding: £42,105
Average class size: GCSE 18, A level 10
Teacher/pupil ratio: 1:8

Tonbridge is one of the leading boys' schools in the UK and is highly respected, both here and internationally, for providing a world-class education.

Our pupils are encouraged to be creative and intellectually curious; to approach new opportunities with confidence; and to learn to think for themselves and develop leadership skills while being mindful of the needs and views of others.

The school has a distinctive mixture of boarders and day boys and enjoys superb indoor and outdoor facilities on a 150 acre site, which lies only 40 minutes by train from central London.

Award-winning

In 2019 Tonbridge was named as Independent Boys' School of the Year (Independent Schools of the Year Awards).

There was recognition for our record of academic and pastoral excellence, for the keen sense of social responsibility that we develop in our boys, and for our charitable activities and community outreach.

Academic achievement

The school is renowned for its high-quality, innovative teaching and learning and for academic achievement. Exam results at GCSE and A-level are outstanding, and each year boys progress to leading universities in the UK and worldwide. In addition to Oxbridge, our leavers regularly take up places at Imperial College, London School of Economics, University College London, Edinburgh, St Andrews, Durham, Bath, Bristol, Manchester, York, Warwick, Leeds and Exeter, to name but some. The large majority of the Upper Sixth achieve their first-choice destination.

Recent international destinations have included Berkeley, University of Pennsylvania, New York University, the University of Toronto and Hong Kong University.

Pastoral care

Pastoral care at Tonbridge is based around an outstanding House system. Strong and positive relationships between boys, staff and parents are central to its success, and the school strives to ensure that each pupil, whether a boarder or a day boy, feels fully at home and well supported.

A culture of House dining supports the family ethos. Mindfulness in schools was first developed at Tonbridge. There is an on-site Medical Centre, Chaplaincy, dedicated school counsellor and welfare group.

Co-curricular

A Tonbridge education includes a vibrant programme of co-curricular breadth and depth. We offer more than 20 sports, and boys of all abilities are encouraged to take part and to enjoy themselves. Tonbridge manages to do 'sporting excellence' (our teams win a good number of trophies) and 'mass participation' equally well.

Plays, musicals and drama workshops take place in the school's own EM Forster Theatre, and there is a strong tradition of musical excellence, with regular performances and concerts. Nearly 300 boys took part in the latest House Music Competition; 70 boys in the Symphony Orchestra performed Holst's The Planets,

in its entirety, to a full house.

The school offers a wide range of activities through clubs and societies, musical and dramatic groups and the popular Combined Cadet Force. There are more than 20 societies, including Junior Science, Beekeeping, Rocketry, Debating, Robotics and Conservation – the latter includes coppicing and looking after pigs! Bridge The Gap was started by boys at the school and is about diversity. Creative Writing is thriving and sees regular trips to the Arvon Foundation. Wide participation in co-curricular activities is encouraged at both House and school levels.

Social responsibility

Boys at Tonbridge develop a strong sense

of social responsibility and of belonging to, and serving, their community. More than 24,000 hours of volunteering time was given by pupils and staff in the past year, while student-led fundraising achieved a record total of £113,000, which was donated to a range of charities.

Our partnership with Child Action Lanka has seen a new Child Development Centre being built in Batticaloa. We became the first UK school to install Join The Pipe's water fountains, which saw the scrapping of single-use plastic bottles, in an initiative which also helps fund water projects in Sri Lanka.

Barton Science Centre

The Barton Science Centre opened in January 2019. This spectacular, three-storey, £20 million building puts science and technology at the very heart of the school. Designed to foster greater curiosity about science, and to stimulate cross-curricular activity and innovation, this new facility places Tonbridge at the cutting edge of science in schools, both nationally and internationally.

Headmaster

James Priory joined Tonbridge as Headmaster in 2018. As well as being focused on young people's all-round development, he is known for his passion for the creative arts and for his commitment to widening access, ensuring that as many boys as possible can continue to benefit from the all-round, top-level educational experience that Tonbridge offers.

Woldingham School

WOLDINGHAM SCHOOL

(Founded 1842)

Marden Park, Woldingham,
Surrey CR3 7YA
Tel: 01883 349431
Fax: 01883 348653
Email: registrar@woldinghamschool.co.uk
Website: www.woldinghamschool.co.uk
Head of School: Dr James Whitehead

School type: Girls' Boarding & Day
Age range of girls: 11–18
No. of pupils enrolled as at 01/01/2021: 585
Fees per annum as at 01/01/2021:
Day: £21,945–£23,910
Full Boarding: £36,135–£39,330

Woldingham is one of the UK's leading boarding and day schools for girls aged 11-18. Set within 700 acres of the most beautiful Surrey countryside, Woldingham provides an inspiring and safe place for students to become confident, compassionate and courageous young women ready to take their place in the world.

Not only is Woldingham's location inspiring, it's remarkably accessible for students from London, Surrey, Kent and West Sussex as well as students from overseas. With direct trains from Clapham Junction taking 25 minutes, Woldingham is a fantastic option for students from London who relish the school's fantastic space and amazing facilities. The school bus service covers a wide range of routes and the school is less than three miles from the M25.

Main House, the stunning 19th century mansion at the centre of the school, sits alongside purpose-built science labs, humanities and language hubs, studios for art, drama and music, and a professional standard 600-seat auditorium. Woldingham has gained a reputation for the outstanding quality of its drama productions over recent years. Students from Year 7 to Upper Sixth take part in plays, musical theatre and reviews, often working with the Music Department. Former students have stellar careers as professional actors and musicians.

Academic excellence goes hand in hand with learning beyond the classroom. Students achieve outstanding GCSE and A Level results to secure places at leading universities opening doors to exciting careers. Woldingham is in the top 10% of schools for added value. This means students thrive academically. Sitting alongside this is an exceptional co-curricular programme of sport, clubs, performing arts and outreach into the local community enabling students to develop a wonderful range of skills, expertise and interests.

Sport is very important at Woldingham, which has excellent indoor and outdoor facilities. The hockey and netball teams compete locally and regionally with first-class training from specialist coaches. The tennis dome means tennis can be played year round, as well as on outside courts in the summer. There is an indoor swimming pool, squash courts, fitness suite, dance studio and sports hall. Woldingham is particularly good at supporting students in specialist sports such as karate and alpine skiing.

Students benefit from a wide range of academic enrichment opportunities, from societies for debating, law and philosophy through to extra qualifications in areas such as mathematics, financial studies and sports leadership.

Scholarships are highly prized with scholarship programmes supporting students to excel in their areas of strength. As well as academic scholarships, there are scholarships for sport, drama, art, music and performing arts.

The beauty and peace of Woldingham

in the Surrey Hills makes it the perfect place to board. Some girls board throughout their time at Woldingham and others move from being a day student to boarder as they go up the school. Flexi-boarding, which is available for up to two nights a week, is a great introduction to boarding.

Boarders live with their own year group in comfortable and well-equipped boarding houses, and there is a great sense of community. The fantastic and experienced team of housemistresses are available round the clock offering support, care and guidance, and really understand how to help new girls settle in quickly and make the most of school life.

Many full boarders stay at school at weekends taking part in a great programme of activities but our family-friendly approach means students can go home at weekends if they prefer.

As one of the UK's oldest girls' schools, Woldingham is proud to be a pioneer of women's education. Its single-sex environment is supportive and stimulating. It enables students to be themselves and to grow into independent women who will make a positive contribution to the world. Whether day or boarding, each student is known and supported as an individual to

develop the resilience and self-worth that will remain with her for life.

Woldingham is a Sacred Heart Catholic school. It warmly welcomes students of all faiths or none.

To find out more about Woldingham School visit www.woldinghamschool. co.uk or contact the Admissions team on +44 (0)1883 654206 or registrar@ woldinghamschool.co.uk

St Swithun's School

St Swithun's
WINCHESTER

(Founded 1884)

Alresford Road, Winchester,
Hampshire SO21 1HA
Tel: 01962 835700
Fax: 01962 835779
Email: office@stswithuns.com
Website: www.stswithuns.com
Head of School:
Jane Gandee MA(Cantab)

Appointed: 2010
School type: Girls' Boarding & Day
Age range of girls: 11–18
No. of pupils enrolled as at 01/01/2021: 510
No. of boarders: 220
Fees per annum as at 01/01/2021:
Day: £20,976
Full Boarding: £34,776

St Swithun's School is a renowned independent day, weekly and full-boarding school for girls set in 45 acres overlooking the Hampshire Downs on the outskirts of Winchester, yet only 50 minutes by train from central London. It offers excellent teaching, sporting and recreational facilities.

The school has a long-standing reputation for academic rigour and success. Girls are prepared for public examinations and higher education in a stimulating environment in which they develop intellectual curiosity, independence of mind and the ability to take responsibility for their own learning. They achieve almost one grade higher at GCSE than their already significant baseline ability would suggest, and approximately half a grade higher at A level. St Swithun's offers a comprehensive careers and higher education support service throughout the school years. Its Oxbridge preparation is part of a whole-school academic enrichment programme providing additional challenge and stimulation.

Whilst achieving academic excellence, girls also have the opportunity to do 'something else'. There is an extensive co-curricular programme of over 100 weekly and 50 weekend activities to choose from.

As well as academic classrooms and science laboratories, there is a magnificent performing arts centre with a 600-seat auditorium, a music school, an art and technology block, a sports hall and a full-size indoor swimming pool. There is an impressive library and ICT facility. The grounds are spacious and encompass sports fields, tennis courts and gardens.

With kindness and tolerance at the heart of its community, St Swithun's provides a civilised and caring environment in which all girls are valued for their individual gifts. By the time a girl leaves she will be courageous, compassionate, committed and self-confident with a love of learning, a moral compass and a sense of humour.

Directory

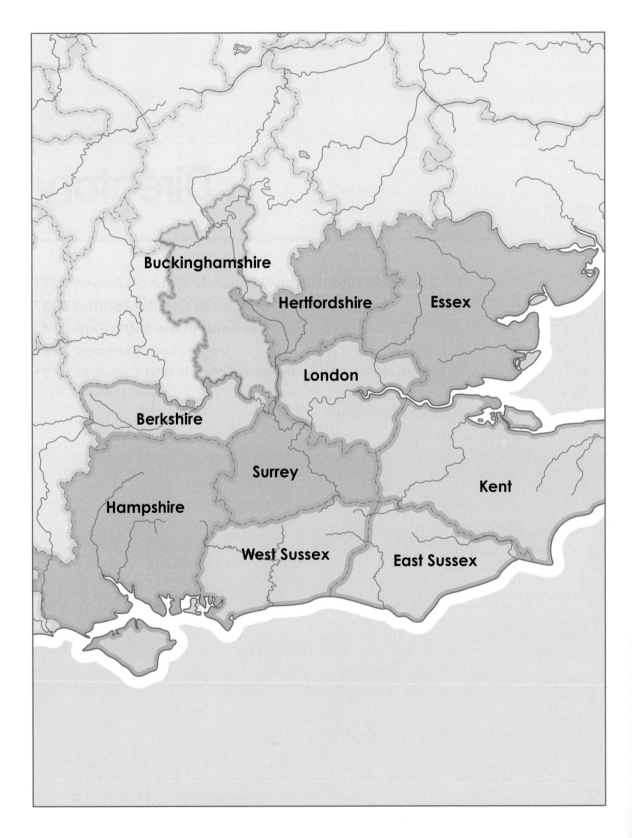

Buckinghamshire

Hertfordshire

Essex

London

Berkshire

Surrey

Kent

Hampshire

West Sussex

East Sussex

Schools and Nursery Schools in Central London

KEY TO SYMBOLS

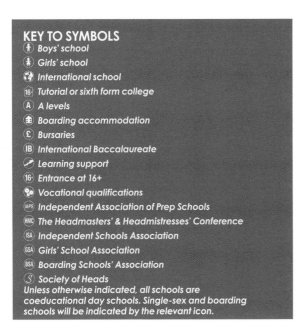

- 👤 Boys' school
- 👤 Girls' school
- 🌐 International school
- 16⁻ Tutorial or sixth form college
- Ⓐ A levels
- 🏫 Boarding accommodation
- £ Bursaries
- IB International Baccalaureate
- ✐ Learning support
- 16⁺ Entrance at 16+
- 🎓 Vocational qualifications
- (IAPS) Independent Association of Prep Schools
- (HMC) The Headmasters' & Headmistresses' Conference
- (ISA) Independent Schools Association
- (GSA) Girls' School Association
- (BSA) Boarding Schools' Association
- Ⓢ Society of Heads

Unless otherwise indicated, all schools are coeducational day schools. Single-sex and boarding schools will be indicated by the relevant icon.

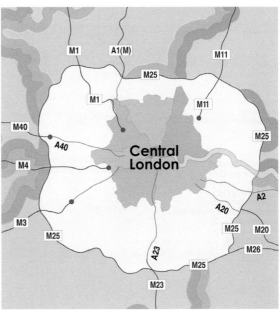

Central London

Accent London
12 Bedford Square,
London WC1B 3JA
Tel: 020 7813 7723
Head: Natasa Blecic

Broadgate Day Nursery
21 Curtain Road, Hackney,
London EC2A 3LW
Tel: 020 7247 3491
Principal: Jacky Roberts NNEB
Age range: 0–5
No. of pupils: 50

CATS London
43-45 Bloomsbury Square,
London WC1A 2RA
Tel: 02078 411580
Principal: Mario Di Clemente
Age range: 15–24

Cavendish College
35-37 Alfred Place,
London WC1E 7DP
Tel: 020 7580 6043
Principal: Dr J Sanders BSc, MBA, PhD

Charterhouse Square School
40 Charterhouse Square,
London EC1M 6EA
Tel: 020 7600 3805
Head of School: Mrs Caroline Lloyd BEd (Hons)
Age range: 3–11
No. of pupils: 196
Fees: Day £5,680

City Lit Centre & Speech Therapy
Keeley House, Keeley Street,
London WC2B 4BA
Tel: 020 7492 2600
Principal: Mr G W Horgan

City of London School
Queen Victoria Street,
London EC4V 3AL
Tel: 020 3680 6300
Head: Mr A R Bird MSc
Age range: B10–18
No. of pupils: 950 VIth250
Fees: Day £18,939

City of London School for Girls
St Giles' Terrace, Barbican,
London EC2Y 8BB
Tel: 020 7847 5500
Headmistress: Mrs E Harrop
Age range: G7–18
No. of pupils: 725

DALLINGTON SCHOOL
For further details see p. 54
8 Dallington Street, Islington,
London EC1V 0BW
Tel: 020 7251 2284
Email: hercules@dallingtonschool.co.uk
Website: www.dallingtonschool.co.uk
Headteacher: Maria Blake
Age range: 3–11
No. of pupils: 103
Fees: Day £11,490–£14,490

ÉCOLE JEANNINE MANUEL – LONDON
For further details see p. 56
43-45 Bedford Square,
London WC1B 3DN
Tel: 020 3829 5970
Email: admissions@jmanuel.uk.net
Website: www.ecolejeannine manuel.org.uk
Head of School: Pauline Prévot
Age range: 3–18 years
No. of pupils: 550
Fees: Day £19,590

Guildhall School of Music & Drama
Barbican, London EC2Y 8DT
Tel: 020 7382 7192
Principal: Barry Ife CBE, FKC, HonFRAM

Hansard Society
40-43 Chancery Lane,
London WC2A 1JA
Tel: 020 7438 1222
Head: Fiona Booth

Italia Conti Academy of Theatre Arts
Italia Conti House, 23 Goswell
Road, London EC1M 7AJ
Tel: 020 7608 0047
Director: Chris White
Age range: 10–21

Kensington College
23 Bloomsbury Square,
London WC1A 2PJ
Tel: 020 7580 1113

London College of English & Advanced Studies Ltd
178 Goswell Road,
London EC1V 7DT
Tel: 020 7250 0610
Fees: Day £0

London College of International Business Studies
Surrey Quays Road,
London SE16 2XU
Tel: 020 7242 1004
Heads: Mr Philip Moore & Ms Irene Chong

Royal Academy of Dramatic Art
62-64 Gower Street,
London WC1E 6ED
Tel: 020 7636 7076
Principal: Nicholas Barter MA, FRSA

Smithfield House Children's Nursery
14 West Smithfield,
London EC1A 9HY
Tel: 020 7236 1000
Manager: Janet MacGregor
Age range: 0–5

ST PAUL'S CATHEDRAL SCHOOL
For further details see p. 79
2 New Change,
London EC4M 9AD
Tel: 020 7248 5156
Email: admissions@spcs.london.sch.uk
Website: www.spcslondon.com
Headmaster: Simon Larter-Evans BA (Hons), PGCE, FRSA
Age range: 4–13
No. of pupils: 260
Fees: Day £14,733–£15,861 FB £8,911

The College of Central London
Tower Bridge Business Centre, 46-48
East Smithfield, London E1W 1AW
Tel: +44 (0) 20 3667 7607

The Courtauld Institute of Art
Somerset House, Strand,
London WC2R 0RN
Tel: 020 7848 2777
Director: Dr Deborah Swallow

The London Film School
24 Shelton Street,
London WC2H 9UB
Tel: 020 7836 9642
Director: Ben Gibson
Fees: Day £0

The Lyceum School
65 Worship Street,
London EC2A 2DU
Tel: +44 (0)20 7247 1588
Head of School: Ms Hilary Wyatt NPQH, MA, PGCE
Age range: 3–11
Fees: Day £16,185

The Method Studio London
Conway Hall, 25 Red Lion
Square, London WC1R 4RL
Tel: 020 7831 7335

Urdang Academy
The Old Finsbury Town
Hall, Rosebery Avenue,
London EC1R 4RP
Tel: +44 (0)20 7713 7710
Age range: 16+

Williams College
Thavies Inn House, 5 Holborn
Circus, London EC1N 2HB
Tel: 020 7583 9222
Head: Mr Mujeeb Pathamanathan

East London

Al-Falah Primary School
48 Kenninghall Road,
Hackney, London E5 8BY
Tel: 020 8985 1059
Headteacher: Mr M A Hussain
Age range: 5–11

Al-Mizan School
46 Whitechapel Road,
London E1 1JX
Tel: 020 7650 3070
Head: Mr Askor Ali
Age range: B7–11

Alphabet House Day (Montessori) Nursery
Methodist Church, Windmill
Lane, Stratford, London E15 1PG
Tel: 020 8519 2023
Principal: Ms Kemi Balogun

Alphabet House Nursery School
23 Harold Road, Upton
Park, London E13 0SQ
Tel: 020 8548 9466
Principal: Ms Kemi Balogun

Ann Tayler Children's Centre
1-13 Triangle Road (off Westgate
Street), Hackney, London E8 3RP
Tel: 020 7275 6022
Fees: Day £10

Azhar Academy
235A Romford Road, Forest
Gate, London E7 9HL
Tel: 020 8534 5959
Headteacher: Mrs R Rehman
Age range: G11–16
No. of pupils: 189

Beis Trana Girls' School
186 Upper Clapton Road,
London E5 9DH
Tel: 020 8815 8000
Head of School: Mrs M Shmaya
Age range: G3–16

Bethnal Green Montessori School
68 Warner Place, Bethnal Green, London E2 7DA
Tel: 020 7739 4343
Head: Sidonie Winter
Age range: 2–6

Building Crafts College
Kennard Road, Stratford, London E15 1AH
Tel: 020 8522 1705
Principal: Mr John Taylor
16⁺ ✿

Busy Bees at Chingford
2 Larkswood Leisure Park, 175 New Road, Chingford, London E4 9EY
Tel: 020 8524 7063
Nursery Manager: Natalie Keyes
Age range: 3 months–5 years

Busy Bees in London ExCel
5 Western Gateway, Royal Victoria Docks, London E16 1XL
Tel: 020 7474 7487
Nursery Manager: Rebecca Davy
Age range: 0–5

Chingford House School
22 Marlborough Road, Waltham Forest, London E4 9AL
Tel: 020 8527 2902; 07749 899 498
Head teacher: Helen McNulty
Age range: 0–5

City of London College
71 Whitechapel High Street, London E1 7PL
Tel: 020 7247 2166
Head: Mr David Nixon
16⁺

East End Computing & Business College
149 Commercial Road, London E1 1PX
Tel: 020 7247 8447
Head: Anthony Wilkinson
16⁺

FARADAY PREP SCHOOL
For further details see p. 57
Old Gate House, 7 Trinity Buoy Wharf, London E14 0JW
Tel: 020 8965 7374
Email: info@ newmodelschool.co.uk
Website: www.faradayschool.co.uk
Head Teacher: Claire Murdoch
Age range: 4–11
No. of pupils: 100
Fees: Day £3,686
£

Forest School
College Place, Snaresbrook, London E17 3PY
Tel: 020 8520 1744
Warden: Mr Cliff Hodges
Age range: 4–18
No. of pupils: 1355 VIth260
Fees: Day £13,095–£18,681
Ⓐ £ ✎ 16⁺

Gatehouse School
Sewardstone Road, Victoria Park, London E2 9JG
Tel: 020 8980 2978
Acting Headmistress: Sevda Corby
Age range: 3–11
No. of pupils: 320
Fees: Day £11,610–£12,225
£ ✎

Grangewood Independent School
Chester Road, Forest Gate, London E7 8QT
Tel: 020 8472 3552
Headteacher: Mrs B A Roberts B.Ed (Hons); PG Cert (SEN)
Age range: 2–11
No. of pupils: 71
Fees: Day £5,157–£6,751
✎

Happy Faces at Wisdom Kids Nursery
524 High Street, London E12 6QN
Tel: 020 8478 2805

Hyland House School
Holcombe Road, Tottenham, London N17 9AD
Tel: 0208 520 4186
Head Teacher: Mrs Gina Abbequaye
Age range: 3–11
Fees: Day £2,520

Independent Place Nursery
26/27 Independent Place, Shacklewell Lane, Hackney, London E8 2HD
Tel: 020 7275 7755
Head: Ms Dawn Pennington
Age range: 0–5
No. of pupils: 43
✎

Kaye Rowe Nursery School
Osborne Road, London E7 0PH
Tel: 020 8534 4403

Kids Inc Day Nursery – Chingford
3 Friday Hill West, Chingford Hatch, London E4 6UP
Tel: 020 8524 6745

Kids Inc Day Nursery – South Woodford
71 Cleveland Road, South Woodford, London E18 2AE
Tel: 020 8518 8855
Manager: Sarah-Jane Smith NNEB
Age range: 3months–5

Lanterns Nursery and Pre-school
Unit D, Great Eastern Enterprise Centre,, 3 Millharbour, London E14 9XP
Tel: 020 7363 0951

Little Green Man Nursery
15 Lemna Road, Waltham Forest, London E11 1HX
Tel: 020 8539 7228
Age range: 0–5
No. of pupils: 46

London East Academy
46 Whitechapel Road, London E1 1JX
Tel: 020 7650 3070
Headteacher: Askor Ali
Age range: B11–18
✶ Ⓐ

London School of Commerce & IT
128 Commercial Road, London E1 1NL
Tel: 020 7702 2509
Head: Dr Abul Kalam
16⁺

Low Hall Nursery
Low Hall Lane, London E17 8BE
Tel: 020 8520 1689

Lubavitch House School (Junior Boys)
135 Clapton Common, London E5 9AE
Tel: 020 8800 1044
Head: Mr R Leach
Age range: B5–11
No. of pupils: 101
✶

Madani Girls School
Myrdle Street, London E1 1HL
Tel: 020 7377 1992
Headteacher: Muhammad S. Rahman
Age range: G11–18 years
✶

Magic Roundabout Nursery – Docklands
Jack Dash House, 2 Lawn House Close, Marsh Wall, London E14 9YQ
Tel: 020 7364 6028

Magic Roundabout Nursery – Walthamstow
161 Wadham Road, Centre Way, Walthamstow, London E17 4HU
Tel: 020 8523 5551

Market Nursery
Wilde Close, Off Pownall Road, Hackney, London E8 4JS
Tel: 020 7241 0978
Head: Ms Hazel Babb
No. of pupils: 24
✎

Noah's Ark Nursery
within Mildmay Hospital, Hackney Road, London E2 7NA
Tel: 020 7613 6346

Normanhurst School
68-74 Station Road, Chingford, London E4 7BA
Tel: 020 8529 4307
Headmistress: Mrs Claire Osborn
Age range: 2–16
No. of pupils: 250
Fees: Day £10,350–£13,050
✎

Oliver Thomas Nursery School
Mathews Avenue, East Ham, London E6 6BU
Tel: 020 8552 1177
Head Teacher: Dianne Walls
Age range: 3–5
✎

Pillar Box Montessori Nursery & Pre-Prep School
107 Bow Road, London E3 2AN
Tel: 020 8980 0700
Director: Lorraine Redknapp
Age range: 0–5
Fees: Day £12,000

PromisedLand Academy
St Cedds Hall, Webb Gardens, Plaistow, London E13 8SR
Tel: 07572 614 770
Head: Mrs M S Coote
Age range: 4–16

Quwwat-ul Islam Girls School
16 Chaucer Road, Forest Gate, London E7 9NB
Tel: 020 8548 4736
Headteacher: Ms Shazia Member
Age range: G4–11
✶

River House Montessori School
3-4 Shadwell Pierhead, Glamis Road, London E1W 3TD
Tel: 020 7538 9886
Headmistress: Miss S Greenwood
Age range: 3–16
Fees: Day £3,410–£3,625
✎

Snaresbrook Preparatory School
75 Woodford Road, South Woodford, London E18 2EA
Tel: 020 8989 2394
Head of School: Mr Ralph Dalton
Age range: 3–11
Fees: Day £8,922–£11,934
✎

Talmud Torah Machzikei Hadass School
1 Belz Terrace, Clapton, London E5 9SN
Tel: 020 8800 6599
Headteacher: Rabbi C Silbiger
Age range: B3–16
✶

The Grove Montessori Nursery
Grosvenor Road, Wanstead, London E11 2EW
Tel: 0203 404 4380
Age range: 3 months–5 years

The Happy Nest Nursery Ltd
Fellows Court Family Centre, Weymouth Terrace, Hackney, London E2 8LR
Tel: 020 7739 3193

The Music School
59a High Street, Wanstead, London E11 2AE
Tel: 020 8502 0932
16

Tom Thumb Nursery
1-7 Beulah Road, London E17 9LG
Tel: 020 8520 1329
Age range: 2–5
No. of pupils: 32

Treehouse Nursery Schools – Cambridge Park
25 Cambridge Park, Wanstead, London E11 2PU
Tel: 020 853 22535
Age range: 3 months–5 years

Treehouse Nursery Schools – Woodbine Place
35 Woodbine Place, London E11 2RH
Tel: 020 8532 2535
Age range: 3 months–5 years

Whitechapel College
67 Maryland Square, Stratford, London E15 1HF
Tel: 020 8555 3355
Principal: Luke Julias Maughan-Pawsey
16

Winston House Preparatory School
140 High Road, London E18 2QS
Tel: 020 8505 6565
Head Teacher: Mrs Marian Kemp
Age range: 3–11

North London

5 E College of London
Selby Centre, Selby Road, London N17 8JL
Tel: 020 8885 3456/5454
Head: Mr Raj Doshi
16

Annemount School
18 Holne Chase, Hampstead Garden Suburb, London N2 0QN
Tel: 020 8455 2132
Principal: Mrs G Maidment BA(Hons), MontDip
Age range: 2–7 years

Asquith Nursery – Crouch Hill
33 Crouch Hill, London N4 4AP
Tel: 020 7561 1533
Age range: 3 months–5

Asquith Nursery – Finsbury Park
Dulas Street, Finsbury Park, Islington, London N4 3AF
Tel: 020 7263 3090
Age range: 3 months–5

Asquith Nursery – Salcombe
33 The Green, Southgate, London N14 6EN
Tel: 020 8882 2136

Avenue Pre-Prep & Nursery School
2 Highgate Avenue, Highgate, London N6 5RX
Tel: 020 8348 6815
Principal: Mrs. Mary Fysh
Age range: 2–8

Beis Chinuch Lebonos Girls School
Woodberry Down Centre, Woodberry Down, London N4 2SH
Tel: 020 88097 737
Age range: G2–16

Beis Malka Girls School
93 Alkham Road, London N16 6XD
Tel: 020 8806 2070
Age range: G2–16

Beis Rochel D'Satmar Girls School
51-57 Amhurst Park, London N16 5DL
Tel: 020 8800 9060
Headmistress: Mrs E Katz
Age range: G2–18

Bnois Jerusalem School
79-81 Amhurst Park, London N16 5DL
Tel: 020 8211 7136
Age range: G3–16

Bobov Primary School
87-90 Egerton Road, London N16 6UE
Tel: 020 8809 1025
Headmaster: Mr Chaim Weissman
Age range: B3–13

Busy Bees at Enfield Highlands Village
2 Florey Square, Highlands Village, London N21 1UJ
Tel: 020 8360 6610
Nursery Manager: Simone Prince
Age range: 3 months–5 years

Busy Bees Nursery
c/o David Lloyd Leisure Club, Leisure Way, High Road, Finchley, London N12 0QZ
Tel: 020 8343 8500
Manager: Toni Difonzo
Age range: 3months–5
No. of pupils: 18

Channing School
The Bank, Highgate, London N6 5HF
Tel: 020 8340 2328
Head: Mrs B M Elliott
Age range: G4–18
No. of pupils: 746 Vlth108
Fees: Day £17,610–£19,410

City of London Business College
Ebenezer House, 726-728 Seven Sisters Road, London N15 5NH
Tel: 020 8800 6621
Head: Mr Kwateng
16

Coconut Nursery
133 Stoke Newington Church Street, London N16 0UH
Tel: 020 7923 0720

Court Theatre Training Co
55 East Road, London N1 6AH
Tel: 020 7739 6868
Artistic Director: June Abbott
16

Dwight School London
6 Friern Barnet Lane, London N11 3LX
Tel: +44 (0)20 8920 0637
Head: Mrs Alison Cobbin BA, Dip Ed, MBA
Age range: 3–18

Finchley & Acton Yochien School
6 Hendon Avenue, Finchley, London N3 1UE
Tel: 020 8343 2191
Headteacher: J Tanabe
Age range: 2–6
No. of pupils: 145

Floral Place Day Nursery
2 Floral Place, Northampton Grove, London N1 2PL
Tel: 020 7354 9945

Grange Park Preparatory School
13 The Chine, Grange Park, Winchmore Hill, London N21 2EA
Tel: 020 8360 1469
Headteacher: Miss F Rizzo
Age range: G4–11
No. of pupils: 90
Fees: Day £10,300–£10,378

Greek Secondary School of London
22 Trinity Road, London N22 8LB
Tel: +44 (0)20 8881 9320
Headteacher: Nikos Kazantzakis
Age range: 13–18
A 16

Hackney Care For Kids
61 Evering Road, Hackney, London N16 7PR
Tel: 020 7923 3471

Highgate
North Road, Highgate, London N6 4AY
Tel: 020 8340 1524
Head Master: Mr A S Pettitt MA
Age range: 3–18
No. of pupils: 1541 Vlth312
Fees: Day £18,165–£20,970
A £ 16

Highgate Junior School
Cholmeley House, 3 Bishopswood Road, London N6 4PL
Tel: 020 8340 9193
Principal: Mr S M James BA
Age range: 7–11
Fees: Day £19,230

Highgate Pre-Preparatory School
7 Bishopswood Road, London N6 4PH
Tel: 020 8340 9196
Principal: Mrs Diane Hecht
Age range: 3–7
No. of pupils: 150
Fees: Day £18,165

Impact Factory
Suite 121, Business Design Centre, 52 Upper Street, London N1 0QH
Tel: 020 7226 1877
Founding Partners: Robin Chandler & Jo Ellen Grzyb
16

Keble Prep
Wades Hill, Winchmore Hill, London N21 1BG
Tel: 020 8360 3359
Headmaster: Mr M J Mitchell
Age range: B4–13
No. of pupils: 228
Fees: Day £3,850–£4,930

Kerem House
18 Kingsley Way, London N2 0ER
Tel: 020 8455 7524
Headmistress: Mrs D Rose
Age range: 2–5
No. of pupils: 96
Fees: Day £2,025–£5,160

Kerem School
Norrice Lea, London N2 0RE
Tel: 020 8455 0909
Head Teacher: Miss Alyson Burns
Age range: 3–11
Fees: Day £9,435

Laurel Way Playgroup
Nansen Village, 21 Woodside Avenue, London N12 8AQ
Tel: 020 8445 7514
Head: Mrs Susan Farber
Age range: 3–5

London Studio Centre
42-50 York Way, Kings Cross, London N1 9AB
Tel: 020 7837 7741
Director & CEO: Mr Nic Espinosa
Age range: 18+

Lubavitch House School (Senior Girls)
107-115 Stamford Hill, Hackney, London N16 5RP
Tel: 020 8800 0022
Headmaster: Rabbi Shmuel Lew FRSA
Age range: G11–18
No. of pupils: 102
Fees: Day £3,900

Lubavitch Orthodox Jewish Nursery – North London
107-115 Stamford Hill, Hackney, London N16 5RP
Tel: 020 8800 0022
Head: Mrs F Sudak

MARS Montessori Islington Green Nursery
4 Collins Yard, Islington Green, London N1 2XU
Tel: 020 7704 2805
Head: Angela Euesden
Age range: 2–5
No. of pupils: 24

New Park Montessori School
67 Highbury New Park, Islington, London N5 2EU
Tel: 020 7226 1109

New Southgate Day and Nursery School
60 Beaconsfield Road, New Southgate, London N11 3AE
Tel: 0333 920 4841
Nursery Manager: Ms Katerina Barotsaki
Age range: 3 months–5 years

Norfolk House School
10 Muswell Avenue, Muswell Hill, London N10 2EG
Tel: 020 8883 4584
Headteacher: Mr Paul Jowett
Age range: 2–11
No. of pupils: 220
Fees: Day £4,143

North London Grammar School
110 Colindeep Lane, Hendon, London NW9 6HB
Tel: 0208 205 0052
Headteacher: Mr Fatih Adak
Age range: 7–18 years

North London Rudolf Steiner School
1-3 The Campsbourne, London N8 7PN
Tel: 020 8341 3770
Age range: 0–7
No. of pupils: 40

One-Tech (UK) Ltd
1st Floor, 12 Cheapside, High Road, London N22 6HH
Tel: 020 8889 0707
Head: Mr Len Sutherland

Palmers Green High School
Hoppers Road, Winchmore Hill, London N21 3LJ
Tel: 020 8886 1135
Headmistress: Mrs Wendy Kempster
Age range: G3–16
No. of pupils: 300
Fees: Day £5,880–£15,930

Pardes House Primary School
Hendon Lane, Finchley, London N3 1SA
Tel: 020 8343 3568
Headteacher: Rabbi J Sager MA, B.Ed, NPQH, FCCT
Age range: B4–11 years

Pentland Day Nursery
224 Squires Lane, Finchley, London N3 2QL
Tel: 020 8970 2441
Principal: Rachele Parker

Phoenix Academy
85 Bounces Road, Edmonton, London N9 8LD
Tel: 020 8887 6888
Headteacher: Mr Paul Kelly
Age range: 5–18
No. of pupils: 19

Phoenix Montessori Nursery
27 Stamford Hill, London N16 5TN
Tel: 020 8880 2550
Manageress: Kelly Murphy
Age range: 0–5 years

Rainbow Nursery
Yorkshire Grove Estate, 22-26 Nevill Road, London N16 8SP
Tel: 020 7254 7930
Age range: 3 months–5 years

Rosemary Works Independent School
1 Branch Place, London N1 5PH
Tel: 020 7739 3950
Head: Rob Dell
Age range: 3–11
No. of pupils: 104
Fees: Day £14,097

Salcombe Preparatory School
224-226 Chase Side, Southgate, London N14 4PL
Tel: 020 8441 5356
Headmistress: Mrs Sarah-Jane Davies BA(Hons) QTS MEd
Age range: 3–11
No. of pupils: 250
Fees: Day £11,673

Salcombe Pre-School
Green Road, Southgate, London N14 4AD
Tel: 020 8441 5356
Headmistress: Mrs Sarah-Jane Davies BA(Hons) QTS MEd

St Andrew's Montessori
St Andrew's Church, Thornhill Square, London N1 1BQ
Tel: 020 7700 2961
Principal: Samantha Rawson MontDip
Age range: 2–6
No. of pupils: 40
Fees: Day £4,200–£6,525

St Paul's Steiner School
1 St Paul's Road, Islington, London N1 2QH
Tel: 020 7226 4454
College of Teachers: College of Teachers
Age range: 2–14
No. of pupils: 136

Sunrise Nursery, Stoke Newington
1 Cazenove Road, Stoke Newington, Hackney, London N16 6PA
Tel: 020 8806 6279
Principal: Didi Ananda Manika

Sunrise Primary School
55 Coniston Road, Tottenham, London N17 0EX
Tel: 020 8806 6279 (Office); 020 8885 3354 (School)
Head: Mrs Mary-Anne Lovage MontDipEd, BA
Age range: 2–11
No. of pupils: 30
Fees: Day £5,550

Talmud Torah Chaim Meirim School
26 Lampard Grove, London N16 6XB
Tel: 020 8806 0898
Principal: Rabbi S Hoffman
Age range: B4–13

Talmud Torah Yetev Lev School
111-115 Cazenove Road, London N16 6AX
Tel: 020 8806 3834
Age range: B2–11

Tawhid Boys School
21 Cazenove Road, London N16 6PA
Tel: 020 8806 2999
Headteacher: Mr Usman Mapara
Age range: B10–15
No. of pupils: 115

Tayyibah Girls School
88 Filey Avenue, Hackney, London N16 6JJ
Tel: 020 8880 0085
Headmistress: Mrs N B Qureishi MSc
Age range: G5–18

The Children's House School
77 Elmore Street, London N1 3AQ
Tel: 020 7354 2113
Head: Kate Orange
Age range: 2–4
No. of pupils: 73
Fees: Day £1,550–£1,675

The Children's House Upper School
King Henry's Walk, London N1 4PB
Tel: 020 7249 6273
Headteacher: Kate Orange
Age range: 4–7
No. of pupils: 60
Fees: Day £14,730

The City College
University House, 55 East Road, London N1 6AH
Tel: 020 7253 1133
Principal: A Andrews MCMI
Age range: 18–40

The Dance Studio
2 Farm Road,, Winchmore Hill, London N21 3JA
Tel: 020 8360 5700

The Gower School Montessori Nursery
18 North Road, Islington, London N7 9EY
Tel: 020 7700 2445
Principal: Miss Emma Gowers
Age range: 3 months–5 years
No. of pupils: 237

The Gower School Montessori Primary
10 Cynthia Street, Barnsbury, London N1 9JF
Tel: 020 7278 2020
Principal: Miss Emma Gowers
Age range: 4–11
No. of pupils: 237
Fees: Day £15,576

The Grove Nursery
Shepperton House, 83-93 Shepperton Road, Islington, London N1 3DF
Tel: 020 7226 4037
Owners: Ms Rebecca Browne & Ms Elaine Catchpole
Age range: 0–5

The Highgate Activity Nurseries
1 Church Road, Highgate, London N6 4QH
Tel: 020 8348 9248
Head: Helena Prior
Age range: 2–5
Fees: Day £5,460–£9,620

The Sam Morris Nursery
Sam Morris Centre, Parkside Crescent, London N7 7JG
Tel: 020 7609 1735

TTTYY School
14 Heathland Road, London N16 5NH
Tel: 020 8802 1348
Head of School: Rabbi A Friesel
Age range: B2–13

Twinkle Stars Day Nursery
416 Seven Sisters Road, Hackney, London N4 2LX
Tel: 020 8802 0550
Admin Officer: Noori Mohamed
Age range: 1–5

Vita et Pax School
Priory Close, Southgate, London N14 4AT
Tel: 020 8449 8336
Headteacher: Miss Gillian Chumbley
Age range: 3–11
Fees: Day £9,360

Woodberry Day Nursery
63 Church Hill, Winchmore Hill, London N21 1LE
Tel: 020 8882 6917
Manager: Michelle Miller
Age range: 6 weeks–5
No. of pupils: 62

Yesodey Hatorah School
Egerton Road, London N16 6UB
Tel: 020 8826 5500
Headteacher: Rabbi Pinter
Age range: 3–16
No. of pupils: 920

North-West London

Abbey Nursery School
Cricklewood Baptist Church, Sneyd Road, Cricklewood, London NW2 6AN
Tel: 020 8208 2202
Head: Mrs Ruby Azam

Abercorn School
38 Portland Place, London W1B 1LS
Tel: 020 7100 4335
Headmaster: Mr Christopher Hammond
Age range: 2 –13 years

Al-Sadiq & Al-Zahra Schools
134 Salusbury Road, London NW6 6PF
Tel: 020 7372 7706
Headteacher: Dr M Movahedi
Age range: 4–16

Arnold House School
1 Loudoun Road, St John's Wood, London NW8 0LH
Tel: 020 7266 4840
Headmaster: Mr Vivian Thomas
Age range: B3–13 years

Asquith Nursery – Golders Green
212 Golders Green Road, Golders Green, London NW11 9AT
Tel: 020 8458 7388
Age range: 1–5
No. of pupils: 68

Asquith Nursery – Hendon
46 Allington Road, Hendon, London NW4 3DE
Tel: 020 8203 9020
Age range: 3 months–5

Asquith Nursery – Hill Park
5 Sunningfields Road, Hendon, London NW4 4QR
Tel: 020 8201 5816
Age range: 3 months–5

Asquith Nursery – West Hampstead
11 Woodchurch Road, West Hampstead, London NW6 3PL
Tel: 020 7328 4787
Age range: 3 months–5

Barnet Hill Academy
10A Montagu Road, Hendon, London NW4 3ES
Tel: 02034112660
Headteacher: Mr Shakil Ahmed
Age range: 3–11 G11–16
Fees: Day £3,000

Beehive On Queens Park Montessori School
147 Chevening Rd, London NW6 6DZ
Tel: 020 8969 2235
Headmistress: Ms Lucilla Baj
Age range: 2–5
Fees: Day £2,550

Beis Soroh Schneirer
Arbiter House, Wilberforce Road, London NW9 6AX
Tel: 020 8201 7771
Head of School: Mrs Sonia Mossberg
Age range: G2–11

Belmont, Mill Hill Preparatory School
The Ridgeway, London NW7 4ED
Tel: 020 8906 7270
Headmaster: Mr Leon Roberts MA
Age range: 7–13
No. of pupils: 550
Fees: Day £18,822

Beth Jacob Grammar School for Girls
Stratford Road, Hendon, London NW4 2AT
Tel: 020 8203 4322
Headteacher: Mrs M Gluck
Age range: G11–17

Bluebells Nursery
Our Lady Help of Christians Church Hall, Lady Margaret Road, London NW5 2NE
Tel: 020 7284 3952
Principal: Ms Anita Pearson
Age range: 2–5
No. of pupils: 20

Brampton College
Lodge House, Lodge Road, Hendon, London NW4 4DQ
Tel: 020 8203 5025
Principal: B Canetti BA(Hons), MSc
Age range: 15–20
Fees: Day £19,935

British American Drama Academy
14 Gloucester Gate, London NW1 4HG
Tel: 020 7487 0730
Head: Paul Costello

Broadhurst School
19 Greencroft Gardens, London NW6 3LP
Tel: 020 7328 4280
Headmistress: Mrs Zoe Sylvester
Age range: 2–5
No. of pupils: 145
Fees: Day £6,480–£10,950

Brondesbury College for Boys
8 Brondesbury Park, London NW6 7BT
Tel: 020 8830 4522
Headteacher: Mr Amzad Ali
Age range: B11–16
No. of pupils: 93

Busy Bees at Mill Hill
30 Mill Way, Mill Hill, London NW7 3RB
Tel: 0208 906 9123
Nursery Manager: Danielle Baker
Age range: 0–5

Camden Community Nurseries
16 Acol Road, London NW6 3AG
Tel: 020 7624 2937

Chaston Nursery & Pre-preparatory School
Chaston Place, Off Grafton Terrace, London NW5 4JH
Tel: 020 7482 0701
Head: Mrs Sandra Witten DipEd, DMS
Age range: 0–5
No. of pupils: 69
Fees: Day £7,020–£12,732

City Mission Nursery
2 Scrub Lane, London NW10 6RB
Tel: 020 8960 0838
Age range: 6 months–5 years

Collège Français Bilingue de Londres
87 Holmes Road, Kentish Town, London NW5 3AX
Tel: 020 7993 7400
Head of School: Mr Denis Bittmann
Age range: 3–15
No. of pupils: 700
Fees: Day £11,115–£11,980

Fine Arts College
Centre Studios, 41-43 England's Lane, London NW3 4YD
Tel: +44 (0)207 586 0312
Principal: Ms Candida Cave
Age range: 13–18
Fees: Day £22,560

Francis Holland School, Regent's Park, NW1
Clarence Gate, Ivor Place, Regent's Park, London NW1 6XR
Tel: 020 7723 0176
Head: Mr C B Fillingham MA (King's College London)
Age range: G11–18
No. of pupils: 495 VIth120
Fees: Day £19,260

Golders Hill School
666 Finchley Road, London NW11 7NT
Tel: 020 8455 2589
Headmistress: Mrs A T Eglash BA(Hons)
Age range: 2–7
No. of pupils: 180
Fees: Day £1,575–£13,827

Goodwyn School
Hammers Lane, Mill Hill,
London NW7 4DB
Tel: 020 8959 3756
Principal: Struan Robertson
Age range: 3–11
No. of pupils: 193
Fees: Day £5,436–£11,943

Grimsdell, Mill Hill Pre-Preparatory School
Winterstoke House, Wills Grove,
Mill Hill, London NW7 1QR
Tel: 020 8959 6884
Head: Mrs Kate Simon BA, PGCE
Age range: 3–7
No. of pupils: 188
Fees: Day £15,492

Hampstead Hill Pre-Prep & Nursery School
St Stephen's Hall, Pond Street,
Hampstead, London NW3 2PP
Tel: 020 7435 6262
Principal: Mrs Andrea Taylor
Age range: B2–7+ G2–7+
Fees: Day £10,175–£16,830

Happy Child Day Nursery
St Anne's & St Andrew's Church
Hall, 125 Salisbury Road, Queens
Park, London NW6 6RG
Tel: 020 7625 1966
Age range: 2–5

Heathside School Hampstead
84a Heath Street, Hampstead,
London NW3 1DN
Tel: +44 (0)20 3058 4011
Headteacher: Katherine Vintiner
Age range: 2–16
No. of pupils: 230
Fees: Day £16,000–£19,200

Hendon Prep School
20 Tenterden Grove, Hendon,
London NW4 1TD
Tel: 020 8203 7727
Head of School: Mrs Tushi Gorasia
Age range: 2–11 years
No. of pupils: 165
Fees: Day £6,975–£15,600

Hereward House School
14 Strathray Gardens,
London NW3 4NY
Tel: 020 7794 4820
Headmaster: Mr P Evans
Age range: B4–13
No. of pupils: 170
Fees: Day £15,615–£16,065

Highgate Day Nursery and Preschool
Highgate Studios, 53–79 Highgate
Road, London NW5 1TL
Tel: 020 7485 5252
Principal: Lorraine Thompson

ICS London
7B Wyndham Place,
London W1H 1PN
Tel: +44 (0) 20 7298 8817
Head of School: Mr. Rod Jackson
Age range: 3–18 years
No. of pupils: 205

Islamia Girls' High School
129 Salusbury Road,
London NW6 6PE
Tel: 020 7372 3472
Headteacher: Mrs Fawziah Islam
Age range: G11–16 years
Fees: Day £6,900

Joel Nursery
214 Colindeep Lane, Colindale,
London NW9 6DF
Tel: 020 820 00189
Age range: 3 months–5 years

Kentish Town Day Nursery
37 Ryland Road, London NW5 3EH
Tel: 020 7284 3600
Manager: Carol Kewley
Age range: 3 months–5 years
No. of pupils: 55

Lakefield Catering & Educational Centre
Maresfield Gardens,
Hampstead, London NW3 5RY
Tel: 020 7794 5669
Course Director: Mrs Maria Brown
Age range: G16–24
No. of pupils: 16
Fees: FB £1,160

London Academy of Dressmaking and Design
18 Dobree Avenue, Willesden,
London NW10 2AE
Tel: 020 8451 7174
Principal: Mrs P A Parkinson MA
Age range: 13+
Fees: Day £2,650

LYNDHURST HOUSE PREP SCHOOL
For further details see p. 64
24 Lyndhurst Gardens,
Hampstead, London NW3 5NW
Tel: 020 7435 4936
Email: office@
lyndhursthouse.co.uk
Website:
www.lyndhursthouse.co.uk
Head of School: Mr Andrew Reid
MA (Oxon)
Age range: B4–13
No. of pupils: 133
Fees: Day £6,470–£7,245

MAPLE WALK PREP SCHOOL
For further details see p. 68
62A Crownhill Road,
London NW10 4EB
Tel: 020 8963 3890
Email: admin@
maplewalkschool.co.uk
Website:
www.maplewalkschool.co.uk
Head Teacher: Mrs S Gillam
Age range: 4–11
No. of pupils: 190
Fees: Day £3,580

Maria Montessori Children's House – West Hampstead
St Mary's Community Hall, 134a
Abbey Road, London NW6 4SN
Tel: 020 7624 5917

Maria Montessori Institute
26 Lyndhurst Gardens,
Hampstead, London NW3 5NW
Tel: 020 7435 3646
Director of Training & School: Mrs
Lynne Lawrence BA, Mont Int Dip(AMI)
Age range: 2–12
No. of pupils: 50
Fees: Day £5,580–£13,560

Maria Montessori School – Hampstead
26 Lyndhurst Gardens,
Hampstead, London NW3 5NW
Tel: +44 (0)20 7435 3646
Director of School: Miss L Kingston
Age range: 2–12
No. of pupils: 100
Fees: Day £6,270–£13,560

Mill Hill School
The Ridgeway, Mill Hill
Village, London NW7 1QS
Tel: 020 8959 1176
Head: Mrs Jane Sanchez BSc (Hons)
PGCE
Age range: 13–18
No. of pupils: 689 VIth259
Fees: Day £21,987 WB
£28,524 FB £33,717

Naima Jewish Preparatory School
21 Andover Place, London NW6 5ED
Tel: 020 7328 2802
Headmaster: Mr Bill Pratt
Age range: 3–11

Nancy Reuben Primary School
Finchley Lane, Hendon,
London NW4 1DJ
Tel: 020 82025646
Head: Anthony Wolfson
Age range: 3–11
No. of pupils: 207

Nicoll Road Nursery School
40 Nicoll Road, Harlesden,
London NW10 9AB
Tel: 020 8961 6648
Age range: 2–5

NORTH BRIDGE HOUSE NURSERY AND PRE-PREP HAMPSTEAD
For further details see p. 70
8 Netherhall Gardens,
London NW3 5RR
Tel: 020 7428 1520
Head of School: Mrs
Christine McLelland
Age range: 2–7 years
No. of pupils: 190

NORTH BRIDGE HOUSE NURSERY AND PRE-PREP WEST HAMPSTEAD
For further details see p. 70
85-87 Fordwych Rd,
London NW2 3TL
Tel: 020 7428 1520
Head of School: Mrs
Christine McLelland
Age range: 2–7 years

NORTH BRIDGE HOUSE PREP SCHOOL REGENT'S PARK
For further details see p. 70
1 Gloucester Avenue,
London NW1 7AB
Tel: 020 7428 1520
Head of School: Mr
James Stenning
Age range: 7–13 years
Fees: Day £20,520

NORTH BRIDGE HOUSE SENIOR CANONBURY
For further details see p. 70
6-9 Canonbury Place,
Islington, London N1 2NQ
Tel: 020 7428 1520
Head of School: Mr
Brendan Pavey
Age range: 11–18 years
Fees: Day £19,230–£21,735

NORTH BRIDGE HOUSE SENIOR HAMPSTEAD
For further details see p. 70
65 Rosslyn Hill, London NW3 5UD
Tel: 020 7428 1520
Email: admissionsenquiries@
northbridgehouse.com
Website:
www.northbridgehouse.com
Head of School: Mr Brendan Pavey
Age range: 11–16 years
Fees: Day £20,520

NW5 Theatre School
14 Fortess Road, London NW5 2EU
Tel: 020 8340 1498
Age range: 16–30

Octagon Nursery School
St Saviour's Church Hall, Eton
Road, London NW3 4SU
Tel: 020 7586 3206

Rainbow Montessori School
13 Woodchurch Road,
Hampstead, London NW6 3PL
Tel: 020 7328 8986
Head Mistress: Maggy Miller MontDip
Age range: 2–5
Fees: Day £12,240–£12,417

Ready Steady Go – Camden
123 St Pancras Way,
London NW1 0SY
Tel: 020 7586 5862
Age range: 2–4

Ready Steady Go – Fitzroy Road
Primrose Hill Community Centre,
29 Hopkinson's Place, Fitzroy
Road, London NW1 8TN
Tel: 020 7586 5862
Age range: 2–3

Ready Steady Go – Primrose Hill
12a King Henry's Road,
London NW3 3RP
Tel: 020 7586 5862
Age range: 3–5

Ready Steady Go – St John's Wood
21 Alexandra Road,
London NW8 0DP
Tel: 020 7586 5862
Age range: 2–5

Saint Christina's School
25 St Edmunds Terrace, Regent's
Park, London NW8 7PY
Tel: 020 7722 8784
Headteacher: Miss J Finlayson
Age range: 3–11
No. of pupils: 224
Fees: Day £13,500

SARUM HALL SCHOOL
For further details see p. 74
15 Eton Avenue,
London NW3 3EL
Tel: 020 7794 2261
Email: admissions@
sarumhallschool.co.uk
Website:
www.sarumhallschool.co.uk
Headteacher: Victoria Savage
Age range: G3–11
No. of pupils: 184

South Hampstead High School GDST
3 Maresfield Gardens,
London NW3 5SS
Tel: 020 7435 2899
Head of School: Mrs V Bingham
Age range: G4–18
No. of pupils: 900
Fees: Day £15,327–£18,654

Southbank International School – Hampstead
16 Netherhall Gardens,
London NW3 5TH
Tel: 020 7243 3803
Principal: Shirley Harwood
Age range: 3–11
No. of pupils: 210

St Anthony's School for Boys
90 Fitzjohn's Avenue, Hampstead,
London NW3 6NP
Tel: 020 7431 1066
Headmaster: Mr Paul Keyte
Age range: B4–13
No. of pupils: 310

St Christopher's School
32 Belsize Lane, Hampstead,
London NW3 5AE
Tel: 020 7435 1521
Head: Emma Crawford-Nash
Age range: G4–11
No. of pupils: 235
Fees: Day £14,700

ST JOHN'S WOOD PRE-PREPARATORY SCHOOL
For further details see p. 75
St Johns Hall, Lords Roundabout,
London NW8 7NE
Tel: 020 7722 7149
Email: info@sjwpre-prep.org.uk
Website:
www.sjwpre-prep.org.uk
Principal: Adrian Ellis
Age range: 3–7

St Margaret's School
18 Kidderpore Gardens,
Hampstead, London NW3 7SR
Tel: 020 7435 2439
Principal: Mr M Webster BSc, PGCE
Age range: G4–16
No. of pupils: 156
Fees: Day £12,591–£14,589

St Marks Square Nursery School
St Mark's Church, St Mark's
Square, Regents Park Road,
London NW1 7TN
Tel: +44 (0)20 7586 8383
Head: Dr Sheema Parsons B.Ed OBE
Age range: 2–6

St Martin's School
22 Goodwyn Avenue, Mill
Hill, London NW7 3RG
Tel: 020 8959 1965
Head Teacher: Mrs Samantha Mbah
Age range: 3–11
No. of pupils: 90
Fees: Day £7,800

ST MARY'S SCHOOL HAMPSTEAD
For further details see p. 78
47 Fitzjohn's Avenue,
Hampstead, London NW3 6PG
Tel: 020 7435 1868
Email: office@stmh.co.uk
Website: www.stmh.co.uk
Head Teacher: Mrs Harriet Connor-Earl
Age range: G2 years 9
months–11 years
No. of pupils: 300
Fees: Day £8,625–£15,945

St Nicholas School
22 Salmon Street, London NW9 8PN
Tel: 020 8205 7153
Headmaster: Mr Matt Donaldson
BA (Hons), PGCE, PGDip (Surv)
Age range: 3 months–11
No. of pupils: 80
Fees: Day £8,550–£8,850

The Academy School
3 Pilgrims Place, Rosslyn Hill,
Hampstead, London NW3 1NG
Tel: 020 7435 6621
Headteacher: Mr Garth Evans BA (Lond)

The American School in London
One Waverley Place,
London NW8 0NP
Tel: 020 7449 1221
Head: Robin Appleby
Age range: 4–18
No. of pupils: 1350
Fees: Day £27,050–£31,200

The Beehive Montessori on Queen's Park
147 Chevening Road,
London NW6 6DZ
Tel: 020 8969 2235
Age range: 2–5

The Cavendish School
31 Inverness Street, Camden
Town, London NW1 7HB
Tel: 020 7485 1958
Headmistress: Miss Jane Rogers
Age range: G3–11
No. of pupils: 260
Fees: Day £15,300

The Hall School
23 Crossfield Road, Hampstead,
London NW3 4NU
Tel: 020 7722 1700
Headmaster: Mr Chris Godwin
Age range: B4–13
No. of pupils: 440
Fees: Day £17,940–£18,486

The Interior Design School
22 Lonsdale Road, Queens
Park, London NW6 6RD
Tel: 020 7372 2811
Principal: Ms Iris Dunbar

The Islamia Schools' Trust
129 Salusbury Road,
London NW6 6PE
Tel: 020 7372 3472

The King Alfred School
Manor Wood, North End
Road, London NW11 7HY
Tel: 020 8457 5200
Head: Robert Lobatto MA (Oxon)
Age range: 4–18
No. of pupils: 650 VIth100
Fees: Day £15,531–£18,723

The Mount, Mill Hill International
Milespit Hill, London NW7 2RX
Tel: +44 (0)20 3826 33
Head of School: Ms Sarah Bellotti
Age range: 13–17
No. of pupils: 80
Fees: Day £25,989 WB
£34,461 FB £40,539

THE MULBERRY HOUSE SCHOOL
For further details see p. 82
7 Minster Road, West
Hampstead, London NW2 3SD
Tel: 020 8452 7340
Email: admissions@
mulberryhouseschool.com
Website: www.mulberryhouse
school.com
Headteacher: Ms Victoria
Playford BA Hons, QTS
Age range: 2–7 years
No. of pupils: 223

The Oak Tree Nursery
2 Arkwright Road, Hampstead,
London NW3 6AD
Tel: 020 7435 1916
Head: Mrs S Alexander
Age range: 2–3
Fees: Day £4,650

The School of the Islamic Republic of Iran
100 Carlton Vale, London NW6 5HE
Tel: 020 7372 8051
Headteacher: Mr Seyed Abbas
Hosseini
Age range: 6–16

The Village School
2 Parkhill Road, Belsize
Park, London NW3 2YN
Tel: 020 7485 4673
Headmistress: Miss C E F Gay
BSc(Hons), PGCE
Age range: G3–11
No. of pupils: 106
Fees: Day £15,525

Theatretrain
69 Great North Way,
London NW4 1HS
Tel: 020 8202 2006
Director: Kevin Dowsett CertEd,
AdvDip(Drama in Education)
Age range: 6–18

Toddlers Inn Nursery School
Cicely Davies Hall, Cochrane Street, London NW8 7NX
Tel: 020 7586 0520
Principal: Ms Laura McCole

Torah Vodaas
Brent Park Road, West Hendon Broadway, London NW9 7AJ
Tel: 020 3670 4670
Head of School: Rabbi Y Feldman
Age range: B2–11

Trevor-Roberts School
55-57 Eton Avenue, London NW3 3ET
Tel: 020 7586 1444
Headmaster: Simon Trevor-Roberts BA
Age range: 5–13
Fees: Day £14,700–£16,200

University College School Hampstead (UCS)
Frognal, Hampstead, London NW3 6XH
Tel: 020 7435 2215
Headteacher: Mr Mark J Beard
Age range: B11–18 G16–18

University College School Hampstead (UCS) Junior
11 Holly Hill, London NW3 6QN
Tel: 020 7435 3068
Headmaster: Mr Lewis Hayward MA (Oxon Lit. Hum), MA (OU, ED. Management), PGCE
Age range: B7–11

University College School Hampstead (UCS) Pre-Prep
36 College Crescent, Hampstead, London NW3 5LF
Tel: 020 7722 4433
Headmistress: Dr Zoe Dunn
Age range: B4–7

Wentworth College
6-10 Brentmead Place, London NW11 9LH
Tel: 020 8458 8524/5
Principal: Manuel Guimaraes
Age range: 14–19
No. of pupils: 115

York Rise Nursery
St Mary Brookfield Hall, York Rise, London NW5 1SB
Tel: 020 7485 7962
Headmistress: Miss Becca Coles
Age range: 2–5

South-East London

Alleyn's School
Townley Road, Dulwich, London SE22 8SU
Tel: 020 8557 1500
Head of School: Jane Lunnon
Age range: 4–18 years

Anerley Montessori Nursery
45 Anerley Park, London SE20 8NQ
Tel: 020 8778 2810
Headmistress: Mrs P Bhatia
Age range: 3 months–5
Fees: Day £2,750–£4,600

Asquith Nursery – Elizabeth Terrace
18-22 Elizabeth Terrace, Eltham, London SE9 5DR
Tel: 020 8294 0377
Age range: 3 months–5

Asquith Nursery – New Eltham
699 Sidcup Road, New Eltham, London SE9 3AQ
Tel: 020 8851 5057
Age range: 3 months–5

Asquith Nursery – Peckham Rye
24 Waveney Avenue, Peckham Rye, London SE15 3UE
Tel: 020 7635 5501
Age range: 4 months–5

Asquith Nursery – West Dulwich
Old Church, 226c Gipsy Road, West Dulwich, London SE27 9RB
Tel: 0330 134 7934
Age range: 3 months–5

Bellenden Day Nursery
Faith Chapel, 198 Bellenden Road, London SE15 4BW
Tel: 020 7639 4896
Manager: Jason Cranston

Bellerbys College London
Bounty House, Greenwich, London SE8 3DE
Tel: +44 (0)208 694 7000
Principal: Ms Alison Baines
Age range: 15–19

Blackheath Day Nursery
The Rectory Field, Charlton, London SE3 8SR
Tel: 020 8305 2526
Headmistress: Mrs Shipley
Age range: 0–5
No. of pupils: 61

Blackheath High School GDST
Vanbrugh Park, Blackheath, London SE3 7AG
Tel: 020 8853 2929
Head: Mrs Carol Chandler-Thompson BA (Hons) Exeter, PGCE Exeter
Age range: G3–18
No. of pupils: 780

Blackheath Montessori Centre
Independents Road, Blackheath, London SE3 9LF
Tel: 020 8852 6765
Headmistress: Mrs Jane Skillen MontDip
Age range: 3–5
No. of pupils: 36

Blackheath Prep
4 St Germans Place, Blackheath, London SE3 0NJ
Tel: 020 8858 0692
Head: Alex Matthews
Age range: 3–11
No. of pupils: 384

Bright Horizons at Tabard Square
10-12 Empire Square, Tabard Street, London SE1 4NA
Tel: 020 7407 2068

Broadfields Day Nursery
96 Broadfields Road, Catford, London SE6 1NG
Tel: 020 8697 1488
Head: Elainne Dalton
Age range: 4 months–5

Clive Hall Day Nursery
rear of 54 Clive Road, London SE21 8BY
Tel: 020 8761 9000

Colfe's Junior School
Horn Park Lane, Lee, London SE12 8AW
Tel: 020 8463 8240
Head: Ms C Macleod
Age range: 3–11
No. of pupils: 355
Fees: Day £13,230–£13,995

Colfe's School
Horn Park Lane, Lee, London SE12 8AW
Tel: 020 8852 2283
Head: Mr R F Russell MA(Cantab)
Age range: 3–18
No. of pupils: 1120

DLD College London
199 Westminster Bridge Road, London SE1 7FX
Tel: +44 (0)20 7935 8411
Principal: Irfan H Latif BSc (Hons) PGCE FRSA FRSC
No. of pupils: 426
Fees: Day £23,500–£29,950 FB £18,000–£28,000

Dulwich College
Dulwich Common, London SE21 7LD
Tel: 020 8693 3601
Master: Dr J A F Spence
Age range: B0–18
No. of pupils: 1589 VIth470
Fees: Day £21,246 WB £41,557 FB £44,346

Dulwich College Kindergarten & Infants School
Eller Bank, 87 College Road, London SE21 7HH
Tel: 020 8693 1538
Head: Mrs Miranda Norris
Age range: 3 months–7 years
No. of pupils: 251

Dulwich Nursery
adj Sainsbury's Dulwich Store, 80 Dog Kennel Hill, London SE22 8DB
Tel: 020 7738 4007
Principal: Amanda Shead

Dulwich Prep London
42 Alleyn Park, Dulwich, London SE21 7AA
Tel: 020 8766 5500
Headmaster: Mr M W Roulston MBE, MEd
Age range: B3–13 G3–5
No. of pupils: 817
Fees: Day £13,074–£19,314

East Greenwich Day Nursery and Preschool
Chavening Road, Greenwich, London SE10 0LB
Tel: 0203 7803053
Nursery Manager: Ms Loraine Thorpe
Age range: 3 months–5 years

Eltham College
Grove Park Road, Mottingham, London SE9 4QF
Tel: 0208 857 1455
Headmaster: Guy Sanderson
Age range: 7–18
No. of pupils: 911 VIth199

Eltham Green Day Nursery
5 Lionel Road, Eltham, London SE9 6DQ
Tel: 0800 085 4074
Age range: 3months–5
No. of pupils: 30

First Steps Montessori Day Nursery & Pre School
254 Upland Road, East Dulwich, London SE22 0DN
Tel: 020 8299 6897
Principal: Karime Dinkha
Age range: 2–5
No. of pupils: 43

Five Steps Community Nursery
31-32 Alpine Road, London SE16 2RE
Tel: 020 7237 2376

Greenwich Steiner School
Woodlands, 90 Mycenae Road, Blackheath, London SE3 7SE
Tel: 020 8858 4404
Head of School: Mr Adrian Dow
Age range: 3–14
No. of pupils: 180
Fees: Day £7,310–£8,100
(£)

GSM London
Meridian House, Royal Hill, Greenwich, London SE10 8RD
Tel: 0203 544 3171
Head: Dr W G Hunt
(16+)

Half Moon Montessori Nursery
Methodist Church Hall, 155 Half Moon Lane, London SE24 9HU
Tel: 020 7326 5300
Age range: 2–5

Happy Faces Nursery
161 Sumner Road, Peckham, London SE15 6JL
Tel: 020 7701 3320

Heath House Preparatory School
37 Wemyss Road, Blackheath, London SE3 0TG
Tel: 020 8297 1900
Head Teacher: Mrs Sophia Laslett CertEd PGDE
Age range: 3–11
No. of pupils: 125
Fees: Day £13,485–£14,985
(£)(✎)

Herne Hill School
The Old Vicarage, 127 Herne Hill, London SE24 9LY
Tel: 020 7274 6336
Headteacher: Mrs Ngaire Telford
Age range: 2–7
No. of pupils: 296
Fees: Day £6,225–£14,955

Hillyfields Day Nursery
41 Harcourt Road, Brockley, London SE4 2AJ
Tel: 020 8694 1069
Head: Ms Lisa Reeves

James Allen's Girls' School
144 East Dulwich Grove, Dulwich, London SE22 8TE
Tel: 020 8693 1181
Head of School: Mrs Sally-Anne Huang MA, MSc
Age range: G4–18
No. of pupils: 1075
(♿)(A)(£)(✎)(16+)

Kings Kids Christian School
100 Woodpecker Road, Newcross, London SE14 6EU
Tel: 020 8691 5813
Headteacher: Mrs M Okenwa
Age range: 5–11

Little Cherubs Day Nursery
2a Bell Green Lane, London SE26 5TB
Tel: 020 8778 3232

Lollipops Child Care Ltd
88 Southwood Road, London SE9 3QT
Tel: 020 8859 5832
Principal: Miss L Thompson

London Bridge Business Academy
7-13 Melior Street, London SE1 3QP
Tel: 020 7378 1000
Head: Shmina Mandal
(16+)

London Christian School
40 Tabard Street, London SE1 4JU
Tel: 020 3130 6430
Headmistress: Miss N Collett-White
Age range: 3–11
No. of pupils: 105
Fees: Day £9,390
(£)

London College of Engineering & Management
18-36 Wellington Street, London SE18 6PF
Tel: 020 8854 6158
Head: Mr Shakhar Sharman
(16+)

Magic Roundabout Nursery – Kennington
35 Sutherland House, Sutherland Square, London SE17 3EE
Tel: 020 7277 3643

Marathon Science School
1-9 Evelyn Street, Surrey Quays, London SE8 5RQ
Tel: +44 (0)20 7231 3232
Headteacher: Mr Uzeyir Onur
Age range: B11–16
No. of pupils: 67
(♂)(♀)

McAlpine Dance Studio
Longfield Hall, 50 Knatchbull Road, London SE5 9QY
Tel: 020 8673 4992
(16+)

Mother Goose Nursery
248 Upland Road, East Dulwich, London SE22 0NU
Tel: 020 8693 9429
Age range: 1–5

Mother Goose Nursery
34 Waveney Avenue, Nunhead, London SE15 3UE
Tel: 020 7277 5951
Age range: 1–5

Mother Goose Nursery
The Pavilion, 65 Greendale Fields, off Wanley Road, London SE5 8JZ
Tel: 020 7738 7700
Age range: 0–5

Mother Goose Nursery (Head Office)
133 Brookbank Road, Lewisham, London SE13 7DA
Tel: 020 8694 8700
Age range: 1–5

Nell Gwynn Nursery
Meeting House Lane, London SE15 2TT
Tel: 020 7252 8265
Executive Head Teacher: Lynne Cooper

Oakfield Preparatory School
125-128 Thurlow Park Road, West Dulwich, London SE21 8HP
Tel: 020 8670 4206
Head of School: Mr Patrick Gush
Age range: 2–11 years
No. of pupils: 420
Fees: Day £10,785

Octavia House School, Kennington
214b Kennington Road, London SE11 6AU
Tel: 020 3651 4396 (option 3)
Executive Headteacher: Mr P Foster

Octavia House School, Vauxhall
Vauxhall Primary School, Vauxhall Street, London SE11 5LG
Tel: 020 3651 4396 (option 1)
Executive Headteacher: Mr P Foster
Age range: 5–14

Octavia House School, Walworth
Larcom House, Larcom Street, London SE17 1RT
Tel: 020 3651 4396 (option 2)
Executive Headteacher: Mr P Foster

Riverston School
63-69 Eltham Road, Lee Green, London SE12 8UF
Tel: 020 8318 4327
Principal: Michael Lewis
Age range: 9 months–19 years
(£)(✎)(16+)(♿)

Rosemead Preparatory School & Nursery, Dulwich
70 Thurlow Park Road, London SE21 8HZ
Tel: 020 8670 5865
Headmaster: Mr Phil Soutar
Age range: 2–11
No. of pupils: 366
Fees: Day £10,272–£11,286
(£)(✎)

School of Technology & Management
Kingshead House, Kingshead Yard, London SE1 1NA
Tel: 020 7378 0052
(16+)

Skallywags Nursery
St Crispin Hall, Southwark Park Road, Rotherhithe, London SE16 2HU
Tel: 020 7252 3225
Headmistress: Miss Allison Armstrong NVQ
Age range: 3 months–5 years

St Dunstan's College
Stanstead Road, London SE6 4TY
Tel: 020 8516 7200
Headmaster: Mr Nicholas Hewlett
Age range: 3–18
No. of pupils: 870
(♿)(A)(£)(16+)

St Olave's Preparatory School
106 Southwood Road, New Eltham, London SE9 3QS
Tel: 020 8294 8930
Headteacher: Miss Claire Holloway BEd, QTS
Age range: 3–11
No. of pupils: 220
Fees: Day £10,848–£12,300
(✎)

St. Patrick's Montessori Day Nursery
91 Cornwall Road, London SE1 8TH
Tel: 020 7928 5557

SYDENHAM HIGH SCHOOL GDST
For further details see p. 80
15 & 19 Westwood Hill, London SE26 6BL
Tel: 020 8557 7004
Email: admissions@syd.gdst.net
Website: www.sydenhamhighschool.gdst.net
Headmistress: Mrs Katharine Woodcock
Age range: G4–18
No. of pupils: 665
(♿)(A)(£)(✎)(16+)

The British School of Osteopathy
275 Borough High Street, London SE1 1JE
Tel: 020 7407 0222
Principal & Chief Executive: Martin Collins BSc(Hons), PhD, MSc, Cbiol, MIBiol, FRSH, DO, ILTM
Fees: Day £0

The Pavilion Nursery
Catford Cricket Club Pavilion, Penerley Road, London SE6 2LQ
Tel: 020 8698 0878
Head: Mrs Karen Weller
Age range: 2–5

The Pointer School
19 Stratheden Road, Blackheath, London SE3 7TH
Tel: 020 8293 1331
Headmaster: Mr Adam M Greenwood BSc (Hons), PGCE, GCGI, MBA
Age range: 3–11 years

The Villa School & Nursery
54 Lyndhurst Grove, Peckham, London SE15 5AH
Tel: 020 7703 6216
Head Teacher: Louise Maughan
Age range: 2–7

The Village Montessori
Kingswood Hall, Kingswood Place, London SE13 5BU
Tel: 020 8318 6720

The Village Nursery
St Mary's Centre, 180 Ladywell Road, Lewisham, London SE13 7HU
Tel: 020 8690 6766
Principal: Frances Rogers

Toad Hall Montessori Nursery School
37 St Mary's Gardens, Kennington, London SE11 4UF
Tel: 020 7735 5087
Principal: Mrs V K Rees NNEB, MontDip
Age range: 2–5
No. of pupils: 40
Fees: Day £6,300

Trinity Child Care
Holy Trinity Church Hall, Bryan Road, London SE16 5HF
Tel: 020 7231 5842
Manager: Sharron Williams
Age range: 2–5
No. of pupils: 60
Fees: Day £6,240

Waterloo Day Nursery
The Chandlery, 50 Westminster Bridge Road, London SE1 7QY
Tel: 020 7721 7432
Principal: Julie Ellis

West Dulwich Day Nursery and Pre-School
Old Church, 226c Gipsy Road, London SE27 9RB
Tel: 0333 122 1189
Nursery Manager: Ms Nazmin Uddin
Age range: 3 months–5 years

Willow Park
19 Glenlyon Road, Eltham, London SE9 1AL
Tel: 020 8850 8753
Principal: Mrs McMahon

South-West London

345 Nursery School
Fitzhugh Community Clubroom, Fitzhugh Grove, Trinity Road, London SW18 3SA
Tel: 020 8870 8441
Principal: Mrs Annabel Dixon
Age range: 3–5
No. of pupils: 42
Fees: Day £3,555

ABACUS Early Learning Nursery School – Balham Day Nursery
135 Laitwood Road, Balham, London SW12 9QH
Tel: 020 8675 8093

ABACUS Early Learning Nursery School – Stretham Day Nursery
7 Drewstead Road, Streatham Hill, London SW16 1LY
Tel: 020 8677 9117
Principals: Mrs M Taylor BEd & Ms S Petgrave
Age range: 12 mths–5 years
No. of pupils: 40

Academy of Live & Recorded Arts
Studio1, Royal Victoria Patriotic Building, John Archer Way, London SW18 3SX
Tel: 020 8870 6475
Principal: Anthony Castro
Age range: 18+
No. of pupils: 108
Fees: Day £3,000–£9,888

Alphabet Nursery School
Chatham Hall, Northcote Road, Battersea, London SW11 6DY
Tel: 020 8871 7473
Principal: Mrs A McKenzie-Lewis
No. of pupils: 40
Fees: Day £1,500–£1,800

Al-Risalah Nursery
10A Gatton Road, Tooting, London SW17 0EE
Tel: 020 8767 0716
Head of School: Nasir Qurashi

Al-Risalah Secondary School
145 Upper Tooting Road, London SW17 7TJ
Tel: 020 8767 6057
Executive Principal: Suhayl Lee
Age range: 11–16 years

Asquith Nursery – Balham
36 Radbourne Road, Balham, London SW12 0EF
Tel: 020 8673 1405

Asquith Nursery – Battersea
18/30 Latchmere Road, Battersea, London SW11 2DX
Tel: 020 7228 7008
Age range: 3 months–5

Asquith Nursery – Putney
107-109 Norroy Road, Putney, London SW15 1PH
Tel: 020 8246 5611
Age range: 3 months–5

Asquith Nursery – Raynes Park
c/o David Lloyd Leisure Club, Bushey Road, Raynes Park, London SW20 8DE
Tel: 020 8543 9005
Age range: 3 months–5

Battersea Pre-School & Nursery
Riverlight, Nine Elms Lane, Kirtling Street, Battersea, London SW8 5BP
Tel: 020 7720 9336

Beechwood Nursery School
55 Leigham Court Road, Streatham, London SW16 2NJ
Tel: 020 8677 8778
Age range: 0–5

Beehive Nursery School
St Margarets Church Hall, Putney Park Lane, London SW15 5HU
Tel: 020 8780 5333
Headmistress: Lindsay Deans
Age range: 2–5
No. of pupils: 16
Fees: Day £1,140

Bees Knees Nursery School
within Brookside Community Hall, 12 Priory Lane, London SW15 5JL
Tel: 020 8876 8252
Headmistress: Jo Wood
Age range: 2–5

Bertrum House Nursery
290 Balham High Road, London SW17 7AL
Tel: 020 8767 4051
Age range: 2–5

Bobby's Playhouse
16 Lettice Street, London SW6 4EH
Tel: 020 7384 1190
Principal: Mrs Emma Hannay
Age range: 3 months–5 years
Fees: Day £11,000

BROOMWOOD HALL LOWER SCHOOL
For further details see p. 52
50 Nightingale Lane, London SW12 8TE
Tel: 020 8682 8840
Email: admissions@northwoodschools.com
Website: www.northwoodschools.com
Head: Miss Jo Townsend
Age range: 4–8
No. of pupils: 320
Fees: Day £5,610

BROOMWOOD HALL UPPER SCHOOL
For further details see p. 53
68-74 Nightingale Lane, London SW12 8NR
Tel: 020 8682 8810
Email: admissions@northwoodschools.com
Website: www.northwoodschools.com
Head: Mrs Louisa McCafferty
Age range: G8–13
No. of pupils: 250
Fees: Day £6,880

Busy Bee Nursery School
19 Lytton Grove, Putney, London SW15 2EZ
Tel: 020 8789 0132
Headmistress: Dr Sally Corbett
Age range: 2–5

Cameron Vale School
4 The Vale, Chelsea, London SW3 6AH
Tel: 020 7352 4040
Headmistress: Mrs Bridget Saul
Age range: 4–11
Fees: Day £19,305

Carmena Christian Day Nurseries
47 Thrale Road, Streatham, London SW16 1NT
Tel: 020 8677 8231
Head: Mrs S Allen

Centre Academy London
92 St John's Hill, Battersea, London SW11 1SH
Tel: 020 7738 2344
Headteacher: Rachel Maddison
Age range: 9–19

Chelsea Kindergarten
St Andrews Church, Park Walk, Chelsea, London SW10 0AU
Tel: 020 7352 4856
Headmistress: Miss Lulu Tindall MontDip
Age range: 2–5
Fees: Day £3,900–£6,120

Clapham Day Nursery
3 Peardon Street, London SW8 3BW
Tel: 020 7498 3165
Manager: Nicolette Warnes NNEB, NVQ4
Age range: 3 months–5
No. of pupils: 72

Clapham Montessori
St Paul's Community Centre, St Paul's Church, Rectory Grove, London SW4 0DX
Tel: 020 7498 8324
Head: Mrs R Bowles BSc, IntMontDip
Age range: 2–5

Clapham Park Montessori
St James' Church House, 10 West Road, Clapham, London SW4 7DN
Tel: 020 7627 0352
Head: Mrs R Bowles BSc, IntMontDip
Age range: 2–5

Collingham
23 Collingham Gardens, London SW5 0HL
Tel: 020 7244 7414
Principal: Sally Powell
Age range: 14–19
No. of pupils: VIth200
Fees: Day £4,260–£22,560

Crown Kindergartens
Coronation House, Ashcombe Road, Wimbledon, London SW19 8JP
Tel: 020 8540 8820
Principal: Mrs Acres
Age range: 1–5
No. of pupils: 28

Dawmouse Montessori Nursery School
34 Haldane Road, Fulham, London SW6 7EU
Tel: 020 7381 9385
Principal: Mrs Emma V Woodcock NNEB, MontDip
Age range: 2–5
No. of pupils: 72

Dolphin School
106 Northcote Road, London SW11 6QW
Tel: 020 7924 3472
Principal: Mrs. N. Baldwin
Age range: 2–11
No. of pupils: 292
Fees: Day £12,270–£13,485

Donhead
33 Edge Hill, London SW19 4NP
Tel: 020 8946 7000
Headmaster: Mr P J J Barr
Age range: B4–11
No. of pupils: 280
Fees: Day £11,175–£11,622

Eaton House Belgravia
3-5 Eaton Gate, London SW1W 9BA
Tel: 020 7924 6000
Head of School: Mr Huw May
Age range: B3–11
Fees: Day £17,850–£20,700

Eaton House The Manor
58 Clapham Common Northside, London SW4 9RU
Tel: 020 7924 6000
Head: Mr Oliver Snowball
Age range: G4–11
Fees: Day £16,143

Eaton House The Manor Pre Prep and Nursery
58 Clapham Common Northside, London SW4 9RU
Tel: 020 7924 6000
Nursery Head of School: Miss Roosha
Age range: B3.5–8
Fees: Day £16,143

Eaton House The Manor Prep School
58 Clapham Common Northside, London SW4 9RU
Tel: 020 7924 6000
Head: Mrs Sarah Segrave
Age range: B8–13
Fees: Day £19,743

Eaton Square Nursery Schools
28 & 30 Eccleston Street, London SW1W 9PY
Tel: +44 (0)20 7931 9469
Age range: 2–4

Eaton Square School Belgravia
79 Eccleston Square, London SW1V 1PP
Tel: +44 (0)20 7931 9469
Principal: Mr Sebastian Hepher
Age range: 4–11

Eaton Square School Kensington
24 Elvaston Place, London SW7 5NL
Tel: +44 (0)20 7225 3131
Headmistress: Mrs Trish Watt
Age range: 4–11

Ecole Charles De Gaulle – Wix
Clapham Common North Side, London SW4 0AJ
Tel: +44 20 7738 0287
Headteacher: Mr Blanchard
Age range: 5–11
No. of pupils: 100

École Primaire Marie D'Orliac
60 Clancarty Road, London SW6 3AA
Tel: +44 (0)20 7736 5863
Director: Mr Blaise Fenart
Age range: 4–11

Elm Park Nursery School
90 Clarence Avenue, Clapham, London SW4 8JR
Tel: 020 8678 1990
Head: Ms Jacqueline Brooks
No. of pupils: 113

Emanuel School
Battersea Rise, London SW11 1HS
Tel: 020 8870 4171
Headmaster: Mr Robert Milne
Age range: 10–18
No. of pupils: 930
Fees: Day £18,372

Eveline Day & Nursery Schools
14 Trinity Crescent, Upper Tooting, London SW17 7AE
Tel: 020 8672 4673
Headmistress: Ms Eveline Drut
Age range: 3 months–11 years
No. of pupils: 80
Fees: Day £13,859

Falcons School for Girls
11 Woodborough Road, Putney, London SW15 6PY
Tel: 020 8992 5189
Headmistress: Ms Sara Williams-Ryan
Age range: G4–11
Fees: Day £7,800–£15,705

Falkner House
19 Brechin Place, South Kensington, London SW7 4QB
Tel: 020 7373 4501
Headteacher: Mrs Anita Griggs BA(Hons), PGCE
Age range: B3–11 G3–11

Finton House School
171 Trinity Road, London SW17 7HL
Tel: 020 8682 0921
Head of School: Mr Ben Freeman
Age range: 4–11
No. of pupils: 300
Fees: Day £15,378–£15,588

First Steps School of Dance & Drama
234 Lillie Road, London SW6 7QA
Tel: 020 7381 5224
Age range: 3–17
Fees: Day £2,700

Francis Holland School, Sloane Square, SW1
39 Graham Terrace, London SW1W 8JF
Tel: 020 7730 2971
Head: Mrs Lucy Elphinstone MA(Cantab)
Age range: G4–18
No. of pupils: 520 VIth70
Fees: Day £17,760–£20,085

Garden House School
Boys' School & Girls' School, Turk's Row, London SW3 4TW
Tel: 020 7730 1652
Boys' Head: Mr Christian Warland BA(Hons), LLB.
Age range: 3–11
No. of pupils: 490
Fees: Day £17,700–£22,800

Gateway House Nursery School
St Judes Church Hall, Heslop Road, London SW12 8EG
Tel: 020 8675 8258
Principal: Miss Elizabeth Marshall
Age range: 2–4
No. of pupils: 30
Fees: Day £1,010–£1,060

Glendower School
86/87 Queen's Gate, London SW7 5JX
Tel: 020 7370 1927
Headmistress: Mrs Sarah Knollys BA, PGCE
Age range: G4–11+
No. of pupils: 206
Fees: Day £19,200

Hall School Wimbledon
17, The downs, Wimbledon, London SW20 8HF
Tel: 020 8879 9200
Headmaster: Mr. Robert Bannon
Age range: 5–18
No. of pupils: 150
Fees: Day £4,420–£5,950

Hall School Wimbledon Junior School
Beavers Holt, Stroud Crescent, Putney Vale, London SW15 3EQ
Tel: 020 8788 2370
Deputy Head Junior School: Susan Harding
Age range: 4–16
No. of pupils: 520
Fees: Day £13,126–£17,336

Happy Nursery Days
Valens House, 132a Uppertulse Hill, London SW2 2RX
Tel: 020 8674 7804
Age range: 3 months–5

Harrodian School
Lonsdale Road, London SW13 9QN
Tel: 020 8748 6117
Headmaster: James R Hooke
Age range: 4–18
No. of pupils: 890 VIth95
Fees: Day £15,000–£23,040
(A) (✐) (16)

HILL HOUSE INTERNATIONAL JUNIOR SCHOOL
For further details see p. 60
17 Hans Place, Chelsea,
London SW1X 0EP
Tel: 020 7584 1331
Email: info@
hillhouseschool.co.uk
Website:
www.hillhouseschool.co.uk
Proprietors: Richard, Janet,
William & Edmund Townend
Age range: 4–13
No. of pupils: 600
Fees: Day £15,000–£18,600
(🏃) (£) (✐)

Hornsby House School
Hearnville Road, Balham,
London SW12 8RS
Tel: 020 8673 7573
Headmaster: Mr Edward Rees
Age range: 4–11
Fees: Day £14,280–£15,345
(£) (✐)

Hurlingham Nursery School
The Old Methodist Hall, Gwendolen
Avenue, London SW15 6EH
Tel: 020 8103 0807
Headmaster: Mr Simon Gould
Age range: 2–4 years
(✐)

Hurlingham School
122 Putney Bridge Road,
Putney, London SW15 2NQ
Tel: 020 8103 1083
Headmaster: Mr Simon Gould
Age range: 4–11
(£) (✐)

Ibstock Place School
Clarence Lane, London SW15 5PY
Tel: 020 8876 9991
Head of School: Mr Chris Wolsey
Age range: 4–18
No. of pupils: 1000
Fees: Day £17,115–£21,735
(A) (£) (16)

Inchbald School of Design
Interior Design Faculty, 7 Eaton
Gate, London SW1W 9BA
Tel: 020 7730 5508
Principal: Mrs Jacqueline Duncan
FIIDA, FIDDA
Age range: 18–50
No. of pupils: 120
(16)

JJAADA Interior Design Academy
28 Abbeville Mews, 88 Clapham
Park Road, London SW4 7BX
Tel: 020 7494 3363
(16)

Judith Blacklock Flower School
4/5 Kinnerton Place South,
London SW1X 8EH
Tel: 020 7235 6235
Head: Judith Blacklock
(16)

Kensington Prep School
596 Fulham Road, London SW6 5PA
Tel: 0207 731 9300
Head of School: Mrs Caroline
Hulme-McKibbin
Age range: G4–11
No. of pupils: 289
Fees: Day £17,193
(🏃)

Kids Inc Day Nursery – East Sheen
459b Upper Richmond Road West,
East Sheen, London SW14 7PR
Tel: 020 8876 8144

King's College School
Southside, Wimbledon
Common, London SW19 4TT
Tel: 020 8255 5300
Head Master: Mr A D Halls OBE
Age range: B7–18 G16–18
No. of pupils: 1475
(🏃) (👦) (A) (£) (IB) (16)

Knightsbridge School
67 Pont Street, Knightsbridge,
London SW1X 0BD
Tel: +44 (0)20 7590 9000
Head of School: Shona Colaço
Age range: 3–13
Fees: Day £18,756–£19,965

Ladybird Nursery School
9 Knowle Close, London SW9 0TQ
Tel: 020 7924 9505

L'ECOLE DE BATTERSEA
For further details see p. 62
Trott Street, Battersea,
London SW11 3DS
Tel: 020 7371 8350
Email: admin@
lecoledespetits.co.uk
Website:
www.lecoledespetits.co.uk
Principal: Mrs F Brisset
Age range: 3–11
No. of pupils: 260
Fees: Day £13,740

L'ECOLE DES PETITS
For further details see p. 63
2 Hazlebury Road, Fulham,
London SW6 2NB
Tel: 020 7371 8350
Email: admin@
lecoledespetits.co.uk
Website:
www.lecoledespetits.co.uk
Principal: Mrs F Brisset
Age range: 3–6
No. of pupils: 125
Fees: Day £13,365

L'Ecole du Parc
12 Rodenhurst Road,
London SW4 8AR
Tel: 020 8671 5287
Headteacher: Mrs E Sicking-Bressler
Age range: 1–5
No. of pupils: 55
Fees: Day £4,000–£7,500

Little People of Fulham
250a Lillie Road, Fulham,
London SW6 7PX
Tel: 020 7386 0006
Owner: Miss Jane Gleasure
Age range: 4 months–5

Little Red Hen Nursery School
Christchurch Hall, Cabul
Road, London SW11 2PN
Tel: 020 7738 0321
Age range: 2–5
Fees: Day £1,470–£1,740

London Film Academy
The Old Church, 52a Walham
Grove, London SW6 1QR
Tel: 020 7386 7711
Founders & Joint Principals: Daisy
Gili & Anna Macdonald
(16)

London Steiner School
9 Weir Road, Balham,
London SW12 0LT
Tel: 0208 772 3504
Age range: 3–14
(£)

Lycée Français Charles de Gaulle
35 Cromwell Road,
London SW7 2DG
Tel: 020 7584 6322
Head of School: Mr Olivier Rauch
Age range: 5–19
No. of pupils: 4000
(👦) (A) (£) (✐) (16)

Magic Roundabout Nursery – Stockwell
Surrey Hall, Binfield Road,
Stockwell, London SW4 6TB
Tel: 020 7498 1194

MANDER PORTMAN WOODWARD – LONDON
For further details see p. 66
90-92 Queen's Gate,
London SW7 5AB
Tel: 020 7835 1355
Email: london@mpw.ac.uk
Website: www.mpw.ac.uk
Principal: Mr John Southworth
BSc MSc
Age range: 14–19
No. of pupils: 600
Fees: Day £9,905
(16) (A) (£) (✐)

Melrose House Nursery School – SW18
39 Melrose Road, Southfields,
London SW18 1LX
Tel: 020 8874 7769
Head of School: Ruth Oates
Age range: 2–5

Melrose House Nursery School – SW6
55 Finlay Street, Fulham,
London SW6 6HF
Tel: 020 7736 9296
Head of School: Caroline
O'Gorman
Age range: 2–5

Miss Daisy's Nursery School
Fountain Court Club Room, Ebury
Square, London SW1W 9SU
Tel: 020 7730 5797
Head: Daisy Harrison
Age range: 2–5
No. of pupils: 30
Fees: Day £1,050–£5,550

Montessori School
St Paul's Community Centre,
Rectory Grove, Clapham,
London SW4 0DX
Tel: 020 7498 8324
Age range: 6 months–6

MORE HOUSE SCHOOL
For further details see p. 69
22-24 Pont Street, Knightsbridge,
London SW1X 0AA
Tel: 020 7235 2855
Email: office@
morehousemail.org.uk
Website:
www.morehouse.org.uk
Head: Ms Faith Hagerty
Age range: G11–18
No. of pupils: 200
Fees: Day £6,950
(🏃) (A) (£) (✐) (16)

Newton Prep
149 Battersea Park Road,
London SW8 4BX
Tel: 020 7720 4091
Headmistress: Mrs Alison Fleming
BA, MA Ed, PGCE
Age range: 3–13
No. of pupils: 631
Fees: Day £9,600–£20,340
(£) (✐)

Nightingale Montessori Nursery
St Lukes Community Hall, 194 Ramsden Road, London SW12 8RQ
Tel: 020 8675 8070
Principal: Mrs Tejas Earp
Age range: 2–5

Noah's Ark Nursery Schools (Dolphin School Trust)
St Michael's Church Hall, Cobham Close, London SW11 6SP
Tel: 020 7924 3472 opt 2
Head: Miss Annette Miller
Age range: 2–5
No. of pupils: 40
Fees: Day £4,725

Noah's Ark Nursery Schools (Dolphin School Trust)
Endlesham Church Hall, 48 Endlesham Road, London SW12 8JL
Tel: 020 7924 3472 opt 2
Head: Miss Annette Miller
Age range: 2–5
No. of pupils: 32
Fees: Day £4,725

Noddy's Nursery School
Trinity Church Hall, Beaumont Road, Wimbledon, London SW19 6SP
Tel: 020 8785 9191
Principal: Mrs Sarah Edwards NNEB, Mont Dip
Age range: 2–5

NORTHCOTE LODGE
For further details see p. 71
26 Bolingbroke Grove, London SW11 6EL
Tel: 020 8682 8888
Email: admissions@ northwoodschools.com
Website: www.northwoodschools.com
Head: Mr Clive Smith-Langridge
Age range: B8–13
No. of pupils: 260
Fees: Day £6,880

NORTHWOOD SENIOR
For further details see p. 72
3 Garrad's Road, London SW16 1JZ
Tel: 020 8161 0301
Email: NWSsenior@ northwoodschools.com
Website: www.northwoodschools.com
Head: Mrs Susan Brooks
Age range: 11–16
Fees: Day £6,880

Oliver House Preparatory School
7 Nightingale Lane, London SW4 9AH
Tel: 020 8772 1911
Headteacher: Mr Rob Farrell
Age range: 3–11
No. of pupils: 144
Fees: Day £6,600–£15,090

Paint Pots Montessori School – The Boltons
St Mary The Boltons Church Hall, The Boltons, London SW10 9TB
Tel: 07794 678 537
Head Teacher: Georgie Scully
Age range: 2 years 6 months–5 years

Parkgate House School
80 Clapham Common North Side, London SW4 9SD
Tel: +44 (0)20 7350 2461
Principal: Miss Catherine Shanley
Age range: 2.5–11 years
No. of pupils: 220
Fees: Day £5,940–£15,600

Parsons Green Prep School
1 Fulham Park Road, Fulham, London SW6 4LJ
Tel: 020 7371 9009
Headmaster: Tim Cannell
Age range: 4–11
No. of pupils: 200
Fees: Day £16,857–£18,201

Peques Anglo-Spanish School
St John's Church, North End Road, Fulham, London SW6 1PB
Tel: 020 7385 0055
Managing Director: Margarita Morro Beltran
Age range: 3 months–5

Playdays Nursery School Wimbledon
58 Queens Road, Wimbledon, London SW19 8LR
Tel: 020 8946 8139
Nursery Manager: Charline Baker

Pooh Corner Kindergarten
St Stephen's Church Hall, 48 Emperor Gate, London SW7 4HJ
Tel: 020 7373 6111
Headmistress: Sarah Crowther

Prince's Gardens Preparatory School
10–13 Prince's Gardens, London SW7 1ND
Tel: 0207 591 4622
Headmistress: Mrs Alison Melrose
Age range: 3–11

Prospect House School
75 Putney Hill, London SW15 3NT
Tel: 020 8246 4897
Headmaster: Mr Michael Hodge BPED(Rhodes) QTS
Age range: 3–11
No. of pupils: 316
Fees: Day £9,210–£19,200

Putney High School GDST
35 Putney Hill, London SW15 6BH
Tel: 020 8788 4886
Headmistress: Mrs Suzie Longstaff BA, MA, PGCE
Age range: G4–18
No. of pupils: 976 VIth150

Queen's Gate School
133 Queen's Gate, London SW7 5LE
Tel: 020 7589 3587
Principal: Mrs R M Kamaryc BA, MSc, PGCE
Age range: G4–18
No. of pupils: 529 VIth94

Raynes Park Nursery and PreSchool
3 Spencer Road, Raynes Park, Wimbledon, London SW20 0QN
Tel: 0333 920 1909
Nursery Manager: Ms Leanne Eustace
Age range: 3 months–5 years

Redcliffe School Trust Ltd
47 Redcliffe Gardens, Chelsea, London SW10 9JH
Tel: 020 7352 9247
Head: Sarah Lemmon
Age range: 3–11
Fees: Day £6,660–£17,730

Ringrose Kindergarten Chelsea
St Lukes Church Hall, St Lukes Street, London SW3 3RP
Tel: 020 7352 8784
Age range: 2–5 years

Royal Academy of Dance
36 Battersea Square, London SW11 3RA
Tel: 020 7326 8000
Chief Executive: Luke Rittner

Royal College of Art
Kensington Gore, London SW7 2EU
Tel: 020 7590 4444
Rector & Vice-Provost: Professor Christopher Frayling

Sinclair House Preparatory School
59 Fulham High Street, Fulham, London SW6 3JJ
Tel: 0207 736 9182
Principal: Mrs Carlotta T M O'Sullivan
Age range: 2–11
No. of pupils: 120
Fees: Day £5,280–£17,025

Southfields Day Nursery and Pre-School
Duntshill Mill, 21 Riverdale Drive, London SW18 4UR
Tel: 0330 057 6434
Nursery Manager: Ms Lydia Howards
Age range: 3 months–5 years

Square One Nursery School
Lady North Hall, 12 Ravenna Road, Putney, London SW15 6AW
Tel: 020 8788 1546
Principal: Mrs King

St Mary Magdalen Montessori Nursery School
61 North Worple Way, London SW14 8PR
Tel: 020 8878 0756
Head: Liz Maitland NNEB, RSH, MontDip
Age range: 2–5

St Mary's Summerstown Montessori
46 Wimbledon Road, Tooting, London SW17 0UQ
Tel: 020 8947 7359
Head: Liz Maitland NNEB, RSH, MontDip
Age range: 18 months–5 years
No. of pupils: 30
Fees: Day £1,300

St Michael's Montessori Nursery School
St Michael's Church, Elm Bank Gardens, Barnes, London SW13 0NX
Tel: 020 8878 0116
Head Teacher: Debbie Goldberg
Age range: 2 1/2–5

St Paul's Juniors
St Paul's School, Lonsdale Road, London SW13 9JT
Tel: 020 8748 3461
Head of School: Maxine Shaw
Age range: B7–13
No. of pupils: 436
Fees: Day £20,010

St Paul's School
Lonsdale Road, Barnes, London SW13 9JT
Tel: 020 8748 9162
High Master: Prof Mark Bailey
Age range: B13–18
No. of pupils: 897
Fees: Day £25,032 FB £37,611

St Philip's School
6 Wetherby Place, London SW7 4NE
Tel: 020 7373 3944
Headmaster: Mr Wulffen-Thomas
Age range: B7–13
No. of pupils: 110
Fees: Day £16,200

Streatham & Clapham High School GDST
42 Abbotswood Road, London SW16 1AW
Tel: 020 8677 8400
Headmaster: Dr Millan Sachania
Age range: G3–18
No. of pupils: 603 VIth70
Fees: Day £10,431–£19,743

Streatham Day Nursery and Preschool
113 Blegborough Road, Streatham, London SW16 6DL
Tel: 0330 057 6267
Nursery Manager: Ms Nadia Kiani
Age range: 3 months–5 years

Streatham Montessori Nursery & Day Care
66 Blairderry Road, Streatham Hill, London SW2 4SB
Tel: 020 8674 2208
Nursery Manager: Mrs Fehmida Gangji
Age range: 1–5

Sussex House School
68 Cadogan Square, London SW1X 0EA
Tel: 020 7584 1741
Headmaster: Mr N P Kaye MA(Cantab), ACP, FRSA, FRGS
Age range: B8–13
No. of pupils: 182
Fees: Day £19,770

Swedish School
82 Lonsdale Road, London SW13 9JS
Tel: 020 8741 1751
Head of School: Ms. Annika Simonsson Bergqvist
Age range: 3–18
No. of pupils: 300 VIth145
Fees: Day £8,600–£9,100

Thames Christian College
Wye Street, Battersea, London SW11 2HB
Tel: 020 7228 3933
Executive Head: Stephen Holsgrove PhD
Age range: 11–16
No. of pupils: 120
Fees: Day £15,780

The Boltons Nursery School
262b Fulham Road, Chelsea, London SW10 9EL
Tel: 020 7351 6993
Age range: 2–5
No. of pupils: 60
Fees: Day £2,370–£4,200

The Bumble Bee Nursery School
Church of Ascension, Pountney Road, London SW11 5TU
Headmistress: Deepti Bansal

The Castle Kindergarten
20 Henfield Road, London SW19 3HU
Tel: 020 8544 0008
Principal: Ms Beverley Davis DipEd
Age range: 2–5

The Crescent I Kindergarten
Flat 1, No 10 Trinity Crescent, London SW17 7AE
Tel: 020 8767 5882
Principal: Philip Evelegh

The Crescent II Kindergarten
Holy Trinity Church Hall, Trinity Road, London SW17 7SQ
Tel: 020 8682 3020

The Eveline Day Nursery Schools, Furzedown
Seeley Hall, Chillerton Road, Furzedown, London SW17 9BE
Tel: 020 8672 0501

The Eveline Day Nursery Schools, Tooting
30 Ritherdon Road, Upper Tooting, London SW17 8QD
Tel: 020 8672 7549
Principal: Mrs T Larche

The Eveline Day Nursery Schools, Wandsworth
East Hill United Reformed Church Hall, Geraldine Road, Wandsworth, London SW18 2NR
Tel: 020 8870 0966

The Eveline Day Nursery Schools, Wimbledon
89a Quicks Road, Wimbledon, London SW19 1EX
Tel: 020 8545 0699

The Hampshire School, Chelsea
15 Manresa Road, Chelsea, London SW3 6NB
Tel: 020 7352 7077
Head of School: Dr P Edmonds BEd (Hons) MEd EdD
Age range: 3–13
No. of pupils: 300
Fees: Day £16,965–£17,955

The Knightsbridge Kindergarten
St. Peter's Church, 119 Eaton Square, London SW1W 9AL
Tel: 020 7371 2306
Age range: 2–5

The Laurels School
126 Atkins Road, Clapham, London SW12 0AN
Tel: 020 8674 7229
Headmistress: Linda Sanders BA Hons (Bristol), MA (Madrid)
Age range: G11–18

The Maria Montessori Children's House
St John's Ambulance Hall, 122-124 Kingston Road, London SW19 1LY
Tel: 020 8543 6353
Age range: 2–5

The Marmalade Bear Nursery School
St. Magdalene Church Hall, Trinity Road, Tooting, London SW17 7HP
Tel: 0208 265 5224
Principal: Ms Rozzy Hyslop
Age range: 2–5
Fees: Day £3,270–£3,450

The Merlin School
4 Carlton Drive, London SW15 2BZ
Tel: 020 8788 2769
Principal: Mrs Kate Prest
Age range: 4–8
No. of pupils: 155
Fees: Day £5,041

The Moat School
Bishops Avenue, Fulham, London SW6 6EG
Tel: 020 7610 9018
Headteacher: Mr K Claeys
Age range: 9–18
No. of pupils: 140

The Montessori Childrens House Ltd
St John's Church, 1 Spencer Hill, London SW19 4NZ
Tel: 020 8971 9135
Age range: 2–5

The Montessori Pavilion – The Kindergarten School
Vine Road, Barnes, London SW13 0NE
Tel: 07554 277 746
Headmistress: Ms Georgina Dashwood
Age range: 3–8
No. of pupils: 50

The Mouse House Nursery School
27 Mallinson Road, London SW11 1BW
Tel: 020 7924 1893
Headmistress: Amanda White-Spunner
Age range: 2–5
Fees: Day £1,650–£4,125

The Norwegian School
28 Arterberry Road, Wimbledon, London SW20 8AH
Tel: 020 8947 6617
Head: Mr Ivar Chavannes
Age range: 3–16

The Oval Montessori Nursery School
within Vauxhall Park, Fentiman Road, London SW8 1LA
Tel: 020 7735 4816
Head: Ms Louise Norwood
Age range: 2–5
Fees: Day £3,000

The Park Kindergarten
St Saviours Church Hall, 351 Battersea Park Road, London SW11 4LH
Tel: 020 7627 5125
Principal: Miss Lisa Neilsen MontDip
Age range: 2–5
Fees: Day £2,370

The Rainbow Playgroup
St Luke's Church Hall, St Luke's Street, London SW3 3RR
Tel: 020 7352 8156
Age range: 2–5

THE ROCHE SCHOOL
For further details see p. 84
11 Frogmore, London SW18 1HW
Tel: 020 8877 0823
Email: office@ therocheschool.com
Website: www.therocheschool.com
Headmistress: Mrs Vania Adams BA(Hons), PGCE, MA
Age range: 2–11 years
No. of pupils: 302
Fees: Day £14,970–£15,690

The Rowans School
19 Drax Avenue, Wimbledon, London SW20 0EG
Tel: 020 8946 8220
Head Teacher: Mrs. Joanna Hubbard MA BA (Hons) PGCE QTS PGDipSEN
Age range: 3–8
Fees: Day £7,905–£13,170

The Study Preparatory School
Wilberforce House, Camp Road, Wimbledon Common, London SW19 4UN
Tel: 020 8947 6969
Head of School: Miss Vicky Ellis BSc (Hons), QTS, MA
Age range: G4–11
No. of pupils: 320
Fees: Day £4,925

The White House Preparatory School & Woodentops Kindergarten
24 Thornton Road, London SW12 0LF
Tel: 020 8674 9514
Principal: Mrs. Mary McCahery
Age range: 2–11
Fees: Day £4,436–£4,740

The Willow Nursery School
55 Grafton Square, Clapham Old Town, London SW4 0DE
Tel: 020 7498 0319
Head: Mrs Harriet Baring MontDip
Age range: 2–5
Fees: Day £3,000–£3,100

The Zebedee Nursery School
4 Parsons Green, London SW6 4TN
Tel: 020 7371 9224
Headmistress: Miss Su Gahan NNEB, RSH
Age range: 2–5
No. of pupils: 32
Fees: Day £3,900

Thomas's Kindergarten – Battersea
St Mary's Church, Battersea Church Road, London SW11 3NA
Tel: 020 7738 0400
Headmistress: Miss Iona Jennings
Age range: 2–5
Fees: Day £1,365–£2,100

Thomas's Kindergarten – Pimlico
14 Ranelagh Grove,
London SW1W 8PD
Tel: 020 7730 3596
Headmistress: Miss Tamara
Spierenburg HBO

Thomas's Preparatory School – Battersea
28-40 Battersea High Street,
London SW11 3JB
Tel: 020 7978 0900
Head: Simon O'Malley
Age range: 4–13
No. of pupils: 547
Fees: Day £18,747–£20,868

Thomas's Preparatory School – Clapham
Broomwood Road,
London SW11 6JZ
Tel: 020 7326 9300
Headmaster: Mr Philip Ward
BEd(Hons)
Age range: 4–13
No. of pupils: 647
Fees: Day £17,262–£19,518

Thomas's Preparatory School – Fulham
Hugon Road, London SW6 3ES
Tel: 020 7751 8200
Head: Miss Annette Dobson
BEd(Hons), PGCertDys
Age range: 4–11
Fees: Day £17,880–£20,016

Tiggers Nursery School
87 Putney Bridge Road,
London SW15 2PA
Tel: 020 8874 4668
Headmistress: Natasha Green
MontDip
Age range: 2–5
Fees: Day £1,425–£1,725

Toots Day Nursery
214 Totterdown Street,
Tooting, London SW17 8TD
Tel: 020 8767 7017
Principal: Angela Duffell
Age range: 1–5

Tower House School
188 Sheen Lane, London SW14 8LF
Tel: 020 8876 3323
Head: Mr Gregory Evans
Age range: B4–13

Twice Times Nursery School
The Cricket Pavilion in South Park,
Clancarty Road, London SW6 3AF
Tel: 020 7731 4929
Heads: Mrs A Welch MontDip & Mrs
S Henderson MontDip
Age range: 2–5
No. of pupils: 50

Ursuline Preparatory School
18 The Downs, Wimbledon,
London SW20 8HR
Tel: 020 8947 0859
Head Teacher: Mrs Caroline Molina
BA
Age range: B3–4 G3–11
No. of pupils: 202

Wandsworth Nursery & Pre-School Academy
Dolphin House, Riverside West,
Smugglers Way, Wandsworth,
London SW18 1DE
Tel: 020 8877 1135
Nursery Manager: Evelyn Herrera
Age range: 0–5

Wandsworth Preparatory School
The Old Library, 2 Allfarthing
Lane, London SW18 2PQ
Tel: 0208 870 4133
Headteacher: Ms Jo Fife
Age range: 4–11
No. of pupils: 100
Fees: Day £4,710

Westminster Abbey Choir School
Dean's Yard, London SW1P 3NY
Tel: 0207 654 4918
Headmaster: Mr Peter Roberts
Age range: B8–13
No. of pupils: 35
Fees: FB £8,571

Westminster Cathedral Choir School
Ambrosden Avenue,
London SW1P 1QH
Tel: 020 7798 9081
Headmaster: Mr Neil McLaughlan
Age range: B4–13
No. of pupils: 150
Fees: Day £16,350–
£19,233 FB £10,086

Westminster School
Little Dean's Yard, Westminster,
London SW1P 3PF
Tel: 020 7963 1003
Headmaster: Mr Patrick Derham
Age range: B13–18 G16–18
No. of pupils: 744
Fees: Day £26,130–
£28,566 FB £37,740

Westminster Tutors
86 Old Brompton Road, South
Kensington, London SW7 3LQ
Tel: 020 7584 1288
Principal: Joe Mattei
Age range: 14–mature
No. of pupils: VIth40
Fees: Day £4,000–£25,000

Westminster Under School
Adrian House, 27 Vincent
Square, London SW1P 2NN
Tel: 020 7821 5788
Headteacher: Mr Mark O'Donnell
Age range: B7–13
No. of pupils: 265
Fees: Day £19,344

Willington Prep
Worcester Road, Wimbledon,
London SW19 7QQ
Tel: 020 8944 7020
Head of School: Mr Keith Brown
Age range: 3–11
No. of pupils: 220

Wimbledon Common Preparatory
113 Ridgway, Wimbledon,
London SW19 4TA
Tel: 020 8946 1001
Head Teacher: Mrs Tracey Buck
Age range: B4–8
No. of pupils: 160
Fees: Day £13,185

Wimbledon High School GDST
Mansel Road, Wimbledon,
London SW19 4AB
Tel: 020 8971 0900
Headmistress: Mrs Jane Lunnon
Age range: G4–18
No. of pupils: 900 VIth155
Fees: Day £14,622–£18,810

Wimbledon Park Montessori School
206 Heythorp Street, Southfields,
London SW18 5BU
Tel: 020 8944 8584
Head: Ms Clare Collins
Age range: 2–5
Fees: Day £830–£950

Wimbledon School of Art
Merton Hall Road,
London SW19 3QA
Tel: 020 8408 5000
Principal: Professor Roderick Bugg

Young England Kindergarten
St Saviour's Hall, St George's
Square, London SW1V 3QW
Tel: 020 7834 3171
Principal: Mrs Kay C King MontDip
Age range: 2.5–5
Fees: Day £3,300–£4,950

West London

Acorn Nursery School
2 Lansdowne Crescent,
London W11 2NH
Tel: 020 7727 2122
Principal: Mrs Jane Cameron
BEd(Hons)
Age range: 2–5
Fees: Day £2,400

Acton Yochien Nursery School
The Pavilion, Queens Drive Playing
Fields, Acton, London W3 0HT
Tel: 020 8343 2192

Alan D Hairdressing Education
4 West Smithfield, London EC1A 9JX
Tel: 020 7580 1030
Director of Education: Alan
Hemmings
Fees: Day £200 FB £12,400

Albemarle Independent College
18 Dunraven Street,
London W1K 7FE
Tel: 020 7409 7273
Co-Principals: Beverley Mellon &
James Eytle
Age range: 16–19
No. of pupils: 160
Fees: Day £7,000–£24,000

ArtsEd Day School & Sixth Form
14 Bath Road, Chiswick,
London W4 1LY
Tel: 020 8987 6666
Headteacher: Mr Adrian Blake
Age range: 11–18 years

Ashbourne Independent Sixth Form College
17 Old Court Place,
Kensington, London W8 4PL
Tel: 020 7937 3858
Principal: Mr Michael Kirby MSc,
BApSc, MInstD
Age range: 13–19 years

Avenue House School
70 The Avenue, Ealing,
London W13 8LS
Tel: 020 8998 9981
Headteacher: Mr J Sheppard
Age range: 3–11
No. of pupils: 135
Fees: Day £11,250

Bales College
742 Harrow Road, Kensal
Town, London W10 4AA
Tel: 020 8960 5899
Principal: William Moore
Age range: 11–19
No. of pupils: 90
Fees: Day £11,550–£12,750

Bassett House School
60 Bassett Road, London W10 6JP
Tel: 020 8969 0313
Headmistress: Mrs Philippa Cawthorne MA (Soton) PGCE Mont Cert
Age range: 3–11
No. of pupils: 190
Fees: Day £5,499–£19,200

Blake College
162 New Cavendish Street, London W1W 6YS
Tel: 020 7636 0658
Course Director: D A J Cluckie BA, BSc
Fees: Day £4,720–£5,310

BPP University
Aldine Place, 142-144 Uxbridge Road, London W12 8AA
Tel: (+44) 03331 226478
Head: Martin Taylor

Busy Bees at Hammersmith
30-40 Dalling Road, Hammersmith, London W6 0JD
Tel: 020 8741 5382
Nursery Manager: Becky
Age range: 3 months–5 years

Bute House Preparatory School for Girls
Bute House, Luxemburg Gardens, London W6 7EA
Tel: 020 7603 7381
Head: Mrs Helen Lowe
Age range: G4–11
No. of pupils: 306
Fees: Day £16,458

Buttercups Day Nursery
38 Grange Road, Chiswick, London W4 4DD
Tel: 020 8995 6750

Buttercups Day Nursery
9 Florence Road, Ealing, London W5 3TU
Tel: 020 8840 4838

Buttercups Day Nursery
9 Florence Road, Ealing, London W5 3TU
Tel: 020 8840 4838

Buttons Day Nursery School
99 Oaklands Road, London W7 2DT
Tel: 020 8840 3355
Head: Julie Parhar BSc, NVQ3
Age range: 3 months–5
No. of pupils: 62

Campbell Harris Tutors
185 Kensington High Street, London W8 6SH
Tel: 020 7937 0032
Principals: Mr Mark Harris & Ms Claire Campbell
Age range: 13+
Fees: Day £4,000–£9,000

Caterpillar Montessori Nursery School
St Albans Church Hall, South Parade, Chiswick, London W4 3HY
Tel: 020 8747 8531
Head: Mrs Alison Scott
Age range: 2–5
Fees: Day £2,700

Chepstow House School
108a Lancaster Road, London W11 1QS
Tel: 0207 243 0243
Headteacher: Angela Barr
Age range: 2.5–12 years

Chiswick & Bedford Park Prep School
Priory House, Priory Avenue, London W4 1TX
Tel: 020 8994 1804
Headmistress: Mrs S Daniell
Age range: B4–7+ G4–11
No. of pupils: 180
Fees: Day £13,275

Chiswick Nursery and Pre-School
4 Marlborough Road, Chiswick, London W4 4ET
Tel: 020 8742 0011
Nursery Manager: Roxane Lovell
Age range: 0–5

Chiswick Park Nursery and Pre-School
Evershed Walk, London W4 5BW
Tel: 0333 920 0404
Nursery Manager: Ms Rebecca Fergus
Age range: 3 months–5 years

Christie's Education
42 Portland Place, Marylebone, London W1W 5BD
Tel: 0207 389 2004
Academic Director: Jon Waldon

Clifton Lodge
8 Mattock Lane, Ealing, London W5 5BG
Tel: 020 8579 3662
Head of School: Mrs Beth Friel
Age range: 3–13
No. of pupils: 130
Fees: Day £12,240–£14,670

College of Naturopathic & Complementary Medicine Ltd
41 Riding House Street, London W1W 7BE
Tel: 01342 410 505
Head: Hermann Keppler

Connaught House School
47 Connaught Square, London W2 2HL
Tel: 020 7262 8830
Principal: Mrs V Hampton
Age range: 4–11
No. of pupils: 75
Fees: Day £16,650–£18,300

David Game College
31 Jewry Street, London EC3N 2ET
Tel: 020 7221 6665
Principal: D T P Game MA, MPhil
Age range: 14–19
No. of pupils: 200 VIth150
Fees: Day £3,680–£30,630

Devonshire Day Nursery
The Vicarage, Bennet Street, Chiswick, London W4 2AH
Tel: 020 8995 9538
Manager: Dawn Freeman
Age range: 6 weeks–5
No. of pupils: 70

Durston House
12-14 Castlebar Road, Ealing, London W5 2DR
Tel: 020 8991 6530
Headmaster: Mr Giles Entwisle
Age range: B4–13
No. of pupils: 380
Fees: Day £4,160–£5,060

Ealing Independent College
83 New Broadway, Ealing, London W5 5AL
Tel: 020 8579 6668
Principal: Dr Ian Moores
Age range: 13–19
No. of pupils: 100 VIth70
Fees: Day £2,910–£18,120

Eaton Square School Mayfair
106 Piccadilly, Mayfair, London W1J 7NL
Tel: +44 (0)20 7491 7393
Co-Heads: Caroline Townshend (Lower) & John Wilson (Upper)
Age range: 11–18

Ecole Francaise Jacques Prevert
59 Brook Green, London W6 7BE
Tel: 020 7602 6871
Headteacher: Delphine Gentil
Age range: 4–11

Elmwood Montessori School
St Michaels Centre, Elmwood Road, London W4 3DY
Tel: 020 8994 8177/995 2621
Headmistress: Mrs S Herbert BA
Age range: 2–5
Fees: Day £3,480–£4,440

FULHAM SCHOOL
For further details see p. 58
200 Greyhound Road, London W14 9SD
Tel: 020 7386 2444
Email: admissions@fulham.school
Website: fulham.school
Pre-Prep Head: Di Steven
Age range: 4–18
No. of pupils: 700
Fees: Day £18,420–£21,567

Godolphin and Latymer School
Iffley Road, Hammersmith, London W6 0PG
Tel: +44 (0)20 8741 1936
Head Mistress: Dr Frances Ramsey
Age range: G11–18
No. of pupils: 800
Fees: Day £23,085

Great Beginnings Montessori Nursery
39 Brendon Street, London W1H 5JE
Tel: 020 7258 1066
Head: Mrs Wendy Innes
Age range: 2–6

Greek Primary School of London
3 Pierrepoint Road, Acton, London W3 9JR
Tel: 020 899 26156
Primary School Head Teacher: Mrs Despoina Kyriakidou BA, MA, QTS
Age range: 1–11

Halcyon London International School
33 Seymour Place, London W1H 5AU
Tel: +44 (0)20 7258 1169
Headteacher: Mr Barry Mansfield
Age range: 11–18
No. of pupils: 195

Hammersmith Day Nursery & Pre-School
50 Richford Gate, 61-69 Richford Street, London W6 7HZ
Tel: 0207 622 0484
Manager: Marion Bones NVQ
Age range: 3 months–5 years
No. of pupils: 70

Happy Child Day Nursery
283-287 Windmill Road, Ealing, London W5 4DP
Tel: 020 8567 2244
Age range: 3 months–5

Happy Child Training Centre
109 Uxbridge Road, Ealing, London W5 5TL
Tel: 020 8579 3955

Harvington School
20 Castlebar Road, Ealing,
London W5 2DS
Tel: 020 8997 1583
Headmistress: Mrs Anna Evans
Age range: B3–4 G3–11
No. of pupils: 140
Fees: Day £6,525–£12,615

**HAWKESDOWN HOUSE
SCHOOL KENSINGTON**
For further details see p. 59
27 Edge Street, Kensington,
London W8 7PN
Tel: 020 7727 9090
Email: admin@
hawkesdown.co.uk
Website:
www.hawkesdown.co.uk
Headmistress: Mrs. J. A. K.
Mackay B.Ed (Hons)
Age range: 2–11
No. of pupils: 100
Fees: Day £13,800–£20,100

Heathfield House School
Heathfield Gardens,
Chiswick, London W4 4JU
Tel: 020 8994 3385
Headteacher: Mrs Goodsman
Age range: 4–11
No. of pupils: 197
Fees: Day £2,471–£3,676

**Holland Park Day Nursery
and Pre-School**
34 Ladbroke Grove, Notting
Hil, London W11 3BQ
Tel: 0333 363 4009
Age range: 3 months–5
Fees: Day £3,900

**Holland Park Pre Prep
School and Day Nursery**
5, Holland Road, Kensington,
London W14 8HJ
Tel: 020 7602 9066/020
7602 9266
Head Mistress: Mrs Kitty Mason
Age range: 3 months–8 years
No. of pupils: 39
Fees: Day £9,180–£18,120

**Instituto Español Vicente
Cañada Blanch**
317 Portobello Road,
London W10 5SZ
Tel: +44 (0) 20 8969 2664
Principal: Carmen Pinilla Padilla
Age range: 4–19
No. of pupils: 405

**International School
of London (ISL)**
139 Gunnersbury Avenue,
London W3 8LG
Tel: +44 (0)20 8992 5823
Principal: Mr Richard Parker
Age range: 3–18 years
No. of pupils: 500
Fees: Day £19,000–£26,300

James Lee Nursery School
Gliddon Road, London W14 9BH
Tel: 020 8741 8877

King Fahad Academy
Bromyard Avenue, Acton,
London W3 7HD
Tel: 020 8743 0131
Director General: Dr Tahani Aljafari
Age range: 3–19

La Petite Ecole Francaise
73 Saint Charles Square,
London W10 6EJ
Tel: +44 208 960 1278
Principal: Mme Marjorie
Lacassagne
Age range: 3–11

**Ladbroke Square
Montessori School**
43 Ladbroke Square,
London W11 3ND
Tel: 020 7229 0125
Head Teacher: Lucy Morley
Age range: 3–5
Fees: Day £850–£1,350

Latymer Prep School
36 Upper Mall, Hammersmith,
London W6 9TA
Tel: 020 7993 0061
Principal: Ms Andrea Rutterford
B.Ed (Hons)
Age range: 7–11
No. of pupils: 165
Fees: Day £18,330

Latymer Upper School
King Street, Hammersmith,
London W6 9LR
Tel: 020862 92024
Head: Mr D Goodhew MA(Oxon)
Age range: 11–18
No. of pupils: 1400
Fees: Day £6,945

Le Herisson
River Court Methodist
Church, Rover Court Road,
Hammersmith, London W6 9JT
Tel: 020 8563 7664
Director: Maria Frost
Age range: 2–6
Fees: Day £8,730–£8,970

L'Ecole Bilingue
St David's Welsh Church, St
Mary's Terrace, London W2 1SJ
Tel: 020 7224 8427
Headteacher: Ms Veronique
Ferreira
Age range: 3–11
No. of pupils: 68
Fees: Day £9,960–£10,770

**Leiths School of
Food & Wine**
16-20 Wendell Road, Shepherd's
Bush, London W12 9RT
Tel: 020 8749 6400
Managing Director: Camilla
Schneideman
Age range: 17–99
No. of pupils: 96

**Little Cherubs
Nursery School**
The Carmelite Priory, Pitt Street,
Kensington, London W8 4JH
Tel: 020 7376 4460/07810
712241
Principal: Mrs M Colvin MontDip
Age range: 2–5
No. of pupils: 42

Little People of Willow Vale
9 Willow Vale, London W12 0PA
Tel: 020 8749 2877
Head: Miss Jane Gleasure
Age range: 4 months–5

**Little Sweethearts
Montessori**
St Saviours Church Hall, Warwick
Avenue, London W9 2PT
Tel: 020 7266 1616

**LLOYD WILLIAMSON
SCHOOLS**
For further details see p. 61
12 Telford Road, London W10 5SH
Tel: 020 8962 0345
Email: admin@lws.org.uk
Website:
www.lloydwilliamson.co.uk
Co-Principals: Ms Lucy Meyer &
Mr Aaron Williams
Age range: 4 months–16 years
Fees: Day £16,950

**London Academy of
Music & Dramatic Art**
155 Talgarth Road,
London W14 9DA
Tel: 020 8834 0500
Head of Examinations: Dawn
Postans
Age range: 17+

London College
1st Floor, 23-25 Eastcastle
Street, London W1W 8DF
Tel: 020 7580 7552
Head: Mr David Kohn

**London Welsh School
Ysgol Gymraeg Llundain**
Hanwell Community Centre,
Westcott Crescent, London W7 1PD
Tel: 020 8575 0237
Lead Teacher: Mrs Rachel King
Age range: 3–11

MAIDA VALE SCHOOL
For further details see p. 65
18 Saltram Crescent,
London W9 3HR
Tel: 020 4511 6000
Email: admissions@
maidavaleschool.com
Website:
www.maidavaleschool.com
Headmaster: Steven Winter
Age range: 11–18
No. of pupils: 600
Fees: Day £7,450

**Maria Montessori
Children's House
– Notting Hill**
28 Powis Gardens, London W11 1JG
Tel: 020 7221 4141
Head: Mrs L Lawrence
Age range: 2–6
No. of pupils: 20
Fees: Day £4,500

**Maria Montessori
Nursery School**
Church of the Ascension
Hall, Beaufort Road,
Ealing, London W5 3EB
Tel: 07717 050761

**Maria Montessori
School – Bayswater**
St Matthew's Church, St
Petersburgh Place, London W2 4LA
Tel: +44 (0)20 7435 3646

**Melrose Nursery
School – Acton**
St Gabriel's Church Hall, Noel
Road, Acton, London W3 0JE
Tel: 020 8992 0855

Norland Place School
162-166 Holland Park Avenue,
London W11 4UH
Tel: 020 7603 9103
Headmaster: Mr Patrick Mattar MA
Age range: B4–8 years G4–11 years
Fees: Day £16,107–£18,072

**Notting Hill & Ealing
High School GDST**
2 Cleveland Road, West
Ealing, London W13 8AX
Tel: (020) 8799 8400
Headmaster: Mr Matthew Shoults
Age range: G4–18
No. of pupils: 903 VIth150
Fees: Day £14,313–£18,561

**Notting Hill
Preparatory School**
95 Lancaster Road,
London W11 1QQ
Tel: 020 7221 0727
Head of School: Mrs Sarah Knollys
Age range: 4–13
No. of pupils: 370
Fees: Day £7,130

One World Montessori Nursery
Church Court, London W6 0EU
Tel: 020 7603 6065
Age range: 1–4

Orchard House School
16 Newton Grove, Bedford Park, London W4 1LB
Tel: 020 8742 8544
Headmistress: Mrs Maria Edwards BEd(Beds) PGCE(Man) Mont Cert
Age range: 3–11
No. of pupils: 290
Fees: Day £9,210–£19,200
(£)(✐)

Oxford House College – London
24 Great Chapel Street, London W1F 8FS
Tel: +44 (0) 20 7580 9785
Principal: Ms Muberra Orme
(16)

Paint Pots Montessori School – Bayswater
St Stephens Church, Westbourne Park Road, London W2 5QT
Tel: 07527 100534
Head Teacher: Vinni Lewis
Age range: 2 years 6 months–5 years

Pembridge Hall School
18 Pembridge Square, London W2 4EH
Tel: 020 7229 0121
Headmaster: Mr Henry Keighley-Elstub
Age range: G4–11 years
(♀)

Playhouse Day Nursery
Leighton Hall, Elthorne Park Road, London W7 2JJ
Tel: 020 8840 2851
Head of School: Mrs Priti Patel

Portland Place School
56-58 Portland Place, London W1B 1NJ
Tel: 0207 307 8700
Headmaster: Mr David Bradbury
Age range: 10–16 years
(A)(✐)

Queen's College
43-49 Harley Street, London W1G 8BT
Tel: 020 7291 7000
Principal: Mr Richard Tillet
Age range: G11–18
No. of pupils: 360 VIth90
(♀)(A)(£)(16)

Queen's College Preparatory School
61 Portland Place, London W1B 1QP
Tel: 020 7291 0660
Headmistress: Mrs Emma Webb
Age range: G4–11
(♀)

RAVENSCOURT PARK PREPARATORY SCHOOL
For further details see p. 73
16 Ravenscourt Avenue, London W6 0SL
Tel: 020 8846 9153
Email: admissions@rpps.co.uk
Website: www.rpps.co.uk
Headmaster: Mr Carl Howes MA (Cantab), PGCE (Exeter)
Age range: 4–11
No. of pupils: 419
Fees: Day £6,120
(✐)

Ray Cochrane Beauty School
118 Baker Street, London W1U 6TT
Tel: 02033224738
Principal: Miss Baljeet Suri
Age range: 16–50
No. of pupils: 30
Fees: Day £650–£8,495
(16)(16)(✿)

Rolfe's Nursery School
34A Oxford Gardens, London W10 5UG
Tel: 020 7727 8300
Headteacher: Mrs Victoria O'Brien
Age range: 2–5
Fees: Day £4,950–£8,595
(✐)

Sassoon Academy
58 Buckingham Gate,, Westminster, London SW1E 6AJ
Tel: 020 7399 6902
Education Manager: Peter Crossfield
Age range: 16–45
Fees: Day £13,500
(16)(✿)

Southbank International School – Kensington
36-38 Kensington Park Road, London W11 3BU
Tel: +44 (0)20 7243 3803
Principal: Siobhan McGrath
Age range: 3–18
(✈)(IB)(✐)

Southbank International School – Westminster
63-65 Portland Place, London W1B 1QR
Tel: 020 7243 3803
Principal: Dr Paul Wood
Age range: 11–19
(✈)(IB)(✐)(16)

St Augustine's Priory
Hillcrest Road, Ealing, London W5 2JL
Tel: 020 8997 2022
Headteacher: Mrs Sarah Raffray M.A., N.P.Q.H
Age range: B3–4 G3–18
No. of pupils: 485
Fees: Day £11,529–£16,398
(♀)(A)(✐)(16)

ST BENEDICT'S SCHOOL
For further details see p. 76
54 Eaton Rise, Ealing, London W5 2ES
Tel: 020 8862 2000
Email: admissions@ stbenedicts.org.uk
Website: www.stbenedicts.org.uk
Headmaster: Mr A Johnson BA
Age range: 3–18
No. of pupils: 1073 VIth203
Fees: Day £13,485–£17,655
(A)(£)(✐)(16)

St James Preparatory School
Earsby Street, London W14 8SH
Tel: 020 7348 1777
Headmistress: Mrs Catherine Thomlinson BA(Hons)
Age range: 3–11
Fees: Day £16,425–£17,910
(£)

St James Senior Girls' School
Earsby Street, London W14 8SH
Tel: 020 7348 1777
Headmistress: Mrs Sarah Labram BA
Age range: G11–18
No. of pupils: 295 VIth67
Fees: Day £20,100
(♀)(A)(£)(✐)(16)

St Matthews Montessori School
St Matthews Church Hall, North Common Road, London W5 2QA
Tel: 07495 898 760
Head Teacher: Mrs Farah Virani M.A, B.A., PGCE – Primary, Mont. Dip.Adv.
Age range: 2–5

St Patrick's International College
London Sceptre Court Campus, 40 Tower Hill, London EC3N 4DX
Tel: 020 7287 6664
Principal: Mr Girish Chandra
(16)

St Paul's Girls' School
Brook Green, London W6 7BS
Tel: 020 7603 2288
High Mistress: Mrs Sarah Fletcher
Age range: G11–18 years
No. of pupils: 750 VIth200
Fees: Day £24,891–£26,760
(♀)(A)(£)(✐)(16)

St Peter's Nursery
59a Portobello Road, London W11 3DB
Tel: 020 7243 2617
Head of Nursery: Tracey Lloyd

Sylvia Young Theatre School
1 Nutford Place, London W1H 5YZ
Tel: 020 7258 2330
Headteacher: Mrs Frances Chave
Age range: 10–16
(16)(£)(✐)

Tabernacle School
32 St Anns Villas, Holland Park, London W11 4RS
Tel: 020 7602 6232
Headteacher: Mrs P Wilson
Age range: 3–16
Fees: Day £6,500–£9,500

The Falcons Pre-Preparatory School for Boys
2 Burnaby Gardens, Chiswick, London W4 3DT
Tel: 020 8747 8393
Head of School: Ms Liz McLaughlin
Age range: B3–7
Fees: Day £7,500–£15,705
(♂)(✐)

The Japanese School
87 Creffield Road, Acton, London W3 9PU
Tel: 020 8993 7145
Age range: 6–16

The Jordans Montessori Nursery School
Holy Innocents Church, Paddenswick Road, London W6 0UB
Tel: 0208 741 3230
Principal: Ms Sara Green
Age range: 2–5
Fees: Day £1,356–£3,270
(✐)

The Meadows Montessori School
Dukes Meadows Community Centre, Alexandra Gardens, London W4 2TD
Tel: 020 8742 1327/8995 2621
Headmistress: Mrs S Herbert BA
Age range: 2–5
Fees: Day £3,030–£3,870
(✐)

The Minors Nursery School
10 Pembridge Square, London W2 4ED
Tel: 020 7727 7253
Headteacher: Ms Jane Ritchie
Age range: 2–5

The Square Montessori School
18 Holland Park Avenue, London W11 3QU
Tel: 020 7221 6004
Principal: Mrs V Lawson-Tancred
No. of pupils: 20
Fees: Day £2,220

Thomas's Preparatory School – Kensington
17-19 Cottesmore Gardens, London W8 5PR
Tel: 020 7361 6500
Headmistress: Miss Joanna Ebner MA, BEd(Hons)(Cantab), NPQH
Age range: 4–11
Fees: Day £20,526–£21,789
(£)(✐)

Treetops Ealing Common
Woodgrange Avenue, Ealing
Common, London W5 3NY
Tel: 020 8992 0209
Age range: 3 months–5

Treetops West Ealing
Green Man Passage,
Ealing, London W13 0TG
Tel: 020 8566 5515
Age range: 3 months–5

West London College
Gliddon Road, Hammersmith,
London W14 9BL
Tel: 020 8741 1688
Principal: Paul S Smith BA(Hons),
FRSA
16

**Wetherby Preparatory
School**
48 Bryanston Square,
London W1H 2EA
Tel: 020 7535 3520
Headmaster: Mr Nick Baker
Age range: B8–13
🏃

**Wetherby Pre-
Preparatory School**
11 Pembridge Square,
London W2 4ED
Tel: 020 7727 9581
Headmaster: Mr Mark Snell
Age range: B2 1/2–8
No. of pupils: 350
Fees: Day £21,600
🏃 £ ✎

Wetherby Senior School
100 Marylebone Lane,
London W1U 2QU
Tel: 020 7535 3530
Headmaster: Mr Seth Bolderow
Age range: B11–18
Fees: Day £22,995
🏃 Ⓐ

**Windmill Montessori
Nursery School**
62 Shirland Road, London W9 2EH
Tel: 020 7289 3410
Principal: Miss M H Leoni & Miss J
Davidson
No. of pupils: 48
Fees: Day £3,600
✎

World of Children
Log Cabin Childrens Centre, 259
Northfield Avenue, London W5 4UA
Tel: 020 8840 3400

Young Dancers Academy
25 Bulwer Street, London W12 8AR
Tel: 020 8743 3856
Head: Mrs K Williams
Age range: 11–16
Fees: Day £12,237–£12,690

Schools in Greater London

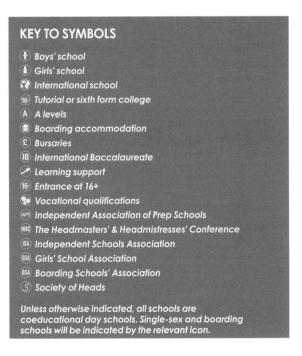

KEY TO SYMBOLS

- ⚤ Boys' school
- ⚤ Girls' school
- 🌐 International school
- 16⁺ Tutorial or sixth form college
- Ⓐ A levels
- 🏠 Boarding accommodation
- £ Bursaries
- IB International Baccalaureate
- ✐ Learning support
- 16⁺ Entrance at 16+
- ✿ Vocational qualifications
- (APS) Independent Association of Prep Schools
- (HMC) The Headmasters' & Headmistresses' Conference
- (ISA) Independent Schools Association
- (GSA) Girls' School Association
- (BSA) Boarding Schools' Association
- Ⓢ Society of Heads

Unless otherwise indicated, all schools are coeducational day schools. Single-sex and boarding schools will be indicated by the relevant icon.

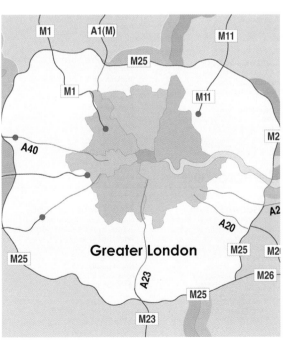

Greater London

Essex

Al-Noor Primary School
619-629 Green Lane, Goodmayes,
Ilford, Essex IG3 9RP
Tel: 020 8597 7576
Headteacher: Mrs Someera Butt
Age range: 4–10

Avon House Preparatory School
490 High Road, Woodford
Green, Essex IG8 0PN
Tel: 020 8504 1749
Headteacher: Mrs Amanda
Campbell
Age range: 3–11
Fees: Day £3,530–£3,950

Bancroft's School
High Road, Woodford
Green, Essex IG8 0RF
Tel: 020 8505 4821
Head: Mr Simon Marshall MA, PGCE
(Cantab), MA, MPhil (Oxon)
Age range: 7–18
No. of pupils: 1120 VIth247

Ⓐ Ⓔ ✎ 16•

Beehive Preparatory School
233 Beehive Lane, Redbridge,
Ilford, Essex IG4 5ED
Tel: 020 8550 3224
Head Teacher: Mr Jamie Gurr
Age range: 4–11

Braeside School
130 High Road, Buckhurst
Hill, Essex IG9 5SD
Tel: 020 8504 1133
Headmistress: Ms Chloe Moon
Age range: G3–16
Fees: Day £3,200–£4,400

Ⓕ

Chigwell School
High Road, Chigwell, Essex IG7 6QF
Tel: 020 8501 5700
Headmaster: Mr M E Punt M.A.
M.Sc. P.G.C.E.
Age range: 4–18
Fees: Day £4,250–£6,295 FB £10,995

Ⓕ Ⓐ Ⓕ Ⓔ ✎ 16•

Daiglen School
68 Palmerston Road, Buckhurst
Hill, Essex IG9 5LG
Tel: 020 8504 7108
Headteacher: Mrs P Dear
Age range: 3–11
Fees: Day £3,375–£3,425

Ⓔ ✎

Eastcourt Independent School
1 Eastwood Road, Goodmayes,
Ilford, Essex IG3 8UW
Tel: 020 8590 5472
Headmistress: Mrs Christine
Redgrave BSc(Hons), DipEd, MEd
Age range: 3–11

Gidea Park College
2 Balgores Lane, Gidea Park,
Romford, Essex RM2 5JR
Tel: 01708 740381
Headmistress: Mrs Katherine Whiskerd
Age range: 3–11
No. of pupils: 177
Fees: Day £9,675

✎

Guru Gobind Singh Khalsa College
Roding Lane, Chigwell,
Essex IG7 6BQ
Tel: 020 8559 9160
Principal: Mr Amarjit Singh Toor
BSc(Hons), BSc, BT
Age range: 3–19
Fees: Day £5,892–£6,720

Immanuel School
Havering Grange, Havering
Road, Romford, Essex RM1 4HR
Tel: 01708 764449
Head of School: Mr Simon Reeves
Age range: 3–16

✎

Loyola Preparatory School
103 Palmerston Road,
Buckhurst Hill, Essex IG9 5NH
Tel: 020 8504 7372
Headteacher: Mrs Kirsty Anthony
Age range: B3–11
No. of pupils: 200
Fees: Day £10,485

Ⓕ Ⓔ ✎

Maytime Montessori Nursery – Cranbrook Road
341 Cranbrook Road,
Ilford, Essex IG1 4UF
Tel: 020 8554 3079

Maytime Montessori Nursery – Eastwood Road
2 Eastwood Road,
Goodmayes, Essex IG3 8XB
Tel: 020 8599 3744

Maytime Montessori Nursery – Wanstead Road
293 Wanstead Park Rd,
Ilford, Essex IG1 3TR
Tel: 020 8554 6344
Age range: 0–6

Oakfields Montessori School
Harwood Hall, Harwood Hall
Lane, Upminster, Essex RM14 2YG
Tel: 01708 220117
Headmistress: Katrina Carroll
Age range: 2–11
No. of pupils: 202
Fees: Day £10,296–£11,121

✎

Oaklands School
8 Albion Hill, Loughton,
Essex IG10 4RA
Tel: 020 8508 3517
Group Managing Principal: Mr M
Hagger
Age range: 2–16
No. of pupils: 243
Fees: Day £10,350–£10,575

Park School for Girls
20-22 Park Avenue,
Ilford, Essex IG1 4RS
Tel: 020 8554 2466
Head Teacher: Mrs Androulla
Nicholas BSc Hons (Econ) PGCE
Age range: G4–16
No. of pupils: 160
Fees: Day £2,375–£3,580

Ⓕ Ⓐ 16•

St Aubyn's School
Bunces Lane, Woodford
Green, Essex IG8 9DU
Tel: 020 8504 1577
Headmaster: Mr Leonard Blom
BEd(Hons) BA NPQH
Age range: 3–13
No. of pupils: 525
Fees: Day £5,370–£12,195

Ⓔ ✎

St Mary's Hare Park School & Nursery
South Drive, Gidea Park,
Romford, Essex RM2 6HH
Tel: 01708 761220
Head Teacher: Mrs K Karwacinski
Age range: 2–11
No. of pupils: 180
Fees: Day £8,775

Stratford College of Management
1-7 Hainault Street,
Ilford, Essex IG1 4EL
Tel: 020 8553 0205
Head: Dr Raza

16•

The Ursuline Preparatory School Ilford
2-8 Coventry Road,
Ilford, Essex IG1 4QR
Tel: 020 8518 4050
Headteacher: Mrs Victoria
McNaughton
Age range: G3–11
No. of pupils: 159
Fees: Day £7,320–£9,828

Ⓕ

Woodford Green Preparatory School
Glengall Road, Woodford
Green, Essex IG8 0BZ
Tel: 020 8504 5045
Headmaster: Mr J P Wadge
Age range: 3–11
No. of pupils: 384
Fees: Day £3,585

Ⓔ ✎

Hertfordshire

Lyonsdown School
3 Richmond Road, New Barnet,
Barnet, Hertfordshire EN5 1SA
Tel: 020 8449 0225
Head of School: Mrs Stanton-Tonner
Age range: B3–7 G3–11
No. of pupils: 180
Fees: Day £4,712–£11,550

✎

Mount House School
Camlet Way, Hadley Wood,
Barnet, Hertfordshire EN4 0NJ
Tel: 020 8449 6889
Principal: Mr Toby Mullins
Age range: 11–18
No. of pupils: 190
Fees: Day £16,560

Ⓕ Ⓐ ✎ 16•

Susi Earnshaw Theatre School
68 High Street, Barnet,
Hertfordshire EN5 5SJ
Tel: 020 8441 5010
Head of School: Julia VanEllis-
Hammond BA Hons
Age range: 9–16
No. of pupils: 60
Fees: Day £9,000–£12,000

Ⓔ

The Royal Masonic School for Girls
Rickmansworth Park,
Rickmansworth,
Hertfordshire WD3 4HF
Tel: 01923 773168
Headmaster: Mr Kevin Carson
M.Phil (Cambridge)
Age range: G4–18
No. of pupils: 930 VIth165
Fees: Day £11,475–£17,475 WB
£20,115–£27,495 FB £21,225–£29,835

Ⓕ Ⓕ Ⓐ Ⓕ Ⓔ ✎ 16•

Kent

Ashgrove School
116 Widmore Road,
Bromley, Kent BR1 3BE
Tel: 020 8460 4143
Principal: Dr Patricia Ash CertEd,
BSc(Hons), PhD, CMath, FIMA
Age range: 3–11 years
🌍

BABINGTON HOUSE SCHOOL
For further details see p. 86
Grange Drive, Chislehurst,
Kent BR7 5ES
Tel: 020 8467 5537
Email: enquiries@
babingtonhouse.com
Website:
www.babingtonhouse.com
Headmaster: Mr Tim Lello MA,
FRSA, NPQH
Age range: 3–18
No. of pupils: 432
Ⓐ £ ✎

Beckenham College
The Clockhouse Business Centre,
Unit 2, Thayers Farm Road,
Beckenham, Kent BR3 4LZ
Tel: 020 8650 3321
Principal: Mrs E Wakeling
Age range: 16+
Fees: Day £100–£3,500
16ᵗ 16ᵗ 🌍

Benedict House Preparatory School
1-5 Victoria Road, Sidcup,
Kent DA15 7HD
Tel: 020 8300 7206
Headteacher: Mr Malcolm Gough
Age range: 3–11
Fees: Day £3,807–£7,929
✎

Bickley Park School
24 Page Heath Lane, Bickley,
Bromley, Kent BR1 2DS
Tel: 020 8467 2195
Headmaster: Mr Patrick Wenham
Age range: B3–13 G3–4
No. of pupils: 370
Fees: Day £6,990–£14,940
⚥ £ ✎

Bird College
The Centre, 27 Station Road,
Sidcup, Kent DA15 7EB
Tel: 020 8300 6004/3031
Principal & Chief Executive: Ms
Shirley Coen BA(Hons), FSRA
16ᵗ

Bishop Challoner School
228 Bromley Road, Shortlands,
Bromley, Kent BR2 0BS
Tel: 020 8460 3546
Headteacher: Mrs Paula Anderson
Age range: 3–18
No. of pupils: 340
Fees: Day £3,150–£4,500
Ⓐ £ ✎ 16ᵗ

Breaside Preparatory School
41-43 Orchard Road,
Bromley, Kent BR1 2PR
Tel: 020 8460 0916
Executive Principal: Mrs Karen A
Nicholson B.Ed, NPQH, Dip EYs
Age range: 2 1/2–11
No. of pupils: 376
Fees: Day £11,580–£13,494

Bromley High School GDST
Blackbrook Lane, Bickley,
Bromley, Kent BR1 2TW
Tel: 020 8781 7000/1
Head: Mrs A M Drew BA(Hons), MBA
(Dunelm)
Age range: G4–18
⚥ Ⓐ £ ✎ 16ᵗ

Darul Uloom London
Foxbury Avenue, Perry Street,
Chislehurst, Kent BR7 6SD
Tel: 020 8295 0637
Principal: Mufti Mustafa
Age range: B11–18
No. of pupils: 160
Fees: FB £2,400
⚥ Ⓐ 🌍 16ᵗ

Farringtons School
Perry Street, Chislehurst,
Kent BR7 6LR
Tel: 020 8467 0256
Head: Mr David Jackson
Age range: 3–18
No. of pupils: 700 VIth100
Fees: Day £15,690 WB
£30,960 FB £32,880
🌍 Ⓐ 🌍 £ ✎ 16ᵗ

Merton Court Preparatory School
38 Knoll Road, Sidcup,
Kent DA14 4QU
Tel: 020 8300 2112
Headmaster: Mr Dominic Price
BEd, MBA
Age range: 3–11
Fees: Day £8,670–£12,765
£

St Christopher's The Hall School
49 Bromley Road,
Beckenham, Kent BR3 5PA
Tel: 020 8650 2200
Headmaster: Mr A Velasco MEd,
BH(Hons), PGCE
Age range: 3–11
No. of pupils: 305
Fees: Day £3,750–£9,165

St. David's Prep
Justin Hall,, Beckenham Road,
West Wickham, Kent BR4 0QS
Tel: 020 8777 5852
Principal: Mrs J Foulger
Age range: 4–11
No. of pupils: 155
Fees: Day £5,850–£8,550
£ ✎

West Lodge School
36 Station Road, Sidcup,
Kent DA15 7DU
Tel: 020 8300 2489
Head Teacher: Mr Robert Francis
Age range: 3–11
No. of pupils: 163
Fees: Day £5,475–£9,150
✎

Wickham Court School
Schiller International,
Layhams Road, West
Wickham, Kent BR4 9HW
Tel: 020 8777 2942
Principal: Mrs Samantha Da Costa
Age range: 2–16
No. of pupils: 121
Fees: Day £6,983.40–£12,344.55

Middlesex

Acorn House College
39-47 High Street, Southall,
Middlesex UB1 3HF
Tel: 020 8571 9900
Principal: Dr Francis Choi
Age range: 13–19
No. of pupils: 121 VIth85
Fees: Day £4,100–£15,525
16ᵗ Ⓐ

ACS Hillingdon International School
Hillingdon Court, 108 Vine
Lane, Hillingdon, Uxbridge,
Middlesex UB10 0BE
Tel: +44 (0) 1895 259 771
Head of School: Mr Martin Hall
Age range: 4–18
🌍 £ ⒾⒷ ✎ 16ᵗ

Alpha Preparatory School
21 Hindes Road, Harrow,
Middlesex HA1 1SH
Tel: 020 8427 1471
Head: Mr P Fahy
Age range: 3–11 years

Ashton House School
50-52 Eversley Crescent,
Isleworth, Middlesex TW7 4LW
Tel: 020 8560 3902
Headteacher: Mrs Angela Stewart
Age range: 3–11
Fees: Day £7,986–£11,586
✎

Buckingham Preparatory School
458 Rayners Lane, Pinner,
Harrow, Middlesex HA5 5DT
Tel: 020 8866 2737
Head of School: Mrs Sarah Hollis
Age range: B3–11 G3–4
Fees: Day £9,600–£12,300
⚥ £ ✎

Buxlow Preparatory School
5/6 Castleton Gardens,
Wembley, Middlesex HA9 7QJ
Tel: 020 8904 3615
Headteacher: Mr Ralf Furse
Age range: 2–11
Fees: Day £8,970–£9,330

Edgware Jewish Girls – Beis Chinuch
296 Hale Lane, Edgware,
Middlesex HA8 8NP
Tel: 020 8905 4376
Headteacher: Mr M Cohen
Age range: G3–11
⚥

Halliford School
Russell Road, Shepperton,
Middlesex TW17 9HX
Tel: 01932 223593
Head: Mr James Davies BMus
(Hons) LGSM FASC ACertCM PGCE
Age range: B11–18 G16–18
No. of pupils: 435
Fees: Day £16,590
⚥ Ⓐ £ ✎ 16ᵗ

Hampton Prep and Pre-Prep School
Gloucester Road, Hampton,
Middlesex TW12 2UQ
Tel: 020 8979 1844
Headmaster: Mr Tim Smith
Age range: 3–11

Hampton School
Hanworth Road, Hampton,
Middlesex TW12 3HD
Tel: 020 8979 9273
Headmaster: Mr Kevin Knibbs MA (Oxon)
Age range: B11–18
No. of pupils: 1200
Fees: Day £6,390

Harrow School
5 High Street, Harrow on the Hill, Middlesex HA1 3HT
Tel: 020 8872 8000
Head Master: Mr Alastair Land
Age range: B13–18
No. of pupils: 830 VIth320
Fees: FB £40,050

Holland House School
1 Broadhurst Avenue, Edgware,
Middlesex HA8 8TP
Tel: 020 8958 6979
Headteacher: Mrs Emily Brown
Age range: 4–11
No. of pupils: 147

Jack and Jill School
30 Nightingale Road, Hampton,
Middlesex TW12 3HX
Tel: 020 8979 3195
Principal: Miss K Papirnik BEd(Hons)
Age range: B2–5 G2–7
No. of pupils: 155
Fees: Day £4,608–£13,143

KEW HOUSE SCHOOL
For further details see p. 88
Kew House, 6 Capital
Interchange Way, London,
Middlesex TW8 0EX
Tel: 0208 742 2038
Email: admissions@
kewhouseschool.com
Website:
www.kewhouseschool.com
Headmaster: Mr Will Williams
Age range: 11–18
No. of pupils: 550
Fees: Day £7,450

Kids Inc Day Nursery – Enfield
8 Glyn Road, Southbury,
Enfield, Middlesex EN3 4JL
Tel: 020 8805 1144

Lady Eleanor Holles
Hanworth Road, Hampton,
Middlesex TW12 3HF
Tel: 020 8979 1601
Head of School: Mrs Heather Hanbury
Age range: G7–18
No. of pupils: 930
Fees: Day £20,802

Lady Nafisa Independent Secondary School for Girls
83A Sunbury Road, Feltham,
Middlesex TW13 4PH
Tel: 020 8751 5610
Headteacher: Ms Fouzia Butt
Age range: G11–16

Menorah Grammar School
Abbots Road, Edgware,
Middlesex HA8 0QS
Tel: 020 8906 9756
Head of School: Mr David Vincent
Age range: B11–21

Merchant Taylors' School
Sandy Lodge, Northwood,
Middlesex HA6 2HT
Tel: 01923 820644
Head: Mr S J Everson MA (Cantab)
Age range: B11–18
No. of pupils: 865 VIth282
Fees: Day £19,998

Newland House School
Waldegrave Park, Twickenham,
Middlesex TW1 4TQ
Tel: 020 8865 1234
Headmaster: Mr D A Alexander
Age range: B3–13 G3–11
No. of pupils: 425
Fees: Day £3,848–£4,306

North London Collegiate School
Canons, Canons Drive,
Edgware, Middlesex HA8 7RJ
Tel: +44 (0)20 8952 0912
Headmistress: Mrs Sarah Clark
Age range: G4–18
No. of pupils: 1080
Fees: Day £5,754–£6,810

Northwood College for Girls GDST
Maxwell Road, Northwood,
Middlesex HA6 2YE
Tel: 01923 825446
Head: Ms Zara Hubble
Age range: G3–18

Oak Heights
3 Red Lion Court, Alexandra Road,
Hounslow, Middlesex TW3 1JS
Tel: 020 8577 1827
Head: Mr S Dhillon
Age range: 11–16
No. of pupils: 48
Fees: Day £6,000

Orley Farm School
South Hill Avenue, Harrow,
Middlesex HA1 3NU
Tel: 020 8869 7600
Headmaster: Mr Tim Calvey
Age range: 4–13
No. of pupils: 497
Fees: Day £14,160–£16,335

Quainton Hall School & Nursery
91 Hindes Road, Harrow,
Middlesex HA1 1RX
Tel: 020 8861 8861
Headmaster: S Ford BEd (Hons), UWE Bristol
Age range: B2–13 G2–11
Fees: Day £11,850–£13,050

RADNOR HOUSE
For further details see p. 90
Pope's Villa, Cross
Deep, Twickenham,
Middlesex TW1 4QG
Tel: 020 8891 6264
Email: admissions@
radnorhouse.org
Website:
www.radnor-twickenham.org
Head: Mr Darryl Wideman MA Oxon, PGCE
Age range: 9–18

Rambert School of Ballet & Contemporary Dance
Clifton Lodge, St Margaret's Drive,
Twickenham, Middlesex TW1 1QN
Tel: 020 8892 9960
Principal: R McKim
Age range: 16+

Reddiford School
36-38 Cecil Park, Pinner,
Middlesex HA5 5HH
Tel: 020 8866 0660
Headteacher: Mrs J Batt CertEd, NPQH
Age range: 3–11
No. of pupils: 320
Fees: Day £4,860–£11,565

Regent College
Sai House, 167 Imperial Drive,
Harrow, Middlesex HA2 7HD
Tel: 020 8966 9900
Principal: Mrs Tharshiny Pankaj
Age range: 11–19
No. of pupils: 167
Fees: Day £4,100–£15,525

Roxeth Mead School
Buckholt House, 25 Middle Road,
Harrow, Middlesex HA2 0HW
Tel: 020 8422 2092
Headmistress: Mrs A Isaacs
Age range: 3–7
No. of pupils: 54
Fees: Day £4,800–£10,665

St Catherine's Prep
Cross Deep, Twickenham,
Middlesex TW1 4QJ
Tel: 020 8891 2898
Headmistress: Mrs Johneen McPherson MA
Age range: G3–11
No. of pupils: 123
Fees: Day £10,500–£12,144

St Catherine's School
Cross Deep, Twickenham,
Middlesex TW1 4QJ
Tel: 020 8891 2898
Headmistress: Mrs Johneen McPherson MA
Age range: G3–18
No. of pupils: 449
Fees: Day £11,205–£15,585

St Christopher's School
71 Wembley Park Drive,
Wembley, Middlesex HA9 8HE
Tel: 020 8902 5069
Headteacher: Mr G. P. Musetti
Age range: 4–11
Fees: Day £9,006–£9,906

St Helen's College
Parkway, Hillingdon, Uxbridge,
Middlesex UB10 9JX
Tel: 01895 234371
Head: Mrs. Shirley Drummond BA, PGCert, MLDP, FCCT
Age range: 2–11
No. of pupils: 373
Fees: Day £9,900–£12,240

St Helen's School
Eastbury Road, Northwood,
Middlesex HA6 3AS
Tel: +44 (0)1923 843210
Headmistress: Dr Mary Short BA, PhD
Age range: G3–18
No. of pupils: VIth165

St John's School
Potter Street Hill, Northwood,
Middlesex HA6 3QY
Tel: 020 8866 0067
Headmaster: Mr M S Robinson BSc
Age range: B3–13 years
No. of pupils: 350
Fees: Day £10,420–£15,110

St Martin's School
40 Moor Park Road, Northwood,
Middlesex HA6 2DJ
Tel: 01923 825740
Headmaster: Mr D T Tidmarsh BSc(Wales)
Age range: B3–13
No. of pupils: 400
Fees: Day £5,775–£15,135

St. John's Senior School
North Lodge, The Ridgeway,
Enfield, Middlesex EN2 8BE
Tel: +44 (0)20 8366 0035
Head Teacher: Mr A Tardios
Age range: 11–18 years
(A) (16)

Tashbar of Edgware
Mowbray Road, Edgware,
Middlesex HA8 8JL
Age range: B3–11
(★)

The Hall Pre-Preparatory School & Nursery
The Grange Country House,
Rickmansworth Road,
Northwood, Middlesex HA6 2RB
Tel: 01923 822807
Headmistress: Mrs S M Goodwin
Age range: 1–7
Fees: Day £4,650–£9,900
(£) (✎)

The John Lyon School
Middle Road, Harrow on the
Hill, Middlesex HA2 0HN
Tel: 020 8515 9443
Head: Miss Katherine Haynes BA,
MEd, NPQH
Age range: B11–18
No. of pupils: 600
(★) (A) (£) (✎) (16)

The Mall School
185 Hampton Road, Twickenham,
Middlesex TW2 5NQ
Tel: 0208 977 2523
Headmaster: Mr D C Price BSc, MA
Age range: B4–13
No. of pupils: 320
Fees: Day £12,240–£13,767
(★) (£) (✎)

The St Michael Steiner School
Park Road, Hanworth Park,
London, Middlesex TW13 6PN
Tel: 0208 893 1299
Age range: 3–16 (17 from Jul 2014)
No. of pupils: 101
Fees: Day £3,850–£9,500
(£) (✎)

Twickenham Preparatory School
Beveree, 43 High Street,
Hampton, Middlesex TW12 2SA
Tel: 020 8979 6216
Head: Mr David Malam BA(Hons)
(Southampton), PGCE(Winchester)
Age range: B4–13 G4–11
No. of pupils: 273
Fees: Day £10,470–£11,340
(£) (✎)

Surrey

Al-Khair School
109-117 Cherry Orchard Road,
Croydon, Surrey CR0 6BE
Tel: 020 8662 8664
Headteacher: Mrs Aisha Chaudhry
Age range: 5–16 years

Broomfield House School
Broomfield Road, Kew Gardens,
Richmond, Surrey TW9 3HS
Tel: 020 8940 3884
Head Teacher: Mr N O York
BA(Hons), MA, MPhil, FRSA
Age range: 3–11
No. of pupils: 160
Fees: Day £4,389–£15,054
(✎)

Cambridge Tutors College
Water Tower Hill, Croydon,
Surrey CR0 5SX
Tel: 020 8688 5284/7363
Principal: Dr Chris Drew
Age range: 15–19
No. of pupils: 215 VIth200
Fees: Day £10,400–£22,995
(16) (A) (★) (£) (16)

Canbury School
Kingston Hill, Kingston upon
Thames, Surrey KT2 7LN
Tel: 020 8549 8622
Headmistress: Ms Louise Clancy
Age range: 11–18
No. of pupils: 58
Fees: Day £16,401
(£) (✎)

Collingwood School
3 Springfield Road, Wallington,
Surrey SM6 0BD
Tel: 020 8647 4607
Headmaster: Mr Leigh Hardie
Age range: 3–11
No. of pupils: 120
Fees: Day £4,980–£8,925
(✎)

Croydon High School GDST
Old Farleigh Road, Selsdon,
South Croydon, Surrey CR2 8YB
Tel: 020 8260 7500
Headmistress: Mrs Emma Pattison
Age range: G3–18
No. of pupils: 580 VIth75
(★) (A) (£) (✎) (16)

Cumnor House Nursery
91 Pampisford Road, South
Croydon, Surrey CR2 6DH
Tel: +44 (0)20 8660 3445
Headmaster: Mr Daniel Cummings
Age range: 2–4
No. of pupils: 200
Fees: Day £4,980–£10,635

Cumnor House School for Boys
168 Pampisford Road, South
Croydon, Surrey CR2 6DA
Tel: 020 8645 2614
Headmaster: Mr Daniel Cummings
Age range: B2–13
No. of pupils: 423
Fees: Day £3,880–£4,655
(★) (✎)

Cumnor House School for Girls
1 Woodcote Lane, Purley,
Surrey CR8 3HB
Tel: 020 8645 2614
Headmistress: Mrs Amanda
McShane
Age range: G2–11
No. of pupils: 138
Fees: Day £3,880–£4,655
(★)

Educare Small School
12 Cowleaze Road, Kingston
upon Thames, Surrey KT2 6DZ
Tel: 020 8547 0144
Head Teacher: Mrs E Steinthal
Age range: 3–11
No. of pupils: 46
Fees: Day £6,240
(✎)

Elmhurst School
44-48 South Park Hill Rd, South
Croydon, Surrey CR2 7DW
Tel: 020 8688 0661
Headmaster: Mr Tony Padfield
Age range: B3–11
No. of pupils: 207
Fees: Day £6,129–£11,403
(★)

Falcons Prep Richmond
41 Kew Foot Road, Richmond,
Surrey TW9 2SS
Tel: 020 8948 9490
Headmistress: Ms Olivia Buchanan
Age range: B7–13
Fees: Day £14,250–£17,835
(★) (✎)

Holy Cross Preparatory School
George Road, Kingston upon
Thames, Surrey KT2 7NU
Tel: 020 8942 0729
Headteacher: Mrs S Hair BEd(Hons)
Age range: G4–11
No. of pupils: 285
Fees: Day £12,996
(★) (£) (✎)

Homefield Preparatory School
Western Road, Sutton,
Surrey SM1 2TE
Tel: 0208 642 0965
Headmaster: Mr John Towers
Age range: B4–13
No. of pupils: 350
Fees: Day £6,345–£13,650
(★) (£) (✎)

Kew College
24-26 Cumberland Road,
Kew, Surrey TW9 3HQ
Tel: 020 8940 2039
Head: Mrs Marianne Austin
BSc(Hons), MA(Hons), ACA, PGCE
Age range: 3–11
No. of pupils: 296
(£) (✎)

KEW GREEN PREPARATORY SCHOOL
For further details see p. 87
Layton House, Ferry Lane,
Kew Green, Richmond,
Surrey TW9 3AF
Tel: 020 8948 5999
Email: admissions@kgps.co.uk
Website: www.kgps.co.uk
Headmaster: Mr J Peck
Age range: 4–11
No. of pupils: 280
Fees: Day £6,120
(✎)

King's House School
68 King's Road, Richmond,
Surrey TW10 6ES
Tel: 020 8940 1878
Head: Mr Mark Turner BA, PGCE,
NPQH
Age range: B3–13 G3–4
No. of pupils: 460
Fees: Day £2,370–£5,560
(★) (£) (✎)

Kingston Grammar School
70 London Rd, Kingston upon
Thames, Surrey KT2 6PY
Tel: 020 8546 5875
Head: Mr Stephen Lehec
Age range: 11–18
(A) (£) (✎) (16)

Laleham Lea School
29 Peaks Hill, Purley, Surrey CR8 3JJ
Tel: 020 8660 3351
Headteacher: Ms K Barry
Age range: 3–11
No. of pupils: 112
Fees: Day £8,940
(£) (✎)

MARYMOUNT LONDON
For further details see p. 89
George Road, Kingston upon
Thames, Surrey KT2 7PE
Tel: +44 (0)20 8949 0571
Email: admissions@
marymountlondon.com
Website:
www.marymountlondon.com
Headmistress: Mrs Margaret
Giblin
Age range: G11–18
No. of pupils: 255
Fees: Day £25,985 WB
£42,135 FB £44,000

Oakwood Independent School
Godstone Road, Purley,
Surrey CR8 2AN
Tel: 020 8668 8080
Headmaster: Mr Ciro Candia
BA(Hons), PGCE
Age range: 3–11
No. of pupils: 176
Fees: Day £9,030–£9,840

Old Palace of John Whitgift School
Old Palace Road, Croydon,
Surrey CR0 1AX
Tel: 020 8686 7347
Head: Mrs. C Jewell
Age range: B3 months–4
years G3 months–19 years
No. of pupils: 740 VIth120
Fees: Day £11,316–£15,366

Old Vicarage School
48 Richmond Hill, Richmond,
Surrey TW10 6QX
Tel: 020 8940 0922
Headmistress: Mrs G D Linthwaite
Age range: G4–11
No. of pupils: 200
Fees: Day £4,740

Park Hill School
8 Queens Road, Kingston upon
Thames, Surrey KT2 7SH
Tel: 020 8546 5496
Headmaster: Mr Alistair Bond
Age range: 2–11
No. of pupils: 100
Fees: Day £10,440

Rokeby School
George Road, Kingston upon
Thames, Surrey KT2 7PB
Tel: 020 8942 2247
Head: Mr J R Peck
Age range: B4–13
No. of pupils: 386
Fees: Day £14,607–£18,189

Royal Botanic Gardens
School of Horticulture, Kew,
Richmond, Surrey TW9 3AB
Tel: 020 8332 5545
Principal: Emma Fox BEd(Hons),
DipHort(Kew)(Hons)
Fees: Day £0

Royal Russell Junior School
Coombe Lane, Croydon,
Surrey CR9 5BX
Tel: 020 8651 5884
Junior School Headmaster: Mr
James C Thompson
Age range: 3–11
No. of pupils: 300
Fees: Day £11,160–£14,220

Royal Russell School
Coombe Lane, Croydon,
Surrey CR9 5BX
Tel: 020 8657 3669
Headmaster: Christopher
Hutchinson
Age range: 11–18
No. of pupils: 590 VIth180
Fees: Day £18,480 FB £36,525

Seaton House School
67 Banstead Road South,
Sutton, Surrey SM2 5LH
Tel: 020 8642 2332
Headmistress: Mrs Debbie Morrison
Higher Diploma in Education (RSA)
Age range: B3–5 G3–11
No. of pupils: 164
Fees: Day £10,188

Shrewsbury House School
107 Ditton Road, Surbiton,
Surrey KT6 6RL
Tel: 020 8399 3066
Headmaster: Mr K Doble BA, PDM,
PGCE
Age range: B7–13
No. of pupils: 320
Fees: Day £18,060

St David's School
23/25 Woodcote Valley Road,
Purley, Surrey CR8 3AL
Tel: 020 8660 0723
Headmistress: Cressida Mardell
Age range: 3–11
No. of pupils: 167
Fees: Day £6,375–£10,650

St James Senior Boys School
Church Road, Ashford,
Surrey TW15 3DZ
Tel: 01784 266930
Headmaster: Mr David Brazier
Age range: B11–18
No. of pupils: 403 VIth65
Fees: Day £18,930

Staines Preparatory School
3 Gresham Road, Staines-upon-
Thames, Surrey TW18 2BT
Tel: 01784 450909
Head of School: Ms Samantha
Sawyer B.Ed (Hons), M.Ed, NPQH
Age range: 3–11
No. of pupils: 339
Fees: Day £10,080–£12,060

Surbiton High School
13-15 Surbiton Crescent, Kingston
upon Thames, Surrey KT1 2JT
Tel: 020 8546 5245
Principal: Mrs Rebecca Glover
Age range: B4–11 G4–18
No. of pupils: 1210 VIth186
Fees: Day £10,857–£17,142

Sutton High School GDST
55 Cheam Road, Sutton,
Surrey SM1 2AX
Tel: 020 8642 0594
Headmistress: Mrs Katharine
Crouch
Age range: G3–18
No. of pupils: 600 VIth60
Fees: Day £10,095–£17,043

The Cedars School
Coombe Road, Lloyd Park,
Croydon, Surrey CR0 5RD
Tel: 020 8185 7770
Headmaster: Robert Teague Bsc
(Hons)
Age range: B11–18

The Royal Ballet School
White Lodge, Richmond,
Surrey TW10 5HR
Tel: 020 8392 8440
Artistic Director: Christopher
Powney
Age range: 11–19 years

The Secretary College
123 South End, Croydon,
Surrey CR0 1BJ
Tel: 0208 688 4440
Principal: Mr J E K Safo

The Study School
57 Thetford Road, New
Malden, Surrey KT3 5DP
Tel: 020 8942 0754
Head of School: Mrs Donna
Brackstone-Drake
Age range: 3–11
No. of pupils: 134
Fees: Day £4,860–£11,388

Trinity School
Shirley Park, Croydon,
Surrey CR9 7AT
Tel: 020 8656 9541
Head: Alasdair Kennedy MA
(Cantab)
Age range: B10–18 G16–18
No. of pupils: 1007
Fees: Day £16,656

Unicorn School
238 Kew Road, Richmond,
Surrey TW9 3JX
Tel: 020 8948 3926
Headmaster: Mr Kil Thompson
Age range: 3–11
Fees: Day £7,170–£13,170

Westbury House
80 Westbury Road, New
Malden, Surrey KT3 5AS
Tel: 020 8942 5885
Head of School: Matthew Burke
Age range: 3–11
Fees: Day £4,860–£11,115

Whitgift School
Haling Park, South Croydon,
Surrey CR2 6YT
Tel: +44 20 8633 9935
Headmaster: Mr Christopher
Ramsey
Age range: B10–18
No. of pupils: 1560
Fees: Day £20,640 WB
£33,081 FB £40,140

Schools in the South-East

KEY TO SYMBOLS

- ⚤ Boys' school
- ⚤ Girls' school
- 🌐 International school
- 16 Tutorial or sixth form college
- Ⓐ A levels
- 🏫 Boarding accommodation
- £ Bursaries
- IB International Baccalaureate
- ✐ Learning support
- 16 Entrance at 16+
- ⚒ Vocational qualifications
- (IAPS) Independent Association of Prep Schools
- (HMC) The Headmasters' & Headmistresses' Conference
- (ISA) Independent Schools Association
- (GSA) Girls' School Association
- (BSA) Boarding Schools' Association
- Ⓢ Society of Heads

Unless otherwise indicated, all schools are coeducational day schools. Single-sex and boarding schools will be indicated by the relevant icon.

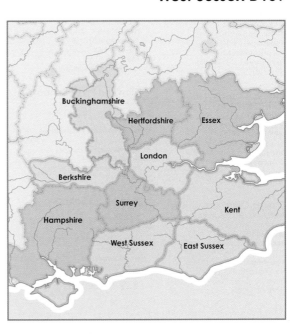

Berkshire

ABI College – Reading Campus
80 London Street, Reading, Berkshire RG1 4SJ
Tel: 01189 569111
16+

Alder Bridge Steiner-Waldorf School
Bridge House, Mill Lane, Padworth, Reading, Berkshire RG7 4JU
Tel: 0118 971 4471
Head of School: Lucia Dimarco
Age range: 3–14 years

Bradfield College
Bradfield, Berkshire RG7 6AU
Tel: 0118 964 4516
Headmaster: Dr Christopher Stevens
Age range: 13–18
No. of pupils: 815
Fees: Day £31,080 FB £38,850

Caversham School
16 Peppard Road, Caversham, Reading, Berkshire RG4 8JZ
Tel: 01189 478 684
Head: Mr Chris Neal
Age range: 4–11
No. of pupils: 60
Fees: Day £9,900

Chiltern College
16 Peppard Road, Caversham, Reading, Berkshire RG4 8JZ
Tel: 0118 947 1847
Head: Christine Lawrence
16+

Claires Court Junior Boys
Maidenhead Thicket, Maidenhead, Berkshire SL6 3QE
Tel: 01628 327700
Head: J M E Spanswick
Age range: B4–11
No. of pupils: 248
Fees: Day £9,270–£15,930

Claires Court Nursery, Girls and Sixth Form
1 College Avenue, Maidenhead, Berkshire SL6 6AW
Tel: 01628 327700
Head of School: Mrs M Heywood
Age range: B16–18 G3–18
No. of pupils: 495 VIth111
Fees: Day £9,270–£16,740

Claires Court Senior Boys
Ray Mill Road East, Maidenhead, Berkshire SL6 8TE
Tel: 01628 327700
Headmaster: Mr J M Rayer BSc, PGCE
Age range: B11–16
No. of pupils: 335 VIth112
Fees: Day £15,930–£16,740

Crosfields School
Shinfield, Reading, Berkshire RG2 9BL
Tel: 0118 987 1810
Headmaster: Mr Craig Watson
Age range: 3–13
No. of pupils: 510
Fees: Day £10,314–£15,159

Dolphin School
Waltham Road, Hurst, Reading, Berkshire RG10 0FR
Tel: 0118 934 1277
Head: Mr Adam Hurst
Age range: 3–13
Fees: Day £10,170–£14,070

Eagle House School
Sandhurst, Berkshire GU47 8PH
Tel: 01344 772134
Headmaster: Mr A P N Barnard BA(Hons), PGCE
Age range: 3–13
No. of pupils: 381
Fees: Day £12,030–£18,810 FB £25,275

Elstree School
Woolhampton, Reading, Berkshire RG7 5TD
Tel: 0118 971 3302
Headmaster: Mr Sid Inglis
Age range: B3–13 G3–13
No. of pupils: 225
Fees: Day £11,550–£21,000 WB £26,250–£26,850 FB £26,700–£27,300

Eton College
Windsor, Berkshire SL4 6DW
Tel: 01753 671249
Head Master: Simon Henderson MA
Age range: B13–18
No. of pupils: 1300 VIth520
Fees: FB £40,668

Eton End PNEU School
35 Eton Road, Datchet, Slough, Berkshire SL3 9AX
Tel: 01753 541075
Headmistress: Sarah Stokes BA(Hons), PGCE
Age range: B3–7 G3–11
No. of pupils: 245
Fees: Day £9,375–£11,985

Heathfield School
London Road, Ascot, Berkshire SL5 8BQ
Tel: 01344 898342
Head of School: Ms Sarah Wilson
Age range: G11–18
No. of pupils: 200
Fees: Day £7,690–£7,900 FB £12,400–£12,700

Hemdean House School
Hemdean Road, Caversham, Reading, Berkshire RG4 7SD
Tel: 0118 947 2590
Head Teacher: Mrs H Chalmers BSc
Age range: B4–11 G4–11
Fees: Day £8,490–£9,300

Herries Preparatory School
Dean Lane, Cookham Dean, Berkshire SL6 9BD
Tel: 01628 483350
Headteacher: Mr Robert Grosse
Age range: 2–11 years

Highfield Preparatory School
2 West Road, Maidenhead, Berkshire SL6 1PD
Tel: 01628 624918
Headteacher: Mrs Joanna Leach
Age range: B3–5 G3–11
No. of pupils: 107
Fees: Day £1,119–£12,675

Holme Grange School
Heathlands Road, Wokingham, Berkshire RG40 3AL
Tel: 0118 978 1566
Headteacher: Mrs Claire Robinson BA (Open) PGCE NPQH
Age range: 3–16 years
No. of pupils: 509
Fees: Day £11,160–£15,525

Impact International College
81 London Street, Reading, Berkshire RG1 4QA
Tel: 0118 956 0610
Head: Mr Alan Loveridge
16+

Kids Inc Day Nursery – Crowthorne
59-61 Dukes Ride, Crowthorne, Berkshire RG45 6NS
Tel: 01344 780670

Lambrook School
Winkfield Row, Nr Ascot, Berkshire RG42 6LU
Tel: 01344 882717
Headmaster: Mr Jonathan Perry
Age range: 3–13
No. of pupils: 570
Fees: Day £12,669–£20,310 WB £22,740–£24,354

LEIGHTON PARK SCHOOL
For further details see p. 98
Shinfield Road, Reading, Berkshire RG2 7ED
Tel: 0118 987 9600
Email: admissions@leightonpark.com
Website: www.leightonpark.com
Head: Mr Matthew L S Judd BA, PGCE
Age range: 11–18
No. of pupils: 520

Long Close School
Upton Court Road, Upton, Slough, Berkshire SL3 7LU
Tel: 01753 520095
Headteacher: Miss K Nijjar BA (Hons), Med, MA
Age range: 2–16
No. of pupils: 329

Luckley House School
Luckley Road, Wokingham, Berkshire RG40 3EU
Tel: 0118 978 4175
Head: Mrs Jane Tudor
Age range: 11–18
No. of pupils: 300
Fees: Day £5,662 WB £9,183 FB £9,907

Ludgrove
Wokingham, Berkshire RG40 3AB
Tel: 0118 978 9881
Head of School: Mr Simon Barber
Age range: B8–13
No. of pupils: 190

LVS ASCOT
For further details see p. 100
London Road, Ascot, Berkshire SL5 8DR
Tel: 01344 882770
Email: enquiries@lvs.ascot.sch.uk
Website: www.lvs.ascot.sch.uk
Principal: Mrs Christine Cunniffe BA (Hons), MMus, MBA
Age range: 4–18
No. of pupils: 800
Fees: Day £10,785–£19,335 FB £27,585–£33,975

Meadowbrook Montessori School
Malt Hill, Warfield, Berkshire RG42 6JQ
Tel: 01344 890869
Director of Education: Ms Serena Gunn
Age range: 18 months–11 years

Newbold School

Popeswood Road, Binfield,
Bracknell, Berkshire RG42 4AH
Tel: 01344 421088
Headteacher: Mrs Jaki Crissey MA,
BA, PGCE Primary
Age range: 3–11
Fees: Day £4,500

Our Lady's Preparatory School

The Avenue, Crowthorne,
Wokingham, Berkshire RG45 6PB
Tel: 01344 773394
Headmistress: Mrs Helene Robinson
Age range: 3 months–11 years
No. of pupils: 100
Fees: Day £7,080

Padworth College

Padworth, Reading,
Berkshire RG7 4NR
Tel: 0118 983 2644
Acting Principal: Mr Chris Randell
Age range: 13–19
No. of pupils: 116 VIth50
Fees: Day £14,400 FB £29,400

Pangbourne College

Pangbourne, Reading,
Berkshire RG8 8LA
Tel: 0118 984 2101
Headmaster: Thomas J C Garnier
Age range: 11–18
No. of pupils: 450 VIth134
Fees: Day £18,000–£25,380
FB £25,860–£36,660

Papplewick School

Windsor Road, Ascot,
Berkshire SL5 7LH
Tel: 01344 621488
Head: Mr Tom Bunbury
Age range: B6–13
No. of pupils: 195

Queen Anne's School

6 Henley Road, Caversham,
Reading, Berkshire RG4 6DX
Tel: 0118 918 7300
Headmistress: Mrs Julia Harrington
BA(Hons), PGCE, NPQH
Age range: G11–18

Reading Blue Coat School

Holme Park, Sonning Lane, Sonning,
Reading, Berkshire RG4 6SU
Tel: 0118 944 1005
Headmaster: Mr Jesse Elzinga
Age range: B11–18 G16–18
No. of pupils: 710 VIth230
Fees: Day £16,695

REDDAM HOUSE BERKSHIRE
For further details see p. 102

Bearwood Road, Sindlesham,
Wokingham, Berkshire RG41 5BG
Tel: 0118 467 8731
Email: registrar@
reddamhouse.org.uk
Website: reddamhouse.org.uk
Principal: Mrs Tammy Howard
Age range: 3 months–18 years
No. of pupils: 650
Fees: Day £11,490–£18,330
WB £27,981–£32,244 FB
£29,526–£33,789

Redroofs School for the Performing Arts (Redroofs Theatre School)

26 Bath Road, Maidenhead,
Berkshire SL6 4JT
Tel: 01628 674092
Principal: June Rose
Age range: 8–18
No. of pupils: 100
Fees: Day £4,882–£5,527

St Andrew's School

Buckhold, Pangbourne,
Reading, Berkshire RG8 8QA
Tel: 0118 974 4276
Headmaster: Mr Jonathan Bartlett
BSc QTS
Age range: 3–13
Fees: Day £5,430–£18,150 WB £3,360

St Bernard's Preparatory School

Hawtrey Close, Slough,
Berkshire SL1 1TB
Tel: 01753 521821
Head Teacher: Mr N Cheesman
Age range: 2–11
Fees: Day £8,850–£10,545

St Edward's Prep

64 Tilehurst Road, Reading,
Berkshire RG30 2JH
Tel: 0118 957 4342
Headmaster: Mr Jonathan Parsons
Age range: 4–11

St George's Ascot

Wells Lane, Ascot, Berkshire SL5 7DZ
Tel: 01344 629920
Headmistress: Mrs Liz Hewer MA
(Hons) (Cantab) PGCE
Age range: G11–18
No. of pupils: 270 VIth70
Fees: Day £22,800 WB
£34,050–£34,680 FB £35,460

St George's School Windsor Castle

Windsor Castle, Windsor,
Berkshire SL4 1QF
Tel: 01753 865553
Head Master: Mr W Goldsmith BA
(Hons), FRSA, FCCT
Age range: 3–13

ST JOHN'S BEAUMONT PREPARATORY SCHOOL
For further details see p. 108

Priest Hill, Old Windsor,
Berkshire SL4 2JN
Tel: 01784 432428
Email: abarker@sjb.email
Website: www.sjbwindsor.uk
Headmaster: Mr G E F Delaney
BA(Hons), PGCE, MSc
Age range: B3–13
No. of pupils: 250
Fees: Day £3,410–£6,525
FB £7,647–£10,005

St Joseph's College

Upper Redlands Road,
Reading, Berkshire RG1 5JT
Tel: 0118 966 1000
Headmaster: Mr Andrew Colpus
Age range: 3–18
No. of pupils: VIth65
Fees: Day £6,672–£11,406

St Mary's School Ascot

St Mary's Road, Ascot,
Berkshire SL5 9JF
Tel: 01344 296614
Headmistress: Mrs Danuta Staunton
Age range: G11–18
No. of pupils: 386 VIth120
Fees: Day £27,630 FB £38,790

St Piran's Preparatory School

Gringer Hill, Maidenhead,
Berkshire SL6 7LZ
Tel: 01628 594302
Headmaster: Mr J A Carroll
BA(Hons), BPhilEd, PGCE, NPQH
Age range: 3–11
Fees: Day £10,857–£16,566

Sunningdale School

Dry Arch Road, Sunningdale,
Berkshire SL5 9PY
Tel: 01344 620159
Headmaster: Tom Dawson MA,
PGCE
Age range: B7–13
No. of pupils: 90

Teikyo School UK

Framewood Road, Wexham,
Slough, Berkshire SL2 4QS
Tel: 01753 663711
Principal: Mr Yukihiro Hamada
Age range: 16–18 years

The Abbey School

Kendrick Road, Reading,
Berkshire RG1 5DZ
Tel: 0118 987 2256
Head: Mr Will le Fleming
Age range: G3–18
No. of pupils: 1000
Fees: Day £10,860–£18,000

The Marist Preparatory School

King's Road, Sunninghill,
Ascot, Berkshire SL5 7PS
Tel: 01344 626137
Vice Principal: Jane Gow
Age range: G2–11
No. of pupils: 225
Fees: Day £9,780–£11,940

The Marist School

King's Road, Sunninghill,
Ascot, Berkshire SL5 7PS
Tel: 01344 624291
Principal: Mr Karl McCloskey
Age range: G3–18

The Oratory Preparatory School

Great Oaks, Goring Heath,
Reading, Berkshire RG8 7SF
Tel: 0118 984 4511
Headmaster: Mr Rob Stewart
Age range: 2–13
No. of pupils: 400
Fees: Day £10,266–£16,443
WB £21,153 FB £24,522

The Oratory School

Woodcote, Reading,
Berkshire RG8 0PJ
Tel: 01491 683500
Head Master: Mr J J Smith BA(Hons),
MEd, PGCE
Age range: B11–18
No. of pupils: 380 VIth120
Fees: Day £24,966 FB £34,299

The Vine Christian School

SORCF Christian Centre,
Basingstoke Road, Three Mile
Cross, Reading, Berkshire RG7 1AT
Tel: 0118 988 6464
Head of School: Mrs Eve Strike
Age range: 5–13
No. of pupils: 9

Upton House School

115 St Leonard's Road,
Windsor, Berkshire SL4 3DF
Tel: 01753 862610
Head: Mrs Rhian Thornton BA (Hons)
NPQH LLE PGCE
Age range: 2–11 years
No. of pupils: 245
Fees: Day £3,143–£5,225

Waverley School
Waverley Way, Finchampstead,
Wokingham, Berkshire RG40 4YD
Tel: 0118 973 1121
Principal: Mr Guy Shore
Age range: 3–11
Fees: Day £8,589–£11,982

Wellington College
Duke's Ride, Crowthorne,
Berkshire RG45 7PU
Tel: +44 (0)1344 444000
Master: Mr James Dahl
Age range: 13–18
No. of pupils: 1080 VIth485
Fees: Day £30,375–
£34,890 FB £41,580

Buckinghamshire

Ashfold School
Dorton House, Dorton, Aylesbury,
Buckinghamshire HP18 9NG
Tel: 01844 238237
Headmaster: Mr Colin MacIntosh
Age range: 3–13 years

**Broughton Manor
Preparatory School**
Newport Road, Broughton, Milton
Keynes, Buckinghamshire MK10 9AA
Tel: 01908 665234
Heads: Mr J Smith & Mrs R Smith
Age range: 2 months–11 years
No. of pupils: 250
Fees: Day £13,980

Caldicott
Crown Lane, Farnham Royal,
Buckinghamshire SL2 3SL
Tel: 01753 649301
Headmaster: Mr Jeremy Banks BA
(Hons) QTS. MEd
Age range: B7–13
No. of pupils: 250
Fees: Day £16,833–£18,780 WB
£24,918–£27,687 FB £24,918–£27,687

**Chesham Preparatory
School**
Two Dells Lane, Chesham,
Buckinghamshire HP5 3QF
Tel: 01494 782619
Headmaster: Mr Jonathan Beale
Age range: 3–13
No. of pupils: 392
Fees: Day £9,270–£14,400

**Child First Aylesbury
Pre-School**
35 Rickfords Hill, Aylesbury,
Buckinghamshire HP20 2RT
Tel: 01296 433224
Pre-School Manager: Sara Foster

**Crown House
Preparatory School**
Bassetsbury Manor, Bassetsbury
Lane, High Wycombe,
Buckinghamshire HP11 1QX
Tel: 01494 529927
Headmaster: Mr David Ward
Age range: 3–11
No. of pupils: 120
Fees: Day £9,005–£10,185

Dair House School
Bishops Blake, Beaconsfield
Road, Farnham Royal,
Buckinghamshire SL2 3BY
Tel: 01753 643964
Headmaster: Mr Terry Wintle
BEd(Hons)
Age range: 3–11
No. of pupils: 125
Fees: Day £3,425–£4,345

DAVENIES SCHOOL
For further details see p. 95
Station Road, Beaconsfield,
Buckinghamshire HP9 1AA
Tel: 01494 685400
Email: office@davenies.co.uk
Website: www.davenies.co.uk
Headmaster: Mr Carl Rycroft
BEd (Hons)
Age range: B4–13
No. of pupils: 343
Fees: Day £11,985–£17,985

**Focus School – Stoke
Poges Campus**
School Lane, Stoke Poges,
Buckinghamshire SL2 4QA
Tel: 01753 662167

Gateway School
1 High Street, Great Missenden,
Buckinghamshire HP16 9AA
Tel: 01494 862407
Head of School: Mrs Cath Bufton-
Green
Age range: 2–11
No. of pupils: 355
Fees: Day £2,235–£11,175

Gayhurst School
Bull Lane, Gerrards Cross,
Buckinghamshire SL9 8RJ
Tel: 01753 882690
Headmaster: Gareth R A Davies
Age range: 3–11
Fees: Day £12,159–£15,438

**Godstowe Preparatory
School**
Shrubbery Road, High Wycombe,
Buckinghamshire HP13 6PR
Tel: 01494 529273
Headmistress: Sophie Green
Age range: B3–7 G3–13
No. of pupils: 409
Fees: Day £10,800–
£16,620 FB £24,645

**Griffin House
Preparatory School**
Little Kimble, Aylesbury,
Buckinghamshire HP17 0XP
Tel: 01844 346154
Headmaster: Mr Tim Walford
Age range: 3–11
No. of pupils: 100
Fees: Day £8,238–£8,580

Heatherton House School
Copperkins Lane,
Chesham Bois, Amersham,
Buckinghamshire HP6 5QB
Tel: 01494 726433
Headteacher: Mrs Debbie
Isaachsen
Age range: B3–4 G3–11
Fees: Day £1,140–£13,335

High March
23 Ledborough Lane, Beaconsfield,
Buckinghamshire HP9 2PZ
Tel: 01494 675186
Head of School: Mrs Kate Gater
Age range: B3–4 G3–11
No. of pupils: 278
Fees: Day £5,850–£15,480

Maltman's Green School
Maltmans Lane, Gerrards Cross,
Buckinghamshire SL9 8RR
Tel: 01753 883022
Headmistress: Mrs Jill Walker BSc
(Hons), MA Ed, PGCE
Age range: G2–11
No. of pupils: 355
Fees: Day £1,925–£5,275

**Milton Keynes
Preparatory School**
Tattenhoe Lane, Milton Keynes,
Buckinghamshire MK3 7EG
Tel: 01908 642111
Heads of School: Mr C Bates & Mr
S Driver
Age range: 2 months–11 years
No. of pupils: 500
Fees: Day £4,560–£15,120

Pipers Corner School
Pipers Lane, Great
Kingshill, High Wycombe,
Buckinghamshire HP15 6LP
Tel: 01494 718 255
Headmistress: Mrs H J Ness-Gifford
BA(Hons), PGCE
Age range: G4–18
No. of pupils: VIth72
Fees: Day £8,880–£18,390

St Mary's School
94 Packhorse Road, Gerrards
Cross, Buckinghamshire SL9 8JQ
Tel: 01753 883370
Head of School: Mrs P Adams
Age range: G3–18
No. of pupils: 350 VIth50
Fees: Day £5,670–£16,980

Stowe School
Buckingham, Buckinghamshire
MK18 5EH
Tel: 01280 818000
Headmaster: Dr Anthony
Wallersteiner
Age range: 13–18
No. of pupils: 769 VIth318
Fees: Day £26,355 FB £36,660

Swanbourne House School
Swanbourne, Milton Keynes,
Buckinghamshire MK17 0HZ
Tel: 01296 720264
Head of School: Mrs Jane Thorpe
Age range: 3–13
No. of pupils: 323
Fees: Day £1,410–£18,360 FB £23,520

The Beacon School
Chesham Bois, Amersham,
Buckinghamshire HP6 5PF
Tel: 01494 433654
Headmaster: William Phelps
Age range: B3–13
No. of pupils: 470
Fees: Day £11,850–£17,250

**The Grove Independent
School**
Redland Drive, Loughton, Milton
Keynes, Buckinghamshire MK5 8HD
Tel: 01908 690590
Principal: Mrs Deborah Berkin
Age range: 3 months–13 years

The Webber Independent School
Soskin Drive, Stantonbury Fields, Milton Keynes, Buckinghamshire MK14 6DP
Tel: 01908 574740
Principal: Mrs Hilary Marsden
Age range: 3–18
No. of pupils: 300 VIth15
Fees: Day £9,030–£12,705
Ⓐ ⓔ ✐ ⑯

Thornton College
College Lane, Thornton, Buckinghamshire MK17 0HJ
Tel: 01280 812610
Headteacher: Mrs Val Holmes
Age range: B2–4 G3–18
No. of pupils: 414
Fees: Day £10,035–£16,005 WB £17,310–£21,900 FB £21,525–£26,700
⚹ ⚘ Ⓐ ⚕ ✐

Thorpe House School
Oval Way, Gerrards Cross, Buckinghamshire SL9 8QA
Tel: 01753 882474
Headmaster: Mr Nicholas Pietrek
Age range: B4–16
Fees: Day £10,950–£16,962
⚹ ⓔ ✐

Wycombe Abbey
High Wycombe, Buckinghamshire HP11 1PE
Tel: +44 (0)1494 897008
Headmistress: Mrs Jo Duncan MA (St Andrews), PGCE (Cantab)
Age range: G11–18
No. of pupils: 649
Fees: Day £30,270 FB £40,350
⚹ ⚘ Ⓐ ⚕ ⓔ ✐ ⑯

East Sussex

Bartholomews Tutorial College
22-23 Prince Albert Street, Brighton, East Sussex BN1 1HF
Tel: 01273 205965/205141
Director of Studies: Mike Balmer BEd
Age range: 16+
No. of pupils: 40 VIth25
Fees: Day £25,000 WB £30,000 FB £30,000
⑯ Ⓐ ✐

Battle Abbey School
Battle, East Sussex TN33 0AD
Tel: 01424 772385
Headmaster: Mr D Clark BA(Hons)
Age range: 2–18
No. of pupils: 286 VIth48
Fees: Day £6,939–£16,914 FB £26,649–£31,932
⚘ Ⓐ ⚕ ⓔ ✐ ⑯ ❀

Bede's School
The Dicker, Upper Dicker, Hailsham, East Sussex BN27 3QH
Tel: +44 (0)1323843252
Head: Mr Peter Goodyer
Age range: 3 months–18
No. of pupils: 800 VIth295
Fees: Day £10,230–£17,400 FB £22,290–£25,650
⚘ Ⓐ ⚕ ⓔ ✐ ⑯ ❀

Bellerbys College Brighton
1 Billinton Way, Brighton, East Sussex BN1 4LF
Tel: +44 (0)1273 339333
Principal: Mr Simon Mower
Age range: 13–18
⚘ ⑯ Ⓐ ⚕

Brighton & Hove Montessori School
67 Stanford Avenue, Brighton, East Sussex BN1 6FB
Tel: 01273 702485
Headteacher: Mrs Daisy Cockburn AMI, MontDip
Age range: 2–11
✐

Brighton College
Eastern Road, Brighton, East Sussex BN2 0AL
Tel: 01273 704200
Head Master: Richard Cairns MA
Age range: 3–18
No. of pupils: 950
Fees: Day £10,050–£24,540 WB £33,390–£34,410 FB £37,470–£45,210
⚘ Ⓐ ⚕ ⓔ ✐ ⑯

Brighton Girls GDST
Montpelier Road, Brighton, East Sussex BN1 3AT
Tel: 01273 280280
Head: Jennifer Smith
Age range: G3–18
No. of pupils: 680 VIth70
Fees: Day £7,191–£14,421
⚹ Ⓐ ⓔ ✐ ⑯

Brighton Steiner School
John Howard House, Roedean Road, Brighton, East Sussex BN2 5RA
Tel: 01273 386300
Chair of the College of Teachers: Carrie Rawle
Age range: 3–16
Fees: Day £7,800–£8,100
ⓔ ✐

Buckswood School
Broomham Hall, Rye Road, Guestling, Hastings, East Sussex TN35 4LT
Tel: 01424 813 813
School Director: Mr Giles Sutton
Age range: 10–19
No. of pupils: 420
⚘ Ⓐ ⚕ ⓔ ⒾⒷ ✐ ⑯

Charters Ancaster
Woodsgate Place, Gunters Lane, Bexhill-on-Sea, East Sussex TN39 4EB
Tel: 01424 216670
Nursery Manager: Susannah Crump
Age range: 6 months–5
No. of pupils: 125
ⓔ ✐

Claremont Preparatory & Nursery School
Ebdens Hill, Baldslow, St Leonards-on-Sea, East Sussex TN37 7PW
Tel: 01424 751555
Headmistress: Abra Stoakley
Age range: 1–13
Fees: Day £6,900–£12,600
Ⓐ ⓔ ✐

Claremont Senior & Sixth Form School
Bodiam, Nr Robertsbridge, East Sussex TN32 5UJ
Tel: 01580 830396
Headmaster: Mr. Giles Perrin
Age range: 14–18
Fees: Day £17,400

Darvell School
Darvell, Brightling Road, Robertsbridge, East Sussex TN32 5DR
Tel: 01580 883300
Head of School: Mr Timothy Maas
Age range: 4–16
✐

Deepdene School
195 New Church Road, Hove, East Sussex BN3 4ED
Tel: 01273 418984
Heads: Mrs Nicola Gane & Miss Elizabeth Brown
Age range: 6 months–11 years
Fees: Day £8,349
ⓔ

Eastbourne College
Old Wish Road, Eastbourne, East Sussex BN21 4JX
Tel: 01323 452323 (Admissions)
Headmaster: Mr Tom Lawson MA (Oxon)
Age range: 13–18
No. of pupils: 650 VIth312
Fees: Day £23,895–£24,375 FB £36,420–£36,975
⚘ Ⓐ ⚕ ⓔ ✐ ⑯

European School of Animal Osteopathy
25 Old Steine, Brighton, East Sussex BN1 1EL
Tel: 01273 673332
Head: Jean-Yves Girard
⑯

Greenfields Independent Day & Boarding School
Priory Road, Forest Row, East Sussex RH18 5JD
Tel: +44 (0)1342 822189
Executive Head: Mr. Jeff Smith
Age range: 2–19
⚘ Ⓐ ⚕ ✐ ⑯

Hove College
48 Cromwell Road, Hove, East Sussex BN3 3ER
Tel: 01273 772577
Director: Mr John Veale
⑯

JeMs Nursery
15 The Upper Drive, Hove, East Sussex BN3 6GR
Tel: 01273 328 675
Head of School: Ms. Penina Efune
Age range: 1–4
✐

Lancing College Preparatory School at Hove
The Droveway, Hove, East Sussex BN3 6LU
Tel: 01273 503452
Headmistress: Mrs Kirsty Keep BEd
Age range: 3–13
No. of pupils: 181
Fees: Day £3,960–£15,975
ⓔ ✐

Lewes Old Grammar School
High Street, Lewes, East Sussex BN7 1XS
Tel: 01273 472634
Headmaster: Mr Robert Blewitt
Age range: 3–18
No. of pupils: 463 VIth50
Fees: Day £8,760–£14,625
Ⓐ ⓔ ✐ ⑯

MAYFIELD SCHOOL
For further details see p. 101
The Old Palace, Mayfield, East Sussex TN20 6PH
Tel: 01435 874642
Email: registrar@mayfieldgirls.org
Website: www.mayfieldgirls.org
Head: Ms Antonia Beary MA, MPhil (Cantab), PGCE
Age range: G11–18
No. of pupils: 385
Fees: Day £7,280 FB £11,750
⚹ ⚘ Ⓐ ⚕ ⓔ ✐ ⑯

Michael Hall School
Kidbrooke Park, Priory Road, Forest Row, East Sussex RH18 5JA
Tel: 01342 822275
Age range: 0 years–18 years
No. of pupils: VIth102
Fees: Day £9,245–£12,670
⚘ Ⓐ ⚕ ✐ ⑯

Roedean Moira House
Upper Carlisle Road, Eastbourne,
East Sussex BN20 7TE
Tel: 01323 644144
Headmaster: Mr Andrew Wood
Age range: G0–18
No. of pupils: 289

ROEDEAN SCHOOL
For further details see p. 104
Roedean Way, Brighton,
East Sussex BN2 5RQ
Tel: 01273 667500
Email: info@roedean.co.uk
Website: www.roedean.co.uk
Headmaster: Mr. Oliver Bond
BA(Essex), PGCE, NPQH
Age range: G11–18
No. of pupils: 630 VIth155
Fees: Day £5,670–£7,415
WB £10,030–£11,185 FB
£10,990–£13,305

Sacred Heart School
Mayfield Lane, Durgates,
Wadhurst, East Sussex TN5 6DQ
Tel: 01892 783414
Headteacher: Mrs H Blake
BA(Hons), PGCE
Age range: 2–11
No. of pupils: 121
Fees: Day £8,355

Skippers Hill Manor Preparatory School
Five Ashes, Mayfield,
East Sussex TN20 6HR
Tel: 01825 830234
Headmaster: Mr Phillip Makhouli
Age range: 2–13
Fees: Day £2,660–£4,615

St Andrew's Prep
Meads Street, Eastbourne,
East Sussex BN20 7RP
Tel: 01323 733203
Headmaster: Gareth Jones MEd,
BA(Hons), PGCE
Age range: 9 months–13 years
No. of pupils: 360

St Bede's Preparatory School
Duke's Drive, Eastbourne,
East Sussex BN20 7XL
Tel: +44 (0)1323 734222
Age range: 3 months–13 years

St Christopher's School
33 New Church Road, Hove,
East Sussex BN3 4AD
Tel: 01273 735404
Headmaster: Mr Julian Withers
Age range: 4–13
Fees: Day £8,370–£12,720

St George's Business & Language College
28-29 Grand Parade, Hastings,
East Sussex TN37 6DN
Tel: 01424 813696
Principal: Mr Richard Lawless

The Academy of Creative Training
8-10 Rock Place, Brighton,
East Sussex BN2 1PF
Tel: 01273 818266

The Drive Prep School
101 The Drive, Hove, East
Sussex BN3 6GE
Tel: 01273 738444
Head Teacher: Mrs S Parkinson
CertEd, CertPerfArts
Age range: 7–16 years

Vinehall
Robertsbridge, East Sussex TN32 5JL
Tel: 01580 880413
Headmaster: Joff Powis
Age range: 2–13
No. of pupils: 220
Fees: Day £10,350–£19,290 WB
£22,575–£23,100 FB £24,525–£25,125

Windlesham School
190 Dyke Road, Brighton,
East Sussex BN1 5AA
Tel: 01273 553645
Headmaster: Mr John Ingrassia
Age range: 3–11
No. of pupils: 195
Fees: Day £6,015–£8,955

Essex

Alleyn Court School
Wakering Road, Southend-
on-Sea, Essex SS3 0PW
Tel: 01702 582553
Headmaster: Mr Rupert W.J. Snow
B.Ed, NPQH
Age range: 2.5–11 years

Brentwood Preparatory School
Shenfield Road, Brentwood,
Essex CM15 8BD
Tel: +44 (0)1277 243300
Headmaster: Mr Jason Whiskerd
Age range: 3–11
No. of pupils: 573

Brentwood School
Middleton Hall Lane,
Brentwood, Essex CM15 8EE
Tel: 01277 243243
Headmaster: Mr Michael Bond
Age range: 3–18
No. of pupils: 1800
Fees: Day £20,097 FB £39,381

Colchester High School
Wellesley Road, Colchester,
Essex CO3 3HD
Tel: 01206 573389
Headteacher: Ms Karen Gracie-
Langrick
Age range: 2–16
No. of pupils: 320
Fees: Day £9,465–£13,620

Coopersale Hall School
Flux's Lane, off Stewards Green
Road, Epping, Essex CM16 7PE
Tel: 01992 577133
Headmistress: Miss Kaye Lovejoy
Age range: 2–11
No. of pupils: 275
Fees: Day £10,350–£10,575

Elm Green Preparatory School
Parsonage Lane, Little Baddow,
Chelmsford, Essex CM3 4SU
Tel: 01245 225230
Principal: Ms Ann Milner
Age range: 4–11
No. of pupils: 220
Fees: Day £8,844

Empire College London
Forest House, 16-20 Clements
Road, Ilford, Essex IG1 1BA
Tel: 020 8553 2683
Head: Ms Aaiesha Tak

Felsted Preparatory School
Felsted, Great Dunmow,
Essex CM6 3JL
Tel: 01371 822610
Headmaster: Mr Simon James
Age range: 4–13
No. of pupils: 460
Fees: Day £9,285–£17,820
FB £23,250–£24,465

Felsted School
Felsted, Great Dunmow,
Essex CM6 3LL
Tel: +44 (0)1371 822608
Headmaster: Mr Chris Townsend
Age range: 4–18

Gosfield School
Cut Hedge Park, Halstead Road,
Gosfield, Halstead, Essex CO9 1PF
Tel: 01787 474040
Headteacher: Mr Guy Martyn
Age range: 4–18
No. of pupils: VIth21
Fees: Day £6,690–£15,525

Heathcote School
Eves Corner, Danbury,
Chelmsford, Essex CM3 4QB
Tel: 01245 223131
Headmistress: Caroline Forgeron
Age range: 2–11
Fees: Day £4,830–£7,245

Herington House School
1 Mount Avenue, Hutton,
Brentwood, Essex CM13 2NS
Tel: 01277 211595
Principal: Mr R. Dudley-Cooke
Age range: 3–11
No. of pupils: 130
Fees: Day £1,955–£3,865

Holmwood House Preparatory School
Chitts Hill, Lexden, Colchester,
Essex CO3 9ST
Tel: 01206 574305
Headmaster: Alexander Mitchell
Age range: 4–13
No. of pupils: 302
Fees: Day £10,140–£17,895 FB £35

Littlegarth School
Horkesley Park, Nayland,
Colchester, Essex CO6 4JR
Tel: 01206 262332
Headmaster: Mr Peter H Jones
Age range: 2–11 years
No. of pupils: 318
Fees: Day £3,205–£3,723

London Academy of Management Sciences
9th Floor Wentworth House,
350 Eastern Avenue,
Ilford, Essex IG2 6NN
Tel: 020 8554 9169
Head: Mr Asif Siddiqui

Maldon Court Preparatory School
Silver Street, Maldon,
Essex CM9 4QE
Tel: 01621 853529
Headteacher: Elaine Mason
Age range: 3–11
Fees: Day £8,236

New Hall School
The Avenue, Boreham,
Chelmsford, Essex CM3 3HS
Tel: 01245 467588
Principal: Mrs Katherine Jeffrey MA,
BA, PGCE, MA(Ed Mg), NPQH
Age range: 1–18
No. of pupils: 1400
Fees: Day £3,096–£6,597 WB
£8,076–£9,735 FB £2,142–£10,233

Oxford House School
2-4 Lexden Road, Colchester,
Essex CO3 3NE
Tel: 01206 576686
Head Teacher: Mrs Sarah Leyshon
Age range: 2–11
No. of pupils: 158

Saint Nicholas School
Hillingdon House, Hobbs Cross
Road, Harlow, Essex CM17 0NJ
Tel: 01279 429910
Headmaster: Mr D Bown
Age range: 4–16
No. of pupils: 400
Fees: Day £9,960–£12,660

Saint Pierre School
16 Leigh Road, Leigh-on-Sea,
Southend-on-Sea, Essex SS9 1LE
Tel: 01702 474164
Headmaster: Mr Chris Perkins
Age range: 2–11+
Fees: Day £7,218–£8,181

St Cedd's School
178a New London Road,
Chelmsford, Essex CM2 0AR
Tel: 01245 392810
Head: Mr Matthew Clarke
Age range: 3–11
No. of pupils: 400
Fees: Day £8,880–£11,370

St John's School
Stock Road, Billericay,
Essex CM12 0AR
Tel: 01277 623070
Head Teacher: Mrs F Armour
BEd(Hons)
Age range: 2–16 years
No. of pupils: 392
Fees: Day £5,328–£13,500

St Margaret's Preparatory School
Hall Drive, Gosfield,
Halstead, Essex CO9 1SE
Tel: 01787 472134
Headteacher: Mrs Carolyn Moss
Age range: 2–11
Fees: Day £3,240–£4,055

St Mary's School
Lexden Road, Colchester,
Essex CO3 3RB
Tel: 01206 572544   Admissions:
01206 216420
Principal: Mrs H K Vipond MEd,
BSc(Hons), NPQH
Age range: B3–4 G3–16
No. of pupils: 430
Fees: Day £6,855–£14,985

St Michael's Church Of England Preparatory School
198 Hadleigh Road, Leigh-on-Sea,
Southend-on-Sea, Essex SS9 2LP
Tel: 01702 478719
Head: Steve Tompkins BSc(Hons),
PGCE, MA, NPQH
Age range: 3–11
No. of pupils: 271
Fees: Day £4,104–£9,600

St Philomena's Catholic School
Hadleigh Road, Frinton-on-
Sea, Essex CO13 9HQ
Tel: 01255 674492
Headmistress: Mrs B McKeown
DipEd
Age range: 4–11
Fees: Day £6,240–£7,500

St. Anne's Preparatory School
154 New London Road,
Chelmsford, Essex CM2 0AW
Tel: 01245 353488
Head of School: Valerie Eveleigh
Age range: 3–11 years

Stephen Perse Junior School, Dame Bradbury's School
Ashdon Road, Saffron
Walden, Essex CB10 2AL
Tel: 01223 454700 (Ext:4000)
Age range: 1–11

The Christian School (Takeley)
Dunmow Road, Brewers End,
Takeley, Bishop's Stortford,
Essex CM22 6QH
Tel: 01279 871182
Headmaster: M E Humphries
Age range: 3–16
Fees: Day £6,012–£8,436

Thorpe Hall School
Wakering Road, Southend-
on-Sea, Essex SS1 3RD
Tel: 01702 582340
Headmaster: Mr Andrew Hampton
Age range: 2–16 years
No. of pupils: 359
Fees: Day £9,000–£12,600

Ursuline Preparatory School
Old Great Ropers, Great
Ropers Lane, Warley,
Brentwood, Essex CM13 3HR
Tel: 01277 227152
Headmistress: Mrs Pauline Wilson
MSc
Age range: 3–11
Fees: Day £6,450–£12,015

Widford Lodge School
Widford Road, Chelmsford,
Essex CM2 9AN
Tel: 01245 352581
Headteacher: Miss Michelle Cole
A.C.I.B. – P.G.C.E.
Age range: 2–11
No. of pupils: 230
Fees: Day £7,800–£9,657

Woodlands School, Great Warley
Warley Street, Great Warley,
Brentwood, Essex CM13 3LA
Tel: 01277 233288
Head: Mr David Bell
Age range: 3 months–11 years

Woodlands School, Hutton Manor
428 Rayleigh Road, Hutton,
Brentwood, Essex CM13 1SD
Tel: 01277 245585
Head: Paula Hobbs
Age range: 3 months–11 years

Hampshire

Alton School
Anstey Lane, Alton,
Hampshire GU34 2NG
Tel: 01420 82070
Head: Karl Guest
Age range: 0–18 years
No. of pupils: 420

Ballard School
Fernhill Lane, New Milton,
Hampshire BH25 5SU
Tel: 01425 626900
Headmaster: Mr Andrew McCleave
Age range: 2–16 years
No. of pupils: 447
Fees: Day £2,945–£5,415

Bedales Prep School, Dunhurst
Petersfield, Hampshire GU32 2DP
Tel: 01730 300200
Head of School: Colin Baty
Age range: 8–13
No. of pupils: 200
Fees: Day £16,920–£18,765
FB £22,215–£24,930

Bedales School
Church Road, Steep, Petersfield,
Hampshire GU32 2DG
Tel: 01730 711733
Head of School: Magnus Bashaarat
Age range: 13–18
No. of pupils: 463
Fees: Day £28,515 FB £36,285

Boundary Oak School
Roche Court, Fareham,
Hampshire PO17 5BL
Tel: 01329 280955/820373
Head: Mr James Polansky
Age range: 2–16
No. of pupils: 348
Fees: Day £9,195–£14,886 WB
£16,155–£21,078 FB £18,144–£23,067

Brockwood Park & Inwoods School
Brockwood Park, Bramdean,
Hampshire SO24 0LQ
Tel: +44 (0)1962 771744
Principal: Mr Antonio Autor
Age range: 14–19
No. of pupils: 112 VIth39
Fees: Day £5,630–£6,400 FB £21,400

Churcher's College
Petersfield, Hampshire GU31 4AS
Tel: 01730 263033
Headmaster: Mr Simon Williams
MA, BSc
Age range: 3–18 years
Fees: Day £10,320–£16,035

Daneshill School
Stratfield Turgis, Basingstoke,
Hampshire RG27 0AR
Tel: 01256 882707
Headmaster: Mr David Griffiths
Age range: 3–13
Fees: Day £10,650–£14,000

Ditcham Park School
Ditcham Park, Petersfield,
Hampshire GU31 5RN
Tel: 01730 825659
Headmaster: Mr Graham
Spawforth MA, MEd
Age range: 2.5–16
No. of pupils: 379
Fees: Day £2,835–£4,753
£ ✎

Durlston Court
Becton Lane, Barton-on-Sea, New
Milton, Hampshire BH25 7AQ
Tel: 01425 610010
Head of School: Mr Richard May
Age range: 2–13
No. of pupils: 296
Fees: Day £3,540–£15,390
£ ✎

Embley
Embley Park, Romsey,
Hampshire SO51 6ZE
Tel: 01794 512206
Headteacher: Mr Cliff Canning
Age range: 2–18
No. of pupils: 500
Fees: Day £8,754–£31,338
⚑ A ⚓ £ ✎ 16

Farleigh School
Red Rice, Andover,
Hampshire SP11 7PW
Tel: 01264 710766
Headmaster: Father Simon Everson
Age range: 3–13
Fees: Day £5,385–£19,590
FB £21,675–£25,485
⚓ £ ✎

Farnborough Hill
Farnborough Road, Farnborough,
Hampshire GU14 8AT
Tel: 01252 545197
Head: Mrs A Neil BA, MEd, PGCE
Age range: G11–18
No. of pupils: 550 VIth90
Fees: Day £14,796
⚑ A £ ✎ 16

Forres Sandle Manor
Fordingbridge, Hampshire SP6 1NS
Tel: 01425 653181
Headmaster: Mr M N Hartley
BSc(Hons)
Age range: 3–13
No. of pupils: 264
⚓ £ ✎

Glenhurst School
16 Beechworth Road, Havant,
Hampshire PO9 1AX
Tel: 023 9248 4054
Principal: Mrs E M Haines
Age range: 3 months–5 years
✎

Highfield and
Brookham Schools
Highfield Lane, Liphook,
Hampshire GU30 7LQ
Tel: 01428 728000
Headteachers: Mr Phillip Evitt MA
(Hons), PGCE & Mrs Sophie Baber
BA (Hons), PGCE, PG Cert
Age range: 2–13
No. of pupils: 441
⚓ £ ✎

King Edward VI School
Wilton Road, Southampton,
Hampshire SO15 5UQ
Tel: 023 8070 4561
Head Master: Mr N T Parker
Age range: 11–18
No. of pupils: 961
Fees: Day £17,130
A £ ✎ 16

Kingscourt School
182 Five Heads Road,
Catherington, Hampshire PO8 9NJ
Tel: 023 9259 3251
Head of School: Amanda
Bembridge
Age range: 3–11
No. of pupils: 158
Fees: Day £2,856

Lord Wandsworth College
Long Sutton, Hook,
Hampshire RG29 1TB
Tel: 01256 862201
Head of School: Mr Adam Williams
Age range: 11–18 years
No. of pupils: 615
Fees: Day £21,240–£24,390
WB £29,400–£33,000 FB
£30,345–£34,650
⚑ A ⚓ £ ✎ 16

Mayville High School
35/37 St Simon's Road, Southsea,
Portsmouth, Hampshire PO5 2PE
Tel: 023 9273 4847
Headteacher: Mrs Rebecca Parkyn
Age range: 6 months–16 years
No. of pupils: 479
Fees: Day £7,635–£11,235
£ ✎

Meoncross School
Burnt House Lane, Stubbington,
Fareham, Hampshire PO14 2EF
Tel: 01329 662182
Headmaster: Mr Mark Cripps
Age range: 2–16
No. of pupils: 405
Fees: Day £8,736–£12,576
£ ✎

Moyles Court School
Moyles Court, Ringwood,
Hampshire BH24 3NF
Tel: 01425 472856
Headmaster: Mr Richard Milner-
Smith
Age range: 3–16
No. of pupils: 195
Fees: Day £6,885–£14,655
FB £21,246–£26,805
⚑ ⚓

Portsmouth High
School GDST
Kent Road, Southsea, Portsmouth,
Hampshire PO5 3EQ
Tel: 023 9282 6714
Headmistress: Mrs Jane Prescott
BSc NPQH
Age range: G3–18
No. of pupils: 500
Fees: Day £2,574–£4,800
⚑ A £ ✎ 16

Prince's Mead School
Worthy Park House, Kings Worthy,
Winchester, Hampshire SO21 1AN
Tel: 01962 888000
Headmaster: Peter Thacker
Age range: 4–11
£ ✎

Ringwood Waldorf School
Folly Farm Lane, Ashley,
Ringwood, Hampshire BH24 2NN
Tel: 01425 472664
Age range: 3–18
No. of pupils: 235
Fees: Day £6,240–£9,000
£ ✎

Rookwood School
Weyhill Road, Andover,
Hampshire SP10 3AL
Tel: 01264 325900
Headmaster: Mr A Kirk-Burgess BSc,
PGCE, MSc (Oxon)
Age range: 2–16
Fees: Day £9,360–£15,600
FB £23,250–£27,465
⚑ ⚓ £ ✎

Salesian College
Reading Road, Farnborough,
Hampshire GU14 6PA
Tel: 01252 893000
Headmaster: Mr Gerard Owens
Age range: B11–18 G16–18
No. of pupils: 650 VIth140
Fees: Day £11,961
⚑ A £ ✎ 16

Sherborne House School
Lakewood Road, Chandlers Ford,
Eastleigh, Hampshire SO53 1EU
Tel: 023 8025 2440
Head Teacher: Mr Mark Beach
Age range: 3–11
No. of pupils: 293
Fees: Day £8,295–£9,675
£ ✎

Sherfield School
South Drive, Sherfield-on-Loddon,
Hook, Hampshire RG27 0HU
Tel: 01256 884800
Headmaster: Mr Nick Brain
BA(Hons), PGCE, MA, NPQH
Age range: 3 months–18 years
No. of pupils: 450
Fees: Day £10,320–£17,085 WB
£18,960–£26,130 FB £22,125–£30,495
⚑ A ⚓ £ ✎ 16 ⚐

St John's College
Grove Road South, Southsea,
Portsmouth, Hampshire PO5 3QW
Tel: 023 9281 5118
Head of School: Mrs Mary Maguire
Age range: 4–18
No. of pupils: 560 VIth86
Fees: Day £9,975–£13,125
FB £28,500–£32,250
⚑ A ⚓ £ ✎ 16 ⚐

ST NEOT'S SCHOOL
For further details see p. 109
St Neot's Road, Eversley,
Hampshire RG27 0PN
Tel: 0118 9739650
Email: admissions@
stneotsprep.co.uk
Website: www.stneotsprep.co.uk
Head of School: Deborah
Henderson
Age range: 2–13 years
No. of pupils: 248
Fees: Day £3,931–£5,624
£ ✎

St Nicholas' School
Redfields House, Redfields
Lane, Church Crookham,
Fleet, Hampshire GU52 0RF
Tel: 01252 850121
Headmistress: Dr O Wright PhD, MA,
BA Hons, PGCE
Age range: B3–7 G3–16
No. of pupils: 325
⚑ £ ✎

St Swithun's Prep
Alresford Road, Winchester,
Hampshire SO21 1HA
Tel: 01962 835750
Head of School: Mr Jonathan
Brough
Age range: B3–4 G3–11
No. of pupils: 200
⚑ ✎

ST SWITHUN'S SCHOOL
For further details see p. 114
Alresford Road, Winchester,
Hampshire SO21 1HA
Tel: 01962 835700
Email: office@stswithuns.com
Website: www.stswithuns.com
Head of School: Jane Gandee
MA(Cantab)
Age range: G11–18
No. of pupils: 510
Fees: Day £20,976 FB £34,776
⚑ A ⚓ £ ✎ 16

Stockton House School
Stockton Avenue, Fleet,
Hampshire GU51 4NS
Tel: 01252 616323
Early Years Manager: Mrs Jenny
Bounds BA EYPS
Age range: 2–5
£ ✎

Stroud School
Highwood House, Highwood Lane,
Romsey, Hampshire SO51 9ZH
Tel: 01794 513231
Headmistress: Mrs Rebecca Smith
Age range: 3–13
✎

The Gregg Prep School
17-19 Winn Road, Southampton,
Hampshire SO17 1EJ
Tel: 023 8055 7352
Head Teacher: Mrs J Caddy
Age range: 3–11
Fees: Day £8,295
£ ✎

The Gregg School
Townhill Park House, Cutbush Lane,
Southampton, Hampshire SO18 2GF
Tel: 023 8047 2133
Headteacher: Mrs S Sellers PGDip,
MSc, BSc(Hons), NPQH, PGCE
Age range: 11–16
No. of pupils: 300
Fees: Day £12,825
£ ✎

The King's School
Lakesmere House, Allington Lane,
Fair Oak, Eastleigh, Southampton,
Hampshire SO50 7DB
Tel: 023 8060 0986
Headteacher: Mrs Heather Bowden
Age range: 4–16 years

**The New Forest
Small School**
1 Southampton Road, Lyndhurst,
Hampshire SO43 7BU
Tel: 02380 284415
Headteacher: Maz Wilberforce
Age range: 3–16 years

The Pilgrims' School
3 The Close, Winchester,
Hampshire SO23 9LT
Tel: 01962 854189
Head: Dr Sarah Essex
Age range: B4–13
No. of pupils: 250
Fees: Day £18,150–£19,245
FB £24,330
👤 🏫 £ ✎

**The Portsmouth
Grammar School**
High Street, Portsmouth,
Hampshire PO1 2LN
Tel: +44 (0)23 9236 0036
Headmistress: Dr Anne Cotton
Age range: 2–18
No. of pupils: 1556 VIth336
Fees: Day £10,233–£15,951
🌐 A £ IB ✎ 16

Thorngrove School
The Mount, Highclere, Newbury,
Hampshire RG20 9PS
Tel: 01635 253172
Headmaster: Mr Adam King
Age range: 2–13
Fees: Day £14,070–£17,595
£ ✎

Twyford School
Twyford, Winchester,
Hampshire SO21 1NW
Tel: 01962 712269
Headmaster: Dr S J Bailey BEd,
PhD, FRSA
Age range: 3–13
Fees: Day £10,953–£19,509
WB £24,552
🏫 £ ✎

Walhampton
Walhampton, Lymington,
Hampshire SO41 5ZG
Tel: 01590 613 300
Headmaster: Mr Titus Mills
Age range: 2–13
No. of pupils: 353
Fees: Day £9,000–£17,625
FB £20,250–£24,750
🏫 £ ✎

**West Hill Park
Preparatory School**
Titchfield, Fareham,
Hampshire PO14 4BS
Tel: 01329 842356
Headmaster: A P Ramsay
BEd(Hons), MSc
Age range: 2–13
No. of pupils: 288
Fees: Day £10,800–£18,300
FB £19,500–£22,650
🏫 £ ✎

Winchester College
College Street, Winchester,
Hampshire SO23 9NA
Tel: 01962 621247
Headmaster: Dr. T R Hands
Age range: B13–18
No. of pupils: 690 VIth280
Fees: FB £39,912
👤 🌐 🏫 £ ✎ 16

Yateley Manor School
51 Reading Road, Yateley,
Hampshire GU46 7UQ
Tel: 01252 405500
Headmaster: Mr Robert Upton
Age range: 3–13
No. of pupils: 453
Fees: Day £11,160–£15,300
£ ✎

Hertfordshire

Abbot's Hill School
Bunkers Lane, Hemel Hempstead,
Hertfordshire HP3 8RP
Tel: 01442 240333
Headmistress: Mrs K Gorman BA,
MEd (Cantab)
Age range: G4–16
No. of pupils: 502
👤 🏫 £ ✎

Aldenham School
Elstree, Hertfordshire WD6 3AJ
Tel: 01923 858122
Head of School: Mr Andrew
Williams
Age range: 3–18
🌐 A 🏫 £ ✎ 16

Aldwickbury School
Wheathampstead Road,
Harpenden, Hertfordshire AL5 1AD
Tel: 01582 713022
Headmaster: Mr V W Hales
Age range: B4–13 years
👤 🏫

Beechwood Park School
Markyate, St Albans,
Hertfordshire AL3 8AW
Tel: 01582 840333
Headmaster: Mr E Balfour BA
(Hons), PGCE
Age range: 3–13
No. of pupils: 547
Fees: Day £11,700–£17,355
WB £21,480
🏫 £ ✎

BERKHAMSTED SCHOOL
For further details see p. 93
Overton House, 131 High
Street, Berkhamsted,
Hertfordshire HP4 2DJ
Tel: 01442 358001
Email: admissions@
berkhamsted.com
Website:
www.berkhamsted.com
Principal: Mr Richard Backhouse
MA(Cantab)
Age range: 3–18
No. of pupils: 1852 VIth406
Fees: Day £10,725–£21,636
WB £29,061 FB £34,620
🌐 A 🏫 £ ✎ 16

**Bhaktivedanta
Manor School**
Hilfield Lane, Aldenham, Watford,
Hertfordshire WD25 8EZ
Tel: 01923 851000 Ext:241
Headteacher: Guru Carana
Padma dasi
Age range: 4–12
No. of pupils: 45
Fees: Day £1,860

Bishop's Stortford College
10 Maze Green Road, Bishop's
Stortford, Hertfordshire CM23 2PJ
Tel: 01279 838575
Headmaster: Mr Jeremy Gladwin
Age range: 13–18
No. of pupils: VIth249
Fees: Day £20,349–£20,532 WB
£31,569–£31,917 FB £33,402–£33,930
🌐 A 🏫 £ 16

**Bishop's Stortford
College Prep School**
Maze Green Road, Bishop's
Stortford, Hertfordshire CM23 2PH
Tel: 01279 838607
Head of the Prep School: Mr Bill
Toleman
Age range: 4–13
No. of pupils: 590
Fees: Day £9,408–£16,281 WB
£22,359–£24,273 FB £23,610–£25,536
🌐 🏫 £

**Champneys International
College of Health & Beauty**
Chesham Road, Wigginton,
Tring, Hertfordshire HP23 6HY
Tel: 01442 291333
College Principal: Ms Pam Clegg
Age range: 16+
No. of pupils: 61
Fees: Day £3,000–£9,050
16 £ ✎ 16

**Charlotte House
Preparatory School**
88 The Drive, Rickmansworth,
Hertfordshire WD3 4DU
Tel: 01923 772101
Head: Miss P Woodcock
Age range: G3–11
No. of pupils: 140
Fees: Day £3,432–£12,102
👤 £ ✎

Duncombe School
4 Warren Park Road, Bengeo,
Hertford, Hertfordshire SG14 3JA
Tel: 01992 414100
Headmaster: Mr Jeremy Phelan
M.A. (Ed)
Age range: 2–11
No. of pupils: 301
Fees: Day £10,380–£14,565
£ ✎

Edge Grove School
Aldenham Village,
Hertfordshire WD25 8NL
Tel: 01923 855724
Head of School: Miss Lisa
McDonald
Age range: 3–13
No. of pupils: 526
Fees: Day £13,140–£17,580
WB £20,550–£23,025
🏫 £ ✎

Egerton Rothesay School
Durrants Lane, Berkhamsted,
Hertfordshire HP4 3UJ
Tel: 01442 865275
Headteacher: Mr Colin Parker
BSc(Hons), Dip.Ed (Oxon), PGCE,
C.Math MIMA
Age range: 6–19
✎

Haberdashers' Aske's School for Girls
Aldenham Road,
Elstree, Borehamwood,
Hertfordshire WD6 3BT
Tel: 020 8266 2300
Head of School: Ms Rose Hardy
Age range: G4–18
No. of pupils: 1190
Fees: Day £17,826–£19,311

Haileybury
Haileybury, Hertford,
Hertfordshire SG13 7NU
Tel: +44 (0)1992 706353
The Master: Mr Martin Collier MA
BA PGCE
Age range: 11–18
No. of pupils: 880 VIth319
Fees: Day £17,712–£26,646
FB £22,929–£36,141

Heath Mount School
Woodhall Park, Watton-at-Stone,
Hertford, Hertfordshire SG14 3NG
Tel: 01920 830230
Headmaster: Mr Chris Gillam
BEd(Hons)
Age range: 3–13
No. of pupils: 515 B291 G224
Fees: Day £11,955–£18,435

High Elms Manor School
High Elms Lane, Watford,
Hertfordshire WD25 0JX
Tel: 01923 681 103
Headmistress: Ms Liadain O'Neill BA
(Hons), AMI 0-3, AMI 3-6, Early Years
FdA Dist.+
Age range: 2–12
No. of pupils: 100
Fees: Day £10,500–£12,675

Howe Green House School
Great Hallingbury, Bishop's
Stortford, Hertfordshire CM22 7UF
Tel: 01279 657706
Headmistress: Ms Deborah Mills BA
(Hons) Q.T.S
Age range: 2–11

Immanuel College
87/91 Elstree Road, Bushey,
Hertfordshire WD23 4EB
Tel: 020 8950 0604
Headmaster: Mr Gary Griffin
Age range: 4–18
No. of pupils: 520 VIth127
Fees: Day £10,995

Kingshott
Stevenage Road, St Ippolyts,
Hitchin, Hertfordshire SG4 7JX
Tel: 01462 432009
Headmaster: Mr David Weston
Age range: 3–13 years
No. of pupils: 400
Fees: Day £6,390–£13,770

Little Acorns Montessori School
Lincolnsfield Centre,
Bushey Hall Drive, Bushey,
Hertfordshire WD23 2ER
Tel: 01923 230705
Head of School: Lola Davies BPA,
AMIDip
Age range: 12 months–6
No. of pupils: 28
Fees: Day £2,120

Lochinver House School
Heath Road, Little Heath, Potters
Bar, Hertfordshire EN6 1LW
Tel: 01707 653064
Headmaster: Ben Walker BA(Hons),
PGCE, CELTA
Age range: B4–13
No. of pupils: 349
Fees: Day £11,175–£14,685

Lockers Park
Lockers Park Lane, Hemel
Hempstead, Hertfordshire HP1 1TL
Tel: 01442 251712
Headmaster: Mr C R Wilson
Age range: B4–13 G4–7
No. of pupils: 171
Fees: Day £11,175–£17,730
WB £16,035–£23,670

Longwood School
Bushey Hall Drive, Bushey,
Hertfordshire WD23 2QG
Tel: 01923 253715
Head Teacher: Claire May
Age range: 3 months–11
Fees: Day £3,705–£7,800

Manor Lodge School
Rectory Lane, Ridge Hill, Shenley,
Hertfordshire WD7 9BG
Tel: 01707 642424
Head of School: Mrs A Lobo
BEd(Hons)
Age range: 3–11
No. of pupils: 427
Fees: Day £11,100–£12,300

Merchant Taylors' Prep
Moor Farm, Sandy Lodge
Road, Rickmansworth,
Hertfordshire WD3 1LW
Tel: 01923 825648
Headmaster: Dr Karen McNerney
BSc (Hons), PGCE, MSc, EdD
Age range: B4–13
No. of pupils: 300
Fees: Day £5,148–£16,000

Queenswood
Shepherd's Way, Brookmans Park,
Hatfield, Hertfordshire AL9 6NS
Tel: 01707 602500
Principal: Mrs Jo Cameron
Age range: G11–18
No. of pupils: 418
Fees: Day £7,115–£8,440 WB
7,325–10,615 FB £8,395–£11,810

Radlett Preparatory School
Kendal Hall, Watling Street,
Radlett, Hertfordshire WD7 7LY
Tel: 01923 856812
Principal: Mr M Pipe BA Hons, QTS
Age range: 4–11

Sherrardswood School
Lockleys, Welwyn,
Hertfordshire AL6 0BJ
Tel: 01438 714282
Headmistress: Mrs Anna Wright
Age range: 2–18
No. of pupils: 357
Fees: Day £10,383–£16,113

St Albans High School for Girls
Townsend Avenue, St Albans,
Hertfordshire AL1 3SJ
Tel: 01727 853800
Headmistress: Amber Waite
Age range: G4–18
No. of pupils: 940 VIth170

St Albans Independent College
69 London Road, St Albans,
Hertfordshire AL1 1LN
Tel: 01727 842348
Principals: Mr. A N Jemal & Mr Elvis
Cotena
Age range: 15+
Fees: Day £2,700–£5,900

St Albans School
Abbey Gateway, St Albans,
Hertfordshire AL3 4HB
Tel: 01727 855521
Headmaster: Mr JWJ Gillespie
MA(Cantab), FRSA
Age range: B11–18 G16–18
No. of pupils: 870
Fees: Day £18,600

St Christopher School
Barrington Road, Letchworth,
Hertfordshire SG6 3JZ
Tel: 01462 650 850
Head: Richard Palmer
Age range: 3–18
No. of pupils: 511 VIth78
Fees: Day £4,590–£18,075 WB
£19,950–£24,675 FB £31,650

St Columba's College
King Harry Lane, St Albans,
Hertfordshire AL3 4AW
Tel: 01727 892040
Head: Mr David Buxton
Age range: B4–18
No. of pupils: 760

St Edmund's College & Prep School
Old Hall Green, Nr Ware,
Hertfordshire SG11 1DS
Tel: 01920 824247
Headmaster: Mr Matthew Mostyn
BA (Hons) MA (Ed)
Age range: 3–18
No. of pupils: 852
Fees: Day £9,882–£18,345 WB
£24,165–£27,630 FB £28,302–£32,460

St Edmund's Prep
Old Hall Green, Ware,
Hertfordshire SG11 1DS
Tel: 01920 824239
Head: Mr Steven Cartwright BSc
(Surrey)
Age range: 3–11
No. of pupils: 185
Fees: Day £10,650–£13,365

St Francis' College
Broadway, Letchworth Garden
City, Hertfordshire SG6 3PJ
Tel: 01462 670511
Headmistress: Mrs B Goulding
Age range: G3–18
No. of pupils: 460 VIth75
Fees: Day £9,990–£16,980 WB
£22,350–£26,475 FB £27,990–£31,995

St Hilda's
High Street, Bushey,
Hertfordshire WD23 3DA
Tel: 020 8950 1751
Headmistress: Miss Sarah-Jane
Styles MA
Age range: B2–4 G2–11
Fees: Day £12,012–£12,843

ST HILDA'S SCHOOL
For further details see p. 105
Douglas Road, Harpenden,
Hertfordshire AL5 2ES
Tel: 01582 712307
Email: office@
sthildasharpenden.co.uk
Website:
www.sthildasharpenden.co.uk
Headmaster: Mr Dan Sayers
Age range: G2.5–11 years
No. of pupils: 150
Fees: Day £3,154–£4,115

St Joseph's In The Park
St Mary's Lane, Hertingfordbury,
Hertford, Hertfordshire SG14 2LX
Tel: 01992 513810
Head of School: Mr Douglas Brown
Age range: 3–11
No. of pupils: 150
Fees: Day £5,718–£16,899

St Margaret's School, Bushey
Merry Hill Road, Bushey,
Hertfordshire WD23 1DT
Tel: +44 (0)20 8416 4400
Headteacher: Lara Péchard
Age range: 3–18 years
No. of pupils: 445

St. John's Prep. School
The Ridgeway, Potters Bar,
Hertfordshire EN6 5QT
Tel: +44 (0)1707 657294
Head Teacher: Mrs C Tardios
Age range: 4–11

Stanborough School
Stanborough Park, Garston,
Watford, Hertfordshire WD25 9JT
Tel: 01923 673268
Acting Head Teacher: Ms Eileen
Hussey
Age range: 3–17
No. of pupils: 300
Fees: Day £6,630–£10,224
WB £10,350–£13,995

Stormont
The Causeway, Potters Bar,
Hertfordshire EN6 5HA
Tel: 01707 654037
Head Teacher: Miss Louise Martin
Age range: G4–11
Fees: Day £12,300–£13,050

The Haberdashers' Aske's Boys' School
Butterfly Lane, Elstree,
Borehamwood,
Hertfordshire WD6 3AF
Tel: 020 8266 1700
Headmaster: Gus Lock MA (Oxon)
Age range: B5–18 years
No. of pupils: 1428
Fees: Day £15,339–£20,346

The King's School
Elmfield, Ambrose Lane,
Harpenden, Hertfordshire AL5 4DU
Tel: 01582 767566
Principal: Mr Clive John Case BA,
HDE
Age range: 4–16
Fees: Day £7,680

The Purcell School, London
Aldenham Road, Bushey,
Hertfordshire WD23 2TS
Tel: 01923 331100
Headteacher: Dr Bernard Trafford
Age range: 10–18
No. of pupils: 180
Fees: Day £25,707 FB £32,826

Tring Park School for the Performing Arts
Tring Park, Tring,
Hertfordshire HP23 5LX
Tel: 01442 824255
Principal: Mr Stefan Anderson MA,
ARCM, ARCT
Age range: 8–19
No. of pupils: 354 VIth150
Fees: Day £15,405–£24,510
FB £26,190–£37,050

Westbrook Hay Prep School
London Road, Hemel Hempstead,
Hertfordshire HP1 2RF
Tel: 01442 256143
Headmaster: Mark Brain
Age range: 3–13
No. of pupils: 340
Fees: Day £10,905–£15,690

York House School
Redheath, Sarratt Road,
Croxley Green, Rickmansworth,
Hertfordshire WD3 4LW
Tel: 01923 772395
Headmaster: Jon Gray BA(Ed)
Age range: 3–13
No. of pupils: 380
Fees: Day £3,393–£4,989

Kent

Ashford School
East Hill, Ashford, Kent TN24 8PB
Tel: 01233 739030
Head: Mr Michael Hall
Age range: 3 months–18 years
No. of pupils: 835 VIth170
Fees: Day £10,500–£16,800
WB £24,000 FB £36,000

Beech Grove School
Forest Drive, Nonington,
Dover, Kent CT15 4FB
Tel: 01304 842980
Head of School: Mr Timothy Maas
Age range: 4–19

Beechwood Sacred Heart
12 Pembury Road, Tunbridge
Wells, Kent TN2 3QD
Tel: 01892 532747
Acting Head: Mrs Helen Rowe
Age range: 3–18
No. of pupils: 400 VIth70
Fees: Day £8,685–£17,385
WB £26,850 FB £29,850

Benenden School
Cranbrook, Kent TN17 4AA
Tel: 01580 240592
Headmistress: Mrs S Price
Age range: G11–18
No. of pupils: 550
Fees: FB £12,650

Bethany School
Curtisden Green, Goudhurst,
Cranbrook, Kent TN17 1LB
Tel: 01580 211273
Headmaster: Mr Francie Healy BSc,
HDipEd, NPQH
Age range: 11–18 years
No. of pupils: 352 VIth86
Fees: Day £17,310–£19,110 WB
£26,865–£29,670 FB £26,865–£29,670

Bronte School
Mayfield, 7 Pelham Road,
Gravesend, Kent DA11 0HN
Tel: 01474 533805
Headmistress: Ms Emma Wood
Age range: 3–11
No. of pupils: 120
Fees: Day £9,330

Bryony School
Marshall Road, Rainham,
Gillingham, Kent ME8 0AJ
Tel: 01634 231511
Joint Head: Mr D Edmunds
Age range: 2–11
No. of pupils: 168
Fees: Day £5,978–£6,511

CATS Canterbury
68 New Dover Road,
Canterbury, Kent CT1 3LQ
Tel: +44 (0)1227866540
Principal: Dr Sarah Lockyer
Age range: 14–18
No. of pupils: 400

Chartfield School
45 Minster Road, Westgate
on Sea, Kent CT8 8DA
Tel: 01843 831716
Head & Proprietor: Miss L P Shipley
Age range: 4–11

COBHAM HALL SCHOOL
For further details see p. 94
Brewers Road, Cobham,
Kent DA12 3BL
Tel: 01474 823371
Email: enquiries@
cobhamhall.com
Website: www.cobhamhall.com
Headteacher: Mrs Wendy
Barrett
Age range: G11–18
No. of pupils: 150
Fees: Day £6,548–£7,936
FB £9,893–£12,349

Derwent Lodge School for Girls
Somerhill, Tonbridge, Kent TN11 0NJ
Tel: 01732 352124
Head of School: Mrs Helen
Hoffmann
Age range: G7–11
No. of pupils: 134
Fees: Day £15,465

Dover College
Effingham Crescent,
Dover, Kent CT17 9RH
Tel: 01304 205969
Headmaster: Mr Gareth Doodes
MA (Hons)
Age range: 3–18
No. of pupils: 301
Fees: Day £7,725–£16,050 WB
£21,000–£25,500 FB £24,750–£31,500

Dulwich Prep Cranbrook
Coursehorn, Cranbrook,
Kent TN17 3NP
Tel: 01580 712179
Headmaster: Mr Paul David
BEd(Hons)
Age range: 3–13
No. of pupils: 535
Fees: Day £5,970–£18,390

Elliott Park School
18-20 Marina Drive, Minster,
Sheerness, Kent ME12 2DP
Tel: 01795 873372
Head: Ms Colleen Hiller
Age range: 3–11

European School of Osteopathy
Boxley House, The Street, Boxley,
Maidstone, Kent ME14 3DZ
Tel: 01622 671 558
Principal: Mr Renzo Molinari DO

Fosse Bank School
Mountains, Noble Tree Road, Hildenborough, Tonbridge, Kent TN11 8ND
Tel: 01732 834212
Headmistress: Miss Alison Cordingley
Age range: 2–11
No. of pupils: 124
Fees: Day £10,605–£13,185
(£)

Gad's Hill School
Higham, Rochester, Medway, Kent ME3 7PA
Tel: 01474 822366
Headmaster: Mr Paul Savage
Age range: 3–16
No. of pupils: 370
Fees: Day £8,988–£12,504
(£)

Haddon Dene School
57 Gladstone Road, Broadstairs, Kent CT10 2HY
Tel: 01843 861176
Head: Miss Alison Hatch
Age range: 3–11
No. of pupils: 200
Fees: Day £5,700–£7,230
(⚲)

Hilden Grange School
62 Dry Hill Park Road, Tonbridge, Kent TN10 3BX
Tel: 01732 352706
Headmaster: Mr J Withers BA(Hons)
Age range: 3–13
No. of pupils: 311
(⚲)

Hilden Oaks School & Nursery
38 Dry Hill Park Road, Tonbridge, Kent TN10 3BU
Tel: 01732 353941
Head of School: Mrs. K Joiner
Age range: 3 months–11 years
No. of pupils: 184
Fees: Day £9,975–£13,290
(£)(⚲)

Holmewood House School
Barrow Lane, Langton Green, Tunbridge Wells, Kent TN3 0EB
Tel: 01892 860000
Headmaster: Mr Scott Carnochan
Age range: 3–13
No. of pupils: 450
(⚑)(£)(⚲)

Kent College Junior School
Harbledown, Canterbury, Kent CT2 9AQ
Tel: 01227 762436
Headmaster: Mr Simon James
Age range: 0–11
No. of pupils: 240
Fees: Day £10,191–£16,332 FB £26,244
(⚑)(⚲)

Kent College Pembury
Old Church Road, Pembury, Tunbridge Wells, Kent TN2 4AX
Tel: +44 (0)1892 822006
Headmistress: Ms Julie Lodrick
Age range: G3–18
No. of pupils: 500
Fees: Day £21,600 WB £26,994 FB £34,419
(⚤)(⚲)(A)(⚑)(⚲)(16+)

Kent College, Canterbury
Whitstable Road, Canterbury, Kent CT2 9DT
Tel: +44 (0)1227 763 231
Executive Head: Dr David Lamper
Age range: 0–18 years (Boarding from 8)
No. of pupils: 770
Fees: Day £5,598–£6,288 FB £8,748–£11,867
(⚲)(A)(⚑)(⚲)(IB)(⚲)(16+)

Kids Inc Day Nursery – Bluewater
West Village, Bluewater, Greenhithe, Kent DA9 9SE
Tel: 01322 386624

King's Preparatory School, Rochester
King Edward Road, Rochester, Medway, Kent ME1 1UB
Tel: 01634 888577
Headmaster: Mr Tom Morgan
Age range: 8–13
(⚑)(⚲)

King's Rochester
Satis House, Boley Hill, Rochester, Kent ME1 1TE
Tel: 01634 888555
Principal: Mr B Charles
Age range: 13–18
No. of pupils: 600 VIth95
Fees: Day £7,440–£20,190 FB £22,950–£33,015
(⚲)(A)(⚑)(£)(⚲)(16+)

Lorenden Preparatory School
Painter's Forstal, Faversham, Kent ME13 0EN
Tel: 01795 590030
Headmistress: Mrs K Uttley
Age range: 3–11
No. of pupils: 120
Fees: Day £8,640–£12,540
(£)(⚲)

Marlborough House School
High Street, Hawkhurst, Kent TN18 4PY
Tel: 01580 753555
Head: Mr Eddy Newton
Age range: 3–13
No. of pupils: 250
Fees: Day £9,165–£18,690
(⚑)(£)(⚲)

Northbourne Park School
Betteshanger, Deal, Kent CT14 0NW
Tel: 01304 611215/218
Headmaster: Mr Sebastian Rees BA(Hons), PGCE, NPQH
Age range: 2–13
No. of pupils: 185
Fees: Day £7,632–£17,007 WB £21,405 FB £24,786
(⚑)(£)(⚲)

OneSchool Global UK Maidstone Campus
Heath Road, Maidstone, Kent ME17 4HT
Tel: 01622 740820
Age range: 7–18

Radnor House, Sevenoaks
Combe Bank Drive, Sevenoaks, Kent TN14 6AE
Tel: 01959 563720
Head: Mr David Paton BComm (Hons) PGCE MA
Age range: 2.5–18
No. of pupils: 250
(A)(£)(⚲)(16+)(⚲)

Rochester Independent College
254 St Margaret's Banks, Rochester, Kent ME1 1HY
Tel: +44 (0)163 482 8115
Head of School: Mr Alistair Brownlow
Age range: 11–18
Fees: Day £13,000–£18,600 WB £12,400 FB £14,100
(⚲)(16+)(⚑)

Rose Hill School
Coniston Avenue, Tunbridge Wells, Kent TN4 9SY
Tel: 01892 525591
Head: Emma Neville
Age range: 3–13
Fees: Day £11,325–£15,225
(£)(⚲)

Russell House School
Station Road, Otford, Sevenoaks, Kent TN14 5QU
Tel: 01959 522352
Headmaster: Mr Craig McCarthy
Age range: 2–11

Sackville School
Tonbridge Rd, Hildenborough, Tonbridge, Kent TN11 9HN
Tel: 01732 838888
Headmaster: Mr Justin Foster-Gandey BSc (hons)
Age range: 11–18
No. of pupils: 160 VIth29
Fees: Day £15,750
(A)(£)(⚲)(16+)(⚲)

Saint Ronan's School
Water Lane, Hawkhurst, Kent TN18 5DJ
Tel: 01580 752271
Headmaster: William Trelawny-Vernon BSc(Hons)
Age range: 3–13
No. of pupils: 300
Fees: Day £10,869–£18,624 FB £22,497
(⚑)(£)(⚲)

Sevenoaks Preparatory School
Godden Green, Sevenoaks, Kent TN15 0JU
Tel: 01732 762336
Headmaster: Mr Luke Harrison
Age range: 2–13
No. of pupils: 388
Fees: Day £10,755–£14,865
(£)(⚲)

Sevenoaks School
High Street, Sevenoaks, Kent TN13 1HU
Tel: +44 (0)1732 455133
Head of School: Mr Jesse R Elzinga AB MSt FCCT
Age range: 11–18
No. of pupils: 1165
Fees: Day £24,291–£27,585 FB £38,790–£42,084
(⚲)(⚑)(£)(IB)(⚲)(16+)

Shernold School
Hill Place, Queens Avenue, Maidstone, Kent ME16 0ER
Tel: 01622 752868
Head Teacher: Ms. Sandra Dinsmore BA Hons. PGCE
Age range: 3–11
No. of pupils: 142
Fees: Day £7,245–£8,190
(£)

Solefield School
Solefield Road, Sevenoaks, Kent TN13 1PH
Tel: 01732 452142
Headmaster: Mr D A Philps BSc(Hons)
Age range: B4–13
No. of pupils: 100
Fees: Day £12,600–£15,345
(⚤)(⚲)

Somerhill Pre-Prep
Somerhill, Five Oak Green Road, Tonbridge, Kent TN11 0NJ
Tel: 01732 352124
Principal of The Schools at Somerhill: Duncan Sinclair
Age range: 3–7
No. of pupils: 245
Fees: Day £10,050–£11,685

Spring Grove School
Harville Road, Wye, Kent TN25 5EZ
Tel: 01233 812337
Head of School: Mrs Therésa Jaggard
Age range: 2–11 years
No. of pupils: 226
Fees: Day £9,000–£12,900
(£)(⚲)

St Andrew's School
24-28 Watts Avenue, Rochester, Medway, Kent ME1 1SA
Tel: 01634 843479
Principal: Mrs E Steinmann-Gilbert
Age range: 2–11
No. of pupils: 367
Fees: Day £7,725–£8,178
(⚲)

St Edmund's Junior School
St Thomas Hill, Canterbury,
Kent CT2 8HU
Tel: 01227 475600
Head: Edward O'Connor
Age range: 3–13
No. of pupils: 230
Fees: Day £9,696–£16,101
WB £25,455 FB £27,933

ST EDMUND'S SCHOOL
For further details see p. 106
St Thomas Hill, Canterbury,
Kent CT2 8HU
Tel: 01227 475601
Email: admissions@
stedmunds.org.uk
Website: www.stedmunds.org.uk
Head: Mr Edward O'Connor MA
(Cantab), MPhil (Oxon), MEd
(Cantab)
Age range: 3–18
No. of pupils: 558

St Faith's at Ash School
5 The Street, Ash, Canterbury,
Kent CT3 2HH
Tel: 01304 813409
Headmaster: Mr Lawrence Groves
Age range: 2–11
No. of pupils: 225
Fees: Day £5,415–£9,885

St Joseph's Convent Prep School
46 Old Road East, Gravesend,
Kent DA12 1NR
Tel: 01474 533012
Head Teacher: Miss D Buckley
Age range: 3–11
No. of pupils: 146
Fees: Day £8,580

St Lawrence College
Ramsgate, Kent CT11 7AE
Tel: 01843 572931
Head of College: Mr Barney Durrant
Age range: 3–18
No. of pupils: 600
Fees: Day £7,845–£16,245
FB £27,765–£36,909

St Michael's Preparatory School
Otford Court, Otford,
Sevenoaks, Kent TN14 5SA
Tel: 01959 522137
Headteacher: Mrs Jill Aisher
Age range: 2–13
No. of pupils: 472
Fees: Day £12,210–£14,835

Steephill School
Off Castle Hill, Fawkham,
Longfield, Kent DA3 7BG
Tel: 01474 702107
Head: Mrs Caroline Birtwell BSc,
MBA, PGCE
Age range: 3–11
No. of pupils: 131
Fees: Day £9,750

Sutton Valence Preparatory School
Chart Sutton, Maidstone,
Kent ME17 3RF
Tel: 01622 842117
Head: Miss C Corkran
Age range: 3–11
No. of pupils: 320
Fees: Day £3,000–£4,610

Sutton Valence School
North Street, Sutton
Valence, Kent ME17 3HL
Tel: 01622 845200
Headmaster: Bruce Grindlay MA
Cantab, MusB, FRCO, CHM
Age range: 11–18
No. of pupils: 570

The Granville School
2 Bradbourne Park Road,
Sevenoaks, Kent TN13 3LJ
Tel: 01732 453039
Headmistress: Mrs Louise Lawrance
B. Prim. Ed. (Hons)
Age range: B3–4 G3–11

The Junior King's School, Canterbury
Milner Court, Sturry,
Canterbury, Kent CT2 0AY
Tel: 01227 714000
Head: Emma Károlyi
Age range: 3–13
Fees: Day £11,475–£19,290
FB £26,475

The King's School, Canterbury
The Precincts, Canterbury,
Kent CT1 2ES
Tel: 01227 595501
Head: Mr Peter Roberts
Age range: 13–18
No. of pupils: 858 VIth385
Fees: Day £27,495 FB £38,955

The Mead School
16 Frant Road, Tunbridge
Wells, Kent TN2 5SN
Tel: 01892 525837
Headmaster: Mr Andrew Webster
Age range: 3–11
No. of pupils: 188
Fees: Day £4,536–£11,625

The New Beacon School
Brittains Lane, Sevenoaks,
Kent TN13 2PB
Tel: 01732 452131
Headmaster: Mr M Piercy BA(Hons)
Age range: B4–13
No. of pupils: 400
Fees: Day £11,400–£16,350

TONBRIDGE SCHOOL
For further details see p. 110
High Street, Tonbridge,
Kent TN9 1JP
Tel: 01732 304297
Email: admissions@
tonbridge-school.org
Website:
www.tonbridge-school.co.uk
Headmaster: Mr James Priory
MA (Oxon)
Age range: B13–18
No. of pupils: 802
Fees: Day £31,587 FB £42,105

Walthamstow Hall Pre-Prep and Junior School
Sevenoaks, Kent TN13 3LD
Tel: 01732 451334
Headmistress: Miss S Ferro
Age range: G2–11
No. of pupils: 218
Fees: Day £12,135–£15,300

Walthamstow Hall School
Sevenoaks, Kent TN13 3UL
Tel: 01732 451334
Headmistress: Miss S Ferro
Age range: G2–18
No. of pupils: 500 VIth80

Wellesley House
114 Ramsgate Road,
Broadstairs, Kent CT10 2DG
Tel: 01843 862991
Headmaster: Mr G D Franklin
Age range: 7–13
No. of pupils: 133
Fees: Day £12,231–£19,917 FB £26,331

Yardley Court
Somerhill, Five Oak Green Road,
Tonbridge, Kent TN11 0NJ
Tel: 01732 352124
Headmaster: Duncan Sinclair
Age range: B7–13
No. of pupils: 260
Fees: Day £15,465

Surrey

ABERDOUR SCHOOL
For further details see p. 92
Brighton Road, Burgh Heath,
Tadworth, Surrey KT20 6AJ
Tel: +44 (0)1737 354119
Email: enquiries@
aberdourschool.co.uk
Website:
www.aberdourschool.co.uk
Headmaster: Mr S. D. Collins
Age range: 2–11 years
No. of pupils: 344
Fees: Day £4,575–£15,270

ACS Cobham International School
Heywood, Portsmouth Road,
Cobham, Surrey KT11 1BL
Tel: +44 (0) 1932 867251
Head of School: Mr Barnaby
Sandow
Age range: 2–18

ACS Egham International School
Woodlee, London Road,
Egham, Surrey TW20 0HS
Tel: +44 (0) 1784 430 800
Head of School: Mr Jeremy Lewis
Age range: 4–18
Fees: Day £11,090–£25,870

Aldro School
Lombard Street, Shackleford,
Godalming, Surrey GU8 6AS
Tel: 01483 810266
Headmaster: Mr Chris Carlier
Age range: 7–13 years

Amesbury
Hazel Grove, Hindhead,
Surrey GU26 6BL
Tel: 01428 604322
Head of School: Mr Jonathan
Whybrow
Age range: 2–13 years
No. of pupils: 360

Banstead Preparatory School
Sutton Lane, Banstead,
Surrey SM7 3RA
Tel: 01737 363601
Headteacher: Miss Vicky Ellis
Age range: 2–11
No. of pupils: 225

Barfield School
Guildford Road, Runfold,
Farnham, Surrey GU10 1PB
Tel: 01252 782271
Headmaster: Mr Andy Boyle
Age range: 2–13 years
No. of pupils: 170
Fees: Day £3,456–£14,895
(£)(✎)

Barrow Hills School
Roke Lane, Witley, Godalming,
Surrey GU8 5NY
Tel: +44 (0)1428 683639
Headmaster: Mr Philip Oldroyd
Age range: 2–13
No. of pupils: 200
Fees: Day £15,975
(£)(✎)

Belmont School
Feldemore, Holmbury St Mary,
Dorking, Surrey RH5 6LQ
Tel: 01306 730852
Headmistress: Mrs Helen Skrine BA,
PGCE, NPQH, FRSA
Age range: 2–16 years
Fees: Day £9,660–£16,740
WB £20,430–£21,300
(⚐)(£)(✎)

Bishopsgate School
Bishopsgate Road, Englefield
Green, Egham, Surrey TW20 0YJ
Tel: 01784 432109
Headmaster: Mr R Williams
Age range: 3–13
Fees: Day £5,580–£15,840
(£)(✎)

Box Hill School
London Road, Mickleham,
Dorking, Surrey RH5 6EA
Tel: 01372 373382
Headmaster: Cory Lowde
Age range: 11–18
No. of pupils: 425
Fees: Day £17,985 WB
£28,350 FB £34,950
(⊕)(⚐)(£)(IB)(✎)(16+)

Cambridge Management College
4-8 Castle Street, Oakington,
Kingston upon Thames,
Surrey KT11SS
Tel: 08003166282
Principal: Dr Peter Holmes
(16+)

Caterham School
Harestone Valley, Caterham,
Surrey CR3 6YA
Tel: 01883 343028
Head: Mr C. W. Jones MA(Cantab)
Age range: 11–18
No. of pupils: VIth321
Fees: Day £18,735–£19,620 WB
£30,936–£33,270 FB £36,795–£38,760
(⊕)(A)(⚐)(£)(✎)(16+)

Charterhouse
Godalming, Surrey GU7 2DX
Tel: +44 (0)1483 291501
Headmaster: Dr Alex Peterken
Age range: B13–18 G16–18
No. of pupils: 820
(⊕)(A)(⚐)(£)(IB)(✎)(16+)

Chinthurst School
Tadworth Street, Tadworth,
Surrey KT20 5QZ
Tel: 01737 812011
Head: Miss Catherine Trundle
Age range: B3–11
No. of pupils: 170
Fees: Day £11,010–£14,850
(£)(✎)

City of London Freemen's School
Ashtead Park, Ashtead,
Surrey KT21 1ET
Tel: 01372 277933
Headmaster: Mr R Martin
Age range: 7–18
No. of pupils: 877 VIth213
Fees: Day £14,067–£19,194 WB
£29,784–£29,841 FB £30,780–£30,816
(⊕)(A)(⚐)(£)(✎)(16+)

Claremont Fan Court School
Claremont Drive, Esher,
Surrey KT10 9LY
Tel: 01372 473780
Head: Mr William Brierly
Age range: 2 1/2–18
No. of pupils: 890
Fees: Day £790–£6,125
(A)(£)(✎)(16+)

Coworth Flexlands School
Valley End, Chobham,
Surrey GU24 8TE
Tel: 01276 855707
Head of School: Miss Nicola Cowell
Age range: B2.5–7 G2.5–11
No. of pupils: 120
(✎)

Cranleigh Preparatory School
Horseshoe Lane, Cranleigh,
Surrey GU6 8QH
Tel: 01483 274199
Headmaster: Mr Neil R Brooks BSc
Age range: 7–13
No. of pupils: 290
Fees: Day £16,062–
£20,838 FB £25,164
(⚐)

Cranleigh School
Horseshoe Lane, Cranleigh,
Surrey GU6 8QQ
Tel: +44 (0) 1483 273666
Headmaster: Mr Martin Reader
MA, MPhil, MBA
Age range: 7–18 (including
Prep School)
No. of pupils: 690 VIth252
Fees: Day £32,370 FB £39,330
(⊕)(A)(⚐)(£)(✎)(16+)

Cranmore School
Epsom Road, West Horsley,
Surrey KT24 6AT
Tel: 01483 280340
Headmaster: Mr Michael Connolly
BSc, BA, MA, MEd
Age range: 2–13
No. of pupils: 420
Fees: Day £12,825–£15,300
(£)(✎)

Danes Hill School
Leatherhead Road, Oxshott,
Surrey KT22 0JG
Tel: 01372 842509
Age range: 3–13
No. of pupils: 872
Fees: Day £14,421–£20,340
(£)(✎)

Danesfield Manor School
Rydens Avenue, Walton-on-
Thames, Surrey KT12 3JB
Tel: 01932 220930
Principal: Mrs Jo Smith
Age range: 2–11
No. of pupils: 170
Fees: Day £9,456–£10,098
(✎)

Downsend School
1 Leatherhead Road,
Leatherhead, Surrey KT22 8TJ
Tel: 01372 372197
Headmaster: Mr Ian Thorpe
Age range: 2–13
No. of pupils: 670
Fees: Day £11,970–£17,985
(✎)

Downsend School (Ashtead Pre-Prep)
Ashtead Lodge, 22 Oakfield
Road, Ashtead, Surrey KT21 2RE
Tel: 01372 385439
Head Teacher: Tessa Roberts
Age range: 2–6
No. of pupils: 66
Fees: Day £11,535

Downsend School (Epsom Pre-Prep)
Epsom Lodge, 6 Norman Avenue,
Epsom, Surrey KT17 3AB
Tel: 01372 385438
Head Teacher: Vanessa Conlan
Age range: 2–6
No. of pupils: 110
Fees: Day £11,535
(✎)

Downsend School (Leatherhead Pre-Prep)
Leatherhead Lodge, Epsom Road,
Leatherhead, Surrey KT22 8ST
Tel: 01372 385437
Headteacher: Mrs Gill Brooks
Age range: 2–6
No. of pupils: 106
Fees: Day £11,535

Drayton House Pre-School and Nursery
35 Austen Road, Guildford,
Surrey GU1 3NP
Tel: 01483 504707
Headmistress: Mrs J Tyson-Jones
Froebel Cert.Ed. London University
Age range: 6 months–5 years
No. of pupils: 65
Fees: Day £4,420–£12,500
(✎)

Duke of Kent School
Peaslake Road, Ewhurst,
Surrey GU6 7NS
Tel: 01483 277313
Head: Mrs Sue Knox
Age range: 3–16
No. of pupils: 234
Fees: Day £7,245–£19,050
(⊕)(⚐)(£)(✎)

Dunottar School
High Trees Road, Reigate,
Surrey RH2 7EL
Tel: 01737 761945
Head of School: Mr Mark Tottman
Age range: 11–18
No. of pupils: 423
Fees: Day £17,739
(A)(£)(16+)

Edgeborough
Frensham, Farnham,
Surrey GU10 3AH
Tel: 01252 792495
Headmaster: Mr Dan Thornburn
Age range: 2–13
No. of pupils: 335
Fees: Day £11,070–£17,970
(⚐)(£)(✎)

Emberhurst School
94 Ember Lane, Esher,
Surrey KT10 8EN
Tel: 020 8398 2933
Headmistress: Mrs P Chadwick BEd
Age range: 2–7
No. of pupils: 70

Epsom College
Epsom, Surrey KT17 4JQ
Tel: 01372 821000
Headmaster: Mr Jay A Piggot MA
Age range: 11–18
No. of pupils: 884
Fees: Day £19,611–£26,151
WB £35,034 FB £38,568
(⊕)(A)(⚐)(£)(✎)(16+)

Essendene Lodge School
Essendene Road, Caterham,
Surrey CR3 5PB
Tel: 01883 348349
Head Teacher: Mrs K Ali
Age range: 2–11
No. of pupils: 153
Fees: Day £3,315–£7,305
(£)(✎)

Ewell Castle School
Church Street, Ewell, Epsom,
Surrey KT17 2AW
Tel: 020 8393 1413
Principal: Mr Silas Edmonds
Age range: 3–18
No. of pupils: 644
Fees: Day £5,175–£17,442
(A)(£)(✎)(16+)

Feltonfleet School
Cobham, Surrey KT11 1DR
Tel: 01932 862264
Head of School: Mrs S Lance
Age range: 3–13
No. of pupils: 435
Fees: Day £12,315–£18,090
WB £18,090

Focus School – Hindhead Campus
Tilford Road, Hindhead,
Surrey GU26 6SJ
Tel: 01428 601800

Frensham Heights
Rowledge, Farnham,
Surrey GU10 4EA
Tel: 01252 792561
Head: Mr Rick Clarke
Age range: 3–18
No. of pupils: 497 VIth105
Fees: Day £7,110–£21,060
FB £27,450–£32,070

Glenesk School
Ockham Road North, East
Horsley, Surrey KT24 6NS
Tel: 01483 282329
Headmistress: Mrs Sarah Bradley
Age range: 2–7
No. of pupils: 100
Fees: Day £11,658–£13,176

Greenfield School
Old Woking Road, Woking,
Surrey GU22 8HY
Tel: 01483 772525
Headmistress: Mrs Tania Botting BEd
Age range: 3–11
No. of pupils: 179
Fees: Day £5,976–£14,079

Guildford High School
London Road, Guildford,
Surrey GU1 1SJ
Tel: 01483 561440
Headmistress: Mrs F J Boulton BSc, MA
Age range: G4–18
No. of pupils: 1000
Fees: Day £11,175–£17,940

Hall Grove School
London Road, Bagshot,
Surrey GU19 5HZ
Tel: 01276 473059
Headmaster: Mr Alastair Graham
Age range: 3–13
No. of pupils: 410
Fees: Day £10,800–£15,450

Halstead Preparatory School
Woodham Rise, Woking,
Surrey GU21 4EE
Tel: 01483 772682
Headmistress: Mrs P Austin
Age range: G3–11
No. of pupils: 220
Fees: Day £10,800–£15,210

Hampton Court House
Hampton Court Road, East
Molesey, Surrey KT8 9BS
Tel: 020 8614 0857
Headmaster: Mr Guy Holloway
Age range: 3–18
(A)

HawleyHurst School
Fernhill Road, Blackwater,
Camberley, Surrey GU17 9HU
Tel: 01276 587190
Head Teacher: Miss V S Smit
Age range: 2–19

Hazelwood School
Wolf's Hill, Limpsfield,
Oxted, Surrey RH8 0QU
Tel: 01883 712194
Head: Mrs Lindie Louw
Age range: 2–13
No. of pupils: 399
Fees: Day £10,275–£16,380

Hoe Bridge School
Hoe Place, Old Woking Road,
Woking, Surrey GU22 8JE
Tel: 01483 760018 &
01483 772194
Headmaster: Mr C Webster MA BSc
(Hons) PGCE
Age range: 3–13
No. of pupils: 460
Fees: Day £5,940–£15,885

Hurtwood House
Holmbury St Mary, Dorking,
Surrey RH5 6NU
Tel: 01483 279000
Principal: Mr Cosmo Jackson
Age range: 16–18
No. of pupils: 360
Fees: Day £29,748 FB £44,622

Kids Inc Day Nursery – Guildford
Railton Road, Queen Elizabeth
Park, Guildford, Surrey GU2 9LX
Tel: 01483 237999

KING EDWARD'S WITLEY
For further details see p. 96
Petworth Road, Godalming,
Surrey GU8 5SG
Tel: 01428 686735
Email: admissions@kesw.org
Website: www.kesw.org
Head: Mrs Joanna Wright
Age range: 11–18 years
No. of pupils: 400

Kingswood House School
56 West Hill, Epsom, Surrey KT19 8LG
Tel: 01372 723590
Headmaster: Mr Duncan Murphy
BA (Hons), MEd, FRSA
Age range: B4–16
No. of pupils: 210

Lanesborough
Maori Road, Guildford,
Surrey GU1 2EL
Tel: 01483 880650
Head: Mrs Clare Turnbull BA(Hons)
MEd
Age range: B3–13
No. of pupils: 350
Fees: Day £10,890–£15,270

Lingfield College
Racecourse Road, Lingfield,
Surrey RH7 6PH
Tel: 01342 832407
Headmaster: Mr R Bool B.A. Hons,
MBA
Age range: 2–18
No. of pupils: 935
Fees: Day £11,250–£21,801

Longacre School
Hullbrook Lane, Shamley Green,
Guildford, Surrey GU5 0NQ
Tel: 01483 893225
Head of School: Mr Matthew Bryan
MA(Cantab.), MA(Oxon.), MSc,
FRSA
Age range: 2–11
No. of pupils: 267
Fees: Day £10,290–£15,300

Lyndhurst School
36 The Avenue, Camberley,
Surrey GU15 3NE
Tel: 01276 22895
Head: Mr A Rudkin BEd(Hons)
Age range: 3–11
No. of pupils: 126

Manor House School, Bookham
Manor House Lane, Little Bookham,
Leatherhead, Surrey KT23 4EN
Tel: 01372 457077
Headteacher: Ms Tracey Fantham
BA (Hons) MA NPQH
Age range: B2–4 G2–16
No. of pupils: 300
Fees: Day £9,555–£17,955

Micklefield School
10/12 Somers Road, Reigate,
Surrey RH2 9DU
Tel: 01737 224212
Head: Mr R Ardé
Age range: 3–11
No. of pupils: 272
Fees: Day £3,465–£13,125

Milbourne Lodge School
Arbrook Lane, Esher,
Surrey KT10 9EG
Tel: 01372 462737
Head: Mrs Judy Waite
Age range: 4–13
No. of pupils: 280
Fees: Day £12,855–£16,155

New Life Christian Primary School
Cairo New Road, Croydon,
Surrey CR0 1XP
Tel: 020 8680 7671 Ext:327

Notre Dame School
Cobham, Surrey KT11 1HA
Tel: 01932 869990
Head of Seniors: Mrs Anna King
MEd, MA (Cantab), PGCE
Age range: 2–18
No. of pupils: 600

Oakhyrst Grange School
160 Stanstead Road,
Caterham, Surrey CR3 6AF
Tel: 01883 343344
Headmaster: Mr Alex Gear
Age range: 4–11 years
No. of pupils: 155

Parkside School
The Manor, Stoke d'Abernon,
Cobham, Surrey KT11 3PX
Tel: 01932 862749
Headteacher: Ms Nicole Janssen
Age range: B2–13 G2–4
No. of pupils: 270

Prior's Field
Priorsfield Road, Godalming,
Surrey GU7 2RH
Tel: 01483 810551
Head of School: Mrs Tracey Kirnig
Age range: G11–18
No. of pupils: 450
Fees: Day £18,900 FB £30,825

Reed's School
Sandy Lane, Cobham,
Surrey KT11 2ES
Tel: 01932 869001
Headmaster: Mr Mark Hoskins BA
MA MSc
Age range: B11–18 G16–18
No. of pupils: 650 VIth230
Fees: Day £20,430–£25,530
FB £27,225–£32,910

Reigate Grammar School
Reigate Road, Reigate,
Surrey RH2 0QS
Tel: 01737 222231
Headmaster: Mr Shaun Fenton MA
(Oxon) MEd (Oxon)
Age range: 11–18
No. of pupils: 969 VIth262
Fees: Day £19,140–£19,350

Reigate St Mary's Prep & Choir School
Chart Lane, Reigate,
Surrey RH2 7RN
Tel: 01737 244880
Headmaster: Mr Marcus Culverwell
MA
Age range: 3–11
No. of pupils: 350
Fees: Day £12,360–£15,300

Ripley Court School

Rose Lane, Ripley, Surrey GU23 6NE
Tel: 01483 225217
Headmistress: Ms Aislinn Clarke
Age range: 3–13

Rowan Preparatory School

6 Fitzalan Road, Claygate,
Surrey KT10 0LX
Tel: 01372 462627
Headmistress: Mrs Susan Clarke
BEd, NPQH
Age range: G2–11
No. of pupils: 317
Fees: Day £11,526–£15,294

Royal Grammar School, Guildford

High Street, Guildford,
Surrey GU1 3BB
Tel: 01483 880600
Headmaster: Dr J M Cox BSc, PhD
Age range: B11–18
No. of pupils: 940
Fees: Day £19,035

Royal School of Needlework

Apartment 12A, Hampton
Court Palace, East Molesey,
Surrey KT8 9AU
Tel: 020 3166 6932

Rydes Hill Preparatory School

Rydes Hill House, Aldershot Road,
Guildford, Surrey GU2 8BP
Tel: 01483 563160
Headmistress: Mrs Sarah Norville
Age range: B3–7 G3–11
No. of pupils: 180
Fees: Day £3,006–£4,565

Shrewsbury House Pre-Preparatory School

22 Milbourne Lane, Esher,
Surrey KT10 9EA
Tel: 01372 462781
Head: Mr Jon Akhurst BA (Hons)
PGCE
Age range: 3–7
Fees: Day £6,225–£13,740

Sir William Perkins's School

Guildford Road, Chertsey,
Surrey KT16 9BN
Tel: 01932 574900
Head: Mr C C Muller
Age range: G11–18 years
No. of pupils: 600
Fees: Day £5,618

St Catherine's, Bramley

Station Road, Bramley,
Guildford, Surrey GU5 0DF
Tel: 01483 899609
Headmistress: Alice Phillips
Age range: G4–18
Fees: Day £9,240–£18,885 FB £31,125

St Christopher's School

6 Downs Road, Epsom,
Surrey KT18 5HE
Tel: 01372 721807
Headteacher: Mrs A C Thackray
MA, BA(Hons)
Age range: 3–7
No. of pupils: 137
Fees: Day £10,485

St Edmund's School

Portsmouth Road, Hindhead,
Surrey GU26 6BH
Tel: 01428 604808
Headmaster: Mr A J Walliker
MA(Cantab), MBA, PGCE
Age range: 2–16
No. of pupils: 410
Fees: Day £9,585–£16,746

St George's College

Weybridge Road, Addlestone,
Weybridge, Surrey KT15 2QS
Tel: 01932 839300
Headmistress: Mrs Rachel Owens
Age range: 11–18
No. of pupils: 909 VIth250
Fees: Day £17,655–£20,100

St George's Junior School

Thames Street, Weybridge,
Surrey KT13 8NL
Tel: 01932 839400
Head Master: Mr Antony Hudson
MA (CANTAB), PGCE, NPQH
Age range: 3–11 years
No. of pupils: 644
Fees: Day £5,640–£14,640

St Hilary's School

Holloway Hill, Godalming,
Surrey GU7 1RZ
Tel: 01483 416551
Headmistress: Mrs Jane
Whittingham BEdCert,
ProfPracSpLD
Age range: B2–11 G2–11
No. of pupils: 250
Fees: Day £10,092–£14,850

St Ives School

Three Gates Lane, Haslemere,
Surrey GU27 2ES
Tel: 01428 643734
Headteacher: Kay Goldsworthy
Age range: 2–11
No. of pupils: 149
Fees: Day £9,900–£13,950

St John's School

Epsom Road, Leatherhead,
Surrey KT22 8SP
Tel: 01372 373000
Head of School: Mrs Rowena Cole
Age range: 11–18
No. of pupils: 840
Fees: Day £19,590–£24,555
WB £24,780–£31,035

St Teresa's Effingham (Preparatory School)

Effingham, Surrey RH5 6ST
Tel: 01372 453456
Headmaster: Mr. Mike Farmer
Age range: B2–4 G2–11
No. of pupils: 100
Fees: Day £1,185–£14,685
WB £25,515 FB £28,665

St Teresa's Effingham (Senior School)

Beech Avenue, Effingham,
Surrey RH5 6ST
Tel: 01372 452037
Executive Director: Mr Mike Farmer
Age range: G11–18
No. of pupils: 640 VIth90
Fees: Day £17,865–£18,465 WB
£28,875–£29,175 FB £30,795–£31,455

St. Andrew's School

Church Hill House, Horsell,
Woking, Surrey GU21 4QW
Tel: 01483 760943
Headmaster: Mr D Fitzgerald
Age range: 3–13
No. of pupils: 300
Fees: Day £4,086–£16,095

Surbiton Preparatory School

3 Avenue Elmers, Surbiton,
Surrey KT6 4SP
Tel: 020 8390 6640
Principal: Mrs Rebecca Glover
Age range: B4–11 G4–11
No. of pupils: 135
Fees: Day £10,857–£13,974

Tante Marie Culinary Academy

Woodham House, Carlton Road,
Woking, Surrey GU21 4HF
Tel: 01483 726957
Principal: Mr Andrew Maxwell
Age range: 16–60
No. of pupils: 72
Fees: Day £20,750

TASIS The American School in England

Coldharbour Lane, Thorpe,
Surrey TW20 8TE
Tel: +44 (0)1932 582316
Head of School: Mr Bryan Nixon
Age range: 3–18
No. of pupils: 620
Fees: Day £11,920–
£25,605 FB £47,565

The Hawthorns School

Pendell Court, Bletchingley,
Redhill, Surrey RH1 4QJ
Tel: 01883 743048
Head of School: Mr Adrian Floyd
Age range: 2–13
No. of pupils: 520
Fees: Day £10,680–£15,780

The Royal Junior School

Portsmouth Road, Hindhead,
Surrey GU26 6BW
Tel: 01428 607977
Principal: Mrs Anne J P Lynch
Age range: 6 weeks–11 years
Fees: Day £10,200–£11,955

The Royal School

Farnham Lane, Haslemere,
Surrey GU27 1HQ
Tel: 01428 605805
Head: Mrs Pippa Smithson
Age range: 11–18 years
Fees: Day £10,506–£18,507
WB £27,747 FB £31,557

Tormead School

27 Cranley Road, Guildford,
Surrey GU1 2JD
Tel: 01483 575101
Headmistress: Mrs Christina Foord
Age range: G4–18
No. of pupils: 760 VIth120
Fees: Day £8,385–£15,915

Warlingham Park School

Chelsham Common,
Warlingham, Surrey CR6 9PB
Tel: 01883 626844
Headmaster: Mrs S S Buist
Age range: 2–11
No. of pupils: 96
Fees: Day £4,230–£8,565

Weston Green School

Weston Green Road. Thames
Ditton, Surrey KT7 0JN
Tel: 020 8398 2778
Headteacher: Mrs Sarah Evans
Age range: 2–11
No. of pupils: 200
Fees: Day £3,389–£3,809

Westward School

47 Hersham Road, Walton-
on-Thames, Surrey KT12 1LE
Tel: 01932 220911
Headmistress: Mrs Shelley
Stevenson
Age range: 3–12
No. of pupils: 140
Fees: Day £7,380–£8,235

WOLDINGHAM SCHOOL
For further details see p. 112
Marden Park, Woldingham,
Surrey CR3 7YA
Tel: 01883 349431
Email: registrar@
woldinghamschool.co.uk
Website:
www.woldinghamschool.co.uk
Head of School: Dr James
Whitehead
Age range: G11–18
No. of pupils: 585
Fees: Day £21,945–£23,910
FB £36,135–£39,330

Woodcote House School
Snows Ride, Windlesham,
Surrey GU20 6PF
Tel: 01276 472115
Headmaster: Mr D.M.K. Paterson
Age range: B7–13
No. of pupils: 100
Fees: Day £18,300 FB £24,600

**World Federation
of Hairdressing &
Beauty Schools**
PO Box 367, Coulsdon,
Surrey CR5 2TP
Tel: 01737 551355

Yehudi Menuhin School
Stoke Road, Stoke d'Abernon,
Cobham, Surrey KT11 3QQ
Tel: 01932 864739
Interim Head: Richard Tanner
Age range: 7–19
No. of pupils: 80 VIth36
Fees: FB £34,299

West Berkshire

**Brockhurst & Marlston
House Schools**
Hermitage, Newbury, West
Berkshire RG18 9UL
Tel: 01635 200293
Head of School: Mr David Fleming
Age range: 2 1/2–13
No. of pupils: 275
Fees: Day £10,650–£17,850
FB £23,925–£25,800

Cheam School
Headley, Newbury, West
Berkshire RG19 8LD
Tel: +44 (0)1635 268242
Headmaster: Mr Martin Harris
Age range: 3–13
No. of pupils: 407
Fees: Day £11,940–£21,285
FB £26,055–£27,630

Downe House School
Downe House, Cold Ash,
Thatcham, West Berkshire RG18 9JJ
Tel: +44 (0)1635 200286
Headmistress: Mrs Emma
McKendrick BA(Liverpool)
Age range: G11–18
No. of pupils: 593
Fees: Day £9,705 FB £13,050

Horris Hill
Newtown, Newbury, West
Berkshire RG20 9DJ
Tel: 01635 40594
Headmaster: Mr G F Tollit B.A.(Hons)
Age range: B4–13

**Marlston House
Preparatory School**
Hermitage, Newbury, West
Berkshire RG18 9UL
Tel: 01635 200293
Headmistress: Mrs Caroline Riley
MA, BEd
Age range: G3–13
No. of pupils: 110
Fees: Day £10,650–
£17,850 FB £23,925

Newbury Hall
Enborne Road, (corner of
Rockingham Road), Newbury,
West Berkshire RG14 6AD
Tel: +44 (0)1635 36879

St Gabriel's
Sandleford Priory, Newbury,
West Berkshire RG20 9BD
Tel: 01635 555680
Principal: Mr Richard Smith MA
(Hons), MEd, PGCE
Age range: B6 months–11
G6 months–18
No. of pupils: 469 VIth40
Fees: Day £10,668–£17,418

St Michael's School
Harts Lane, Burghclere, Newbury,
West Berkshire RG20 9JW
Tel: 01635 278137
Headmaster: Rev. Fr. John Brucciani
Age range: B5–18 G5–11

The Cedars School
Church Road, Aldermaston,
West Berkshire RG7 4LR
Tel: 0118 971 4251
Headteacher: Mrs Jane O'Halloran
Age range: 4–11
No. of pupils: 50
Fees: Day £8,910

West Sussex

Ardingly College
College Road, Ardingly, Haywards
Heath, West Sussex RH17 6SQ
Tel: +44 (0)1444 893320
Headmaster: Mr Ben Figgis
Age range: 13–18
No. of pupils: 559
Fees:–£23,985 FB £35,865–£29,250

**Ardingly College
Preparatory School**
Haywards Heath, West
Sussex RH17 6SQ
Tel: 01444 893200
Headmaster: Mr Harry Hastings
Age range: 2–13 years

Brambletye
Brambletye, East Grinstead,
West Sussex RH19 3PD
Tel: 01342 321004
Headmaster: Will Brooks
Age range: 2–13
No. of pupils: 280
Fees: Day £10,050–£21,660
FB £25,815–£26,415

Burgess Hill Girls
Keymer Road, Burgess Hill,
West Sussex RH15 0EG
Tel: 01444 241050
Head of School: Liz Laybourn
Age range: B2.5–4 G2.5–18
No. of pupils: 505 VIth70
Fees: Day £8,100–£20,100
FB £31,050–£35,850

**Chichester High
Schools Sixth Form**
Kingsham Road, Chichester,
West Sussex PO19 8AE
Tel: +44 1243 832 546

Christ's Hospital
Horsham, West Sussex RH13 0LJ
Tel: 01403 211293
Head Teacher: Mr Simon Reid
Age range: 11–18
No. of pupils: 900
Fees: Day £18,510–£23,310
FB £35,850

Conifers School
Egmont Road, Midhurst,
West Sussex GU29 9BG
Tel: 01730 813243
Headmistress: Mrs Emma Smyth
Age range: 2–13
No. of pupils: 104
Fees: Day £7,350–£9,750

Copthorne Prep School
Effingham Lane, Copthorne,
West Sussex RH10 3HR
Tel: 01342 712311
Headmaster: Mr Chris Jones
Age range: 2–13
No. of pupils: 340
Fees: Day £9,750–£16,740
WB £20,400 FB £25,500

Cottesmore School
Buchan Hill, Pease Pottage,
West Sussex RH11 9AU
Tel: 01293 520648
Head: T F Rogerson
Age range: 4–13
No. of pupils: 170
Fees: Day £3,199–£4,267 FB £9,095

Cumnor House Sussex
London Road, Danehill, Haywards Heath, West Sussex RH17 7HT
Tel: 01825 792 006
Headmaster: Fergus Llewellyn
Age range: 2–13
No. of pupils: 385
Fees: Day £8,985–£19,530 WB £22,635 FB £23,250

Dorset House School
The Manor, Church Lane, Bury, Pulborough, West Sussex RH20 1PB
Tel: 01798 831456
Headmaster: Matt Thomas
Age range: 3–13
No. of pupils: 135
Fees: Day £8,550–£17,850

Farlington School
Strood Park, Horsham, West Sussex RH12 3PN
Tel: 01403 282573
Headmistress: Ms Louise Higson BSc, PGCE
Age range: 3–18
No. of pupils: 300
Fees: Day £5,400–£17,670 WB £23,205–£28,515 FB £24,540–£29,850

Great Ballard School
Eartham House, Eartham, Nr Chichester, West Sussex PO18 0LR
Tel: 01243 814236
Head: Mr Richard Evans
Age range: 2–13
No. of pupils: 136
Fees: Day £0,580–£15,930 WB £17,010

Great Walstead School
East Mascalls Lane, Lindfield, Haywards Heath, West Sussex RH16 2QL
Tel: 01444 483528
Headmaster: Mr Chris Calvey
Age range: 2.5–13
No. of pupils: 465
Fees: Day £11,055–£15,510

Handcross Park School
Handcross, Haywards Heath, West Sussex RH17 6HF
Tel: 01444 400526
Headmaster: Mr Richard Brown
Age range: 2–13
No. of pupils: 339
Fees: Day £3,230–£6,360 WB £5,370–£7,480 FB £6,030–£8,130

Hurstpierpoint College
College Lane, Hurstpierpoint, West Sussex BN6 9JS
Tel: 01273 833636
Headmaster: Mr. T J Manly BA, MSc
Age range: 4–18
No. of pupils: 1156
Fees: Day £8,790–£22,860 WB £28,800

Hurstpierpoint College Prep School
Hurstpierpoint, West Sussex BN6 9JS
Tel: 01273 834975
Head: Mr I D Pattison BSc
Age range: 4–13
No. of pupils: 360

Lancing College
Lancing, West Sussex BN15 0RW
Tel: 01273 465805
Head Master: Mr Dominic T Oliver MPhil
Age range: 13–18
No. of pupils: 550 VIth255
Fees: Day £8,190 FB £11,995

Lancing College Preparatory School at Worthing
Broadwater Road, Worthing, West Sussex BN14 8HU
Tel: 01903 201123
Head: Mrs Heather Beeby
Age range: 2–13
No. of pupils: 165
Fees: Day £8,115–£11,460

Oakwood Preparatory School
Chichester, West Sussex PO18 9AN
Tel: 01243 575209
Headteacher: Mrs Clare Bradbury
Age range: 2.5–11
No. of pupils: 275
Fees: Day £3,170–£5,110

Our Lady of Sion School
Gratwicke Road, Worthing, West Sussex BN11 4BL
Tel: 01903 204063
Headmaster: Dr Simon Orchard
Age range: 3–18
No. of pupils: 410
Fees: Day £8,640–£13,575

Pennthorpe School
Church Street, Horsham, West Sussex RH12 3HJ
Tel: 01403 822391
Headmistress: Alexia Bolton
Age range: 2–13
No. of pupils: 362
Fees: Day £2,070–£16,605

Rikkyo School in England
Guildford Road, Rudgwick, Horsham, West Sussex RH12 3BE
Tel: 01403 822107
Headmaster: Mr Roger Munechika
Age range: 10–18
No. of pupils: 116
Fees: FB £15,000–£21,600

Seaford College
Lavington Park, Petworth, West Sussex GU28 0NB
Tel: 01798 867392
Headmaster: J P Green MA BA
Age range: 6–18
No. of pupils: 869 VIth219
Fees: Day £10,725–£22,230 WB £22,350–£30,120 FB £34,380

Shoreham College
St Julians Lane, Shoreham-by-Sea, West Sussex BN43 6YW
Tel: 01273 592681
Headmaster: Mr R Taylor-West
Age range: 3–16 years
No. of pupils: 375
Fees: Day £9,750–£15,150

Slindon College
Slindon House, Slindon, Arundel, West Sussex BN18 0RH
Tel: 01243 814320
Head Teacher: Mr Mark Birkbeck
Age range: B8–18 years

Sompting Abbotts Preparatory School for Boys and Girls
Church Lane, Sompting, West Sussex BN15 0AZ
Tel: 01903 235960
Principal: Mrs P M Sinclair
Age range: 2–13
No. of pupils: 185
Fees: Day £9,195–£11,805

The Prebendal School
52-55 West Street, Chichester, West Sussex PO19 1RT
Tel: 01243 772220
Headteacher: Mrs L Salmond Smith
Age range: 3–13
No. of pupils: 181
Fees: Day £8,160–£15,495 WB £18,975–£20,100 FB £22,290

Westbourne House School
Shopwyke, Chichester, West Sussex PO20 2BH
Tel: 01243 782739
Headmaster: Mr Martin Barker
Age range: 2.5–13 years
No. of pupils: 420
Fees: Day £10,440–£17,985 FB £21,465–£24,105

Windlesham House School
London Road, Washington, Pulborough, West Sussex RH20 4AY
Tel: 01903 874701
Head of School: Ben Evans
Age range: 4–13
No. of pupils: 280

Worth School
Paddockhurst Road, Turners Hill, Crawley, West Sussex RH10 4SD
Tel: +44 (0)1342 710200
Head Master: Stuart McPherson
Age range: 11–18
No. of pupils: 580 VIth222
Fees: Day £15,960–£23,730 FB £21,210–£33,690

International Schools in London and the South-East

London

Central London

Accent London
12 Bedford Square,
London WC1B 3JA
Tel: 020 7813 7723
Head: Natasa Blecic
🌍 16+

CATS London
43-45 Bloomsbury Square,
London WC1A 2RA
Tel: 02078 411580
Principal: Mario Di Clemente
Age range: 15–24
🌍 Ⓐ 🏛 £ 16+

ÉCOLE JEANNINE MANUEL - LONDON
For further details see p. 56
43-45 Bedford Square,
London WC1B 3DN
Tel: 020 3829 5970
Email: admissions@
jmanuel.uk.net
Website: www.ecolejeannine
manuel.org.uk
Head of School: Pauline Prévot
Age range: 3–18 years
No. of pupils: 550
Fees: Day £19,590
🌍 £ Ⓘ🅑

North London

Dwight School London
6 Friern Barnet Lane,
London N11 3LX
Tel: +44 (0)20 8920 0637
Head: Mrs Alison Cobbin BA, Dip
Ed, MBA
Age range: 3–18
🌍 £ Ⓘ🅑 ✐ 16+

North-West London

Collège Français Bilingue de Londres
87 Holmes Road, Kentish
Town, , London NW5 3AX
Tel: 020 7993 7400
Head of School: Mr Denis Bittmann
Age range: 3–15
No. of pupils: 700
Fees: Day £11,115–£11,980
🌍

ICS London
7B Wyndham Place,
London W1H 1PN
Tel: +44 (0) 20 7298 8817
Head of School: Mr. Rod Jackson
Age range: 3–18 years
No. of pupils: 205
🌍 Ⓘ🅑 ✐ 16+

Mill Hill School
The Ridgeway, Mill Hill
Village, London NW7 1QS
Tel: 020 8959 1176
Head: Mrs Jane Sanchez BSc (Hons)
PGCE
Age range: 13–18
No. of pupils: 689 VIth259
Fees: Day £21,987 WB
£28,524 FB £33,717
🌍 Ⓐ 🏛 £ 16+

Southbank International School - Hampstead
16 Netherhall Gardens,
London NW3 5TH
Tel: 020 7243 3803
Principal: Shirley Harwood
Age range: 3–11
No. of pupils: 210
🌍 Ⓘ🅑 ✐

The American School in London
One Waverley Place,
London NW8 0NP
Tel: 020 7449 1221
Head: Robin Appleby
Age range: 4–18
No. of pupils: 1350
Fees: Day £27,050–£31,200
🌍 16+

The Mount, Mill Hill International
Milespit Hill, London NW7 2RX
Tel: +44 (0)20 3826 33
Head of School: Ms Sarah Bellotti
Age range: 13–17
No. of pupils: 80
Fees: Day £25,989 WB
£34,461 FB £40,539
🌍 🏛

South-East London

Bellerbys College London
Bounty House, Greenwich,
London SE8 3DE
Tel: +44 (0)208 694 7000
Principal: Ms Alison Baines
Age range: 15–19
🌍 16+ Ⓐ 🏛

DLD College London
199 Westminster Bridge
Road, London SE1 7FX
Tel: +44 (0)20 7935 8411
Principal: Irfan H Latif BSc (Hons)
PGCE FRSA FRSC
No. of pupils: 426
Fees: Day £23,500–£29,950
FB £18,000–£28,000
🌍 16+ Ⓐ 🏛 £ ✐

Dulwich College
Dulwich Common, ,
London SE21 7LD
Tel: 020 8693 3601
Master: Dr J A F Spence
Age range: B0–18
No. of pupils: 1589 VIth470
Fees: Day £21,246 WB
£41,557 FB £44,346
👦 🌍 Ⓐ 🏛 £ ✐ 16+

St Dunstan's College
Stanstead Road, London SE6 4TY
Tel: 020 8516 7200
Headmaster: Mr Nicholas Hewlett
Age range: 3–18
No. of pupils: 870
🌍 Ⓐ 🏛 £ 16+

South-West London

Centre Academy London
92 St John's Hill, Battersea,
London SW11 1SH
Tel: 020 7738 2344
Headteacher: Rachel Maddison
Age range: 9–19
🌍 £ ✐ 16+

Eaton Square School Belgravia
79 Eccleston Square,
London SW1V 1PP
Tel: +44 (0)20 7931 9469
Principal: Mr Sebastian Hepher
Age range: 4–11
🌍

Ecole Charles De Gaulle - Wix
Clapham Common North
Side, London SW4 0AJ
Tel: +44 20 7738 0287
Headteacher: Mr Blanchard
Age range: 5–11
No. of pupils: 100
🌍

École Primaire Marie D'Orliac
60 Clancarty Road,
London SW6 3AA
Tel: +44 (0)20 7736 5863
Director: Mr Blaise Fenart
Age range: 4–11
🌍

HILL HOUSE INTERNATIONAL JUNIOR SCHOOL
For further details see p. 60
17 Hans Place, Chelsea,
London SW1X 0EP
Tel: 020 7584 1331
Email: info@
hillhouseschool.co.uk
Website: www.hillhouseschool.co.uk
Proprietors: Richard, Janet,
William & Edmund Townend
Age range: 4–13
No. of pupils: 600
Fees: Day £15,000–£18,600
🌍 £

King's College School
Southside, Wimbledon
Common, London SW19 4TT
Tel: 020 8255 5300
Head Master: Mr A D Halls OBE
Age range: B7–18 G16–18
No. of pupils: 1475
👦 🌍 Ⓐ £ Ⓘ🅑 16+

Lycée Français Charles de Gaulle
35 Cromwell Road,
London SW7 2DG
Tel: 020 7584 6322
Head of School: Mr Olivier Rauch
Age range: 5–19
No. of pupils: 4000
🌍 Ⓐ £ ✐ 16+

St Paul's School
Lonsdale Road, Barnes,
London SW13 9JT
Tel: 020 8748 9162
High Master: Prof Mark Bailey
Age range: B13–18
No. of pupils: 897
Fees: Day £25,032 FB £37,611
👦 🌍 Ⓐ 🏛 £ 16+

Wandsworth Preparatory School
The Old Library, 2 Allfarthing
Lane, London SW18 2PQ
Tel: 0208 870 4133
Headteacher: Ms Jo Fife
Age range: 4–11
No. of pupils: 100
Fees: Day £4,710
🌍 £

Westminster School
Little Dean's Yard, Westminster,
London SW1P 3PF
Tel: 020 7963 1003
Headmaster: Mr Patrick Derham
Age range: B13–18 G16–18
No. of pupils: 744
Fees: Day £26,130–
£28,566 FB £37,740
👦 🌍 Ⓐ 🏛 £ 16+

West London

Bales College
742 Harrow Road, Kensal
Town, London W10 4AA
Tel: 020 8960 5899
Principal: William Moore
Age range: 11–19
No. of pupils: 90
Fees: Day £11,550–£12,750

Ecole Francaise Jacques Prevert
59 Brook Green, London W6 7BE
Tel: 020 7602 6871
Headteacher: Delphine Gentil
Age range: 4–11

FULHAM SCHOOL
For further details see p. 58
200 Greyhound Road,
London W14 9SD
Tel: 020 7386 2444
Email: admissions@
fulham.school
Website: fulham.school
Pre-Prep Head: Di Steven
Age range: 4–18
No. of pupils: 700
Fees: Day £18,420–£21,567

Godolphin and Latymer School
Iffley Road, Hammersmith,
London W6 0PG
Tel: +44 (0)20 8741 1936
Head Mistress: Dr Frances Ramsey
Age range: G11–18
No. of pupils: 800
Fees: Day £23,085

Halcyon London International School
33 Seymour Place, ,
London W1H 5AU
Tel: +44 (0)20 7258 1169
Headteacher: Mr Barry Mansfield
Age range: 11–18
No. of pupils: 195

Instituto Español Vicente Cañada Blanch
317 Portobello Road,
London W10 5SZ
Tel: +44 (0) 20 8969 2664
Principal: Carmen Pinilla Padilla
Age range: 4–19
No. of pupils: 405

International School of London (ISL)
139 Gunnersbury Avenue,
London W3 8LG
Tel: +44 (0)20 8992 5823
Principal: Mr Richard Parker
Age range: 3–18 years
No. of pupils: 500
Fees: Day £19,000–£26,300

King Fahad Academy
Bromyard Avenue, Acton,
London W3 7HD
Tel: 020 8743 0131
Director General: Dr Tahani Aljafari
Age range: 3–19

Southbank International School - Kensington
36-38 Kensington Park
Road, London W11 3BU
Tel: +44 (0)20 7243 3803
Principal: Siobhan McGrath
Age range: 3–18

Southbank International School - Westminster
63-65 Portland Place,
London W1B 1QR
Tel: 020 7243 3803
Principal: Dr Paul Wood
Age range: 11–19

Berkshire

Bradfield College
Bradfield, Berkshire RG7 6AU
Tel: 0118 964 4516
Headmaster: Dr Christopher
Stevens
Age range: 13–18
No. of pupils: 815
Fees: Day £31,080 FB £38,850

Eton College
Windsor, Berkshire SL4 6DW
Tel: 01753 671249
Head Master: Simon Henderson MA
Age range: B13–18
No. of pupils: 1300 VIth520
Fees: FB £40,668

Heathfield School
London Road, Ascot,
Berkshire SL5 8BQ
Tel: 01344 898342
Head of School: Ms Sarah Wilson
Age range: G11–18
No. of pupils: 200
Fees: Day £7,690–£7,900
FB £12,400–£12,700

LEIGHTON PARK SCHOOL
For further details see p. 98
Shinfield Road, Reading,
Berkshire RG2 7ED
Tel: 0118 987 9600
Email: admissions@
leightonpark.com
Website:
www.leightonpark.com
Head: Mr Matthew L S Judd BA,
PGCE
Age range: 11–18
No. of pupils: 520

Luckley House School
Luckley Road, Wokingham,
Berkshire RG40 3EU
Tel: 0118 978 4175
Head: Mrs Jane Tudor
Age range: 11–18
No. of pupils: 300
Fees: Day £5,662 WB £9,183 FB £9,907

LVS ASCOT
For further details see p. 100
London Road, Ascot,
Berkshire SL5 8DR
Tel: 01344 882770
Email: enquiries@lvs.
ascot.sch.uk
Website: www.lvs.ascot.sch.uk
Principal: Mrs Christine Cunniffe
BA (Hons), MMus, MBA
Age range: 4–18
No. of pupils: 800
Fees: Day £10,785–£19,335
FB £27,585–£33,975

Padworth College
Padworth, Reading,
Berkshire RG7 4NR
Tel: 0118 983 2644
Acting Principal: Mr Chris Randell
Age range: 13–19
No. of pupils: 116 VIth50
Fees: Day £14,400 FB £29,400

Pangbourne College
Pangbourne, Reading,
Berkshire RG8 8LA
Tel: 0118 984 2101
Headmaster: Thomas J C Garnier
Age range: 11–18
No. of pupils: 450 VIth134
Fees: Day £18,000–£25,380
FB £25,860–£36,660

Queen Anne's School
6 Henley Road, Caversham,
Reading, Berkshire RG4 6DX
Tel: 0118 918 7300
Headmistress: Mrs Julia Harrington
BA(Hons), PGCE, NPQH
Age range: G11–18

REDDAM HOUSE BERKSHIRE
For further details see p. 102
Bearwood Road, Sindlesham,
Wokingham, Berkshire RG41 5BG
Tel: 0118 467 8731
Email: registrar@
reddamhouse.org.uk
Website:
http://reddamhouse.org.uk
Principal: Mrs Tammy Howard
Age range: 3 months–18 years
No. of pupils: 650
Fees: Day £11,490–£18,330
WB £27,981–£32,244 FB
£29,526–£33,789

St George's Ascot
Wells Lane, Ascot, Berkshire SL5 7DZ
Tel: 01344 629920
Headmistress: Mrs Liz Hewer MA
(Hons) (Cantab) PGCE
Age range: G11–18
No. of pupils: 270 VIth70
Fees: Day £22,800 WB
£34,050–£34,680 FB £35,460

St Mary's School Ascot
St Mary's Road, Ascot,
Berkshire SL5 9JF
Tel: 01344 296614
Headmistress: Mrs Danuta Staunton
Age range: G11–18
No. of pupils: 386 VIth120
Fees: Day £27,630 FB £38,790

The Abbey School
Kendrick Road, Reading,
Berkshire RG1 5DZ
Tel: 0118 987 2256
Head: Mr Will le Fleming
Age range: G3–18
No. of pupils: 1000
Fees: Day £10,860–£18,000

The Oratory School
Woodcote, Reading,
Berkshire RG8 0PJ
Tel: 01491 683500
Head Master: Mr J J Smith BA(Hons),
MEd, PGCE
Age range: B11–18
No. of pupils: 380 VIth120
Fees: Day £24,966 FB £34,299

Wellington College
Duke's Ride, Crowthorne,
Berkshire RG45 7PU
Tel: +44 (0)1344 444000
Master: Mr James Dahl
Age range: 13–18
No. of pupils: 1080 VIth485
Fees: Day £30,375–
£34,890 FB £41,580

Buckinghamshire

Thornton College
College Lane, Thornton,
Buckinghamshire MK17 0HJ
Tel: 01280 812610
Headteacher: Mrs Val Holmes
Age range: B2–4 G3–18
No. of pupils: 414
Fees: Day £10,035–£16,005 WB
£17,310–£21,900 FB £21,525–£26,700

Wycombe Abbey
High Wycombe,
Buckinghamshire HP11 1PE
Tel: +44 (0)1494 897008
Headmistress: Mrs Jo Duncan MA
(St Andrews), PGCE (Cantab)
Age range: G11–18
No. of pupils: 649
Fees: Day £30,270 FB £40,350

East Sussex

Battle Abbey School
Battle, East Sussex TN33 0AD
Tel: 01424 772385
Headmaster: Mr D Clark BA(Hons)
Age range: 2–18
No. of pupils: 286 VIth48
Fees: Day £6,939–£16,914
FB £26,649–£31,932

Bede's School
The Dicker, Upper Dicker,
Hailsham, East Sussex BN27 3QH
Tel: +44 (0)1323843252
Head: Mr Peter Goodyer
Age range: 3 months–18
No. of pupils: 800 VIth295
Fees: Day £10,230–£17,400
FB £22,290–£25,650

Bellerbys College Brighton
1 Billinton Way, Brighton,
East Sussex BN1 4LF
Tel: +44 (0)1273 339333
Principal: Mr Simon Mower
Age range: 13–18

Brighton College
Eastern Road, Brighton,
East Sussex BN2 0AL
Tel: 01273 704200
Head Master: Richard Cairns MA
Age range: 3–18
No. of pupils: 950
Fees: Day £10,050–£24,540 WB
£33,390–£34,410 FB £37,470–£45,210

Buckswood School
Broomham Hall, Rye
Road, Guestling, Hastings,
East Sussex TN35 4LT
Tel: 01424 813 813
School Director: Mr Giles Sutton
Age range: 10–19
No. of pupils: 420

Eastbourne College
Old Wish Road, Eastbourne,
East Sussex BN21 4JX
Tel: 01323 452323 (Admissions)
Headmaster: Mr Tom Lawson MA
(Oxon)
Age range: 13–18
No. of pupils: 650 VIth312
Fees: Day £23,895–£24,375
FB £36,420–£36,975

Greenfields Independent Day & Boarding School
Priory Road, Forest Row,
East Sussex RH18 5JD
Tel: +44 (0)1342 822189
Executive Head: Mr. Jeff Smith
Age range: 2–19

MAYFIELD SCHOOL
For further details see p. 101
The Old Palace, Mayfield,
East Sussex TN20 6PH
Tel: 01435 874642
Email: registrar@
mayfieldgirls.org
Website: www.mayfieldgirls.org
Head: Ms Antonia Beary MA,
MPhil (Cantab), PGCE
Age range: G11–18
No. of pupils: 385
Fees: Day £7,280 FB £11,750

Michael Hall School
Kidbrooke Park, Priory Road,
Forest Row, East Sussex RH18 5JA
Tel: 01342 822275
Age range: 0 years–18 years
No. of pupils: VIth102
Fees: Day £9,245–£12,670

Roedean Moira House
Upper Carlisle Road, Eastbourne,
East Sussex BN20 7TE
Tel: 01323 644144
Headmaster: Mr Andrew Wood
Age range: G0–18
No. of pupils: 289

ROEDEAN SCHOOL
For further details see p. 104
Roedean Way, Brighton,
East Sussex BN2 5RQ
Tel: 01273 667500
Email: info@roedean.co.uk
Website: www.roedean.co.uk
Headmaster: Mr. Oliver Bond
BA(Essex), PGCE, NPQH
Age range: G11–18
No. of pupils: 630 VIth155
Fees: Day £5,670–£7,415
WB £10,030–£11,185 FB
£10,990–£13,305

Essex

Brentwood School
Middleton Hall Lane,
Brentwood, Essex CM15 8EE
Tel: 01277 243243
Headmaster: Mr Michael Bond
Age range: 3–18
No. of pupils: 1800
Fees: Day £20,097 FB £39,381
🌐Ⓐ♟£ⒷⒾ✎⑯

Chigwell School
High Road, Chigwell, Essex IG7 6QF
Tel: 020 8501 5700
Headmaster: Mr M E Punt M.A.
M.Sc. P.G.C.E.
Age range: 4–18
Fees: Day £4,250–£6,295 FB £10,995
🌐Ⓐ♟£✎⑯

Felsted School
Felsted, Great Dunmow,
Essex CM6 3LL
Tel: +44 (0)1371 822608
Headmaster: Mr Chris Townsend
Age range: 4–18
🌐Ⓐ♟£ⒾⒷ✎⑯

Gosfield School
Cut Hedge Park, Halstead Road,
Gosfield, Halstead, Essex CO9 1PF
Tel: 01787 474040
Headteacher: Mr Guy Martyn
Age range: 4–18
No. of pupils: VIth21
Fees: Day £6,690–£15,525
🌐Ⓐ♟£✎⑯

New Hall School
The Avenue, Boreham,
Chelmsford, Essex CM3 3HS
Tel: 01245 467588
Principal: Mrs Katherine Jeffrey MA,
BA, PGCE, MA(Ed Mg), NPQH
Age range: 1–18
No. of pupils: 1400
Fees: Day £3,096–£6,597 WB
£8,076–£9,735 FB £2,142–£10,233
🌐Ⓐ♟£✎⑯

Hampshire

Bedales School
Church Road, Steep, Petersfield,
Hampshire GU32 2DG
Tel: 01730 711733
Head of School: Magnus Bashaarat
Age range: 13–18
No. of pupils: 463
Fees: Day £28,515 FB £36,285
🌐Ⓐ♟£✎⑯

Brockwood Park & Inwoods School
Brockwood Park, Bramdean,
Hampshire SO24 0LQ
Tel: +44 (0)1962 771744
Principal: Mr Antonio Autor
Age range: 14–19
No. of pupils: 112 VIth39
Fees: Day £5,630–£6,400 FB £21,400
🌐Ⓐ♟£✎⑯

Embley
Embley Park, Romsey,
Hampshire SO51 6ZE
Tel: 01794 512206
Headteacher: Mr Cliff Canning
Age range: 2–18
No. of pupils: 500
Fees: Day £8,754–£31,338
🌐Ⓐ♟£✎⑯

Lord Wandsworth College
Long Sutton, Hook,
Hampshire RG29 1TB
Tel: 01256 862201
Head of School: Mr Adam Williams
Age range: 11–18 years
No. of pupils: 615
Fees: Day £21,240–£24,390
WB £29,400–£33,000 FB
£30,345–£34,650
🌐Ⓐ♟£✎⑯

Moyles Court School
Moyles Court, Ringwood,
Hampshire BH24 3NF
Tel: 01425 472856
Headmaster: Mr Richard Milner-Smith
Age range: 3–16
No. of pupils: 195
Fees: Day £6,885–£14,655
FB £21,246–£26,805
🌐♟

Rookwood School
Weyhill Road, Andover,
Hampshire SP10 3AL
Tel: 01264 325900
Headmaster: Mr A Kirk-Burgess BSc,
PGCE, MSc (Oxon)
Age range: 2–16
Fees: Day £9,360–£15,600
FB £23,250–£27,465
🌐♟£✎

Sherfield School
South Drive, Sherfield-on-Loddon,
Hook, Hampshire RG27 0HU
Tel: 01256 884800
Headmaster: Mr Nick Brain
BA(Hons), PGCE, MA, NPQH
Age range: 3 months–18 years
No. of pupils: 450
Fees: Day £10,320–£17,085 WB
£18,960–£26,130 FB £22,125–£30,495
🌐Ⓐ♟£✎⑯🐾

St John's College
Grove Road South, Southsea,
Portsmouth, Hampshire PO5 3QW
Tel: 023 9281 5118
Head of School: Mrs Mary Maguire
Age range: 4–18
No. of pupils: 560 VIth86
Fees: Day £9,975–£13,125
FB £28,500–£32,250
🌐Ⓐ♟£✎⑯🐾

ST SWITHUN'S SCHOOL
For further details see p. 114
Alresford Road, Winchester,
Hampshire SO21 1HA
Tel: 01962 835700
Email: office@stswithuns.com
Website: www.stswithuns.com
Head of School: Jane Gandee
MA(Cantab)
Age range: G11–18
No. of pupils: 510
Fees: Day £20,976 FB £34,776
🧍🌐Ⓐ♟£✎⑯

The Portsmouth Grammar School
High Street, Portsmouth,
Hampshire PO1 2LN
Tel: +44 (0)23 9236 0036
Headmistress: Dr Anne Cotton
Age range: 2–18
No. of pupils: 1556 VIth336
Fees: Day £10,233–£15,951
🌐Ⓐ£ⒷⒾ✎⑯

Winchester College
College Street, Winchester,
Hampshire SO23 9NA
Tel: 01962 621247
Headmaster: Dr T R Hands
Age range: B13–18
No. of pupils: 690 VIth280
Fees: FB £39,912
🧍🌐♟£✎⑯

Hertfordshire

Aldenham School
Elstree, Hertfordshire WD6 3AJ
Tel: 01923 858122
Head of School: Mr Andrew Williams
Age range: 3–18
🌐 Ⓐ 🏫 £ ✎ 16

BERKHAMSTED SCHOOL
For further details see p. 93
Overton House, 131 High Street, Berkhamsted, Hertfordshire HP4 2DJ
Tel: 01442 358001
Email: admissions@berkhamsted.com
Website: www.berkhamsted.com
Principal: Mr Richard Backhouse MA(Cantab)
Age range: 3–18
No. of pupils: 1852 VIth406
Fees: Day £10,725–£21,636 WB £29,061 FB £34,620
🌐 Ⓐ 🏫 £ ✎ 16

Bishop's Stortford College
10 Maze Green Road, Bishop's Stortford, Hertfordshire CM23 2PJ
Tel: 01279 838575
Headmaster: Mr Jeremy Gladwin
Age range: 13–18
No. of pupils: VIth249
Fees: Day £20,349–£20,532 WB £31,569–£31,917 FB £33,402–£33,930
🌐 Ⓐ 🏫 £ 16

Bishop's Stortford College Prep School
Maze Green Road, Bishop's Stortford, Hertfordshire CM23 2PH
Tel: 01279 838607
Head of the Prep School: Mr Bill Toleman
Age range: 4–13
No. of pupils: 590
Fees: Day £9,408–£16,281 WB £22,359–£24,273 FB £23,610–£25,536
🌐 🏫 £

Haileybury
Haileybury, Hertford, Hertfordshire SG13 7NU
Tel: +44 (0)1992 706353
The Master: Mr Martin Collier MA BA PGCE
Age range: 11–18
No. of pupils: 880 VIth319
Fees: Day £17,712–£26,646 FB £22,929–£36,141
🌐 Ⓐ 🏫 £ IB ✎ 16

St Christopher School
Barrington Road, Letchworth, Hertfordshire SG6 3JZ
Tel: 01462 650 850
Head: Richard Palmer
Age range: 3–18
No. of pupils: 511 VIth78
Fees: Day £4,590–£18,075 WB £19,950–£24,675 FB £31,650
🌐 Ⓐ 🏫 £ ✎ 16 🐾

St Edmund's College & Prep School
Old Hall Green, Nr Ware, Hertfordshire SG11 1DS
Tel: 01920 824247
Headmaster: Mr Matthew Mostyn BA (Hons) MA (Ed)
Age range: 3–18
No. of pupils: 852
Fees: Day £9,882–£18,345 WB £24,165–£27,630 FB £28,302–£32,460
🌐 Ⓐ 🏫 £ ✎ 16

St Francis' College
Broadway, Letchworth Garden City, Hertfordshire SG6 3PJ
Tel: 01462 670511
Headmistress: Mrs B Goulding
Age range: G3–18
No. of pupils: 460 VIth75
Fees: Day £9,990–£16,980 WB £22,350–£26,475 FB £27,990–£31,995
🚹 🌐 Ⓐ 🏫 £ 16

St Margaret's School, Bushey
Merry Hill Road, Bushey, Hertfordshire WD23 1DT
Tel: +44 (0)20 8416 4400
Headteacher: Lara Péchard
Age range: 3–18 years
No. of pupils: 445
🌐 Ⓐ 🏫 £ ✎ 16

Stanborough School
Stanborough Park, Garston, Watford, Hertfordshire WD25 9JT
Tel: 01923 673268
Acting Head Teacher: Ms Eileen Hussey
Age range: 3–17
No. of pupils: 300
Fees: Day £6,630–£10,224 WB £10,350–£13,995
🌐 🏫 16

The Purcell School, London
Aldenham Road, Bushey, Hertfordshire WD23 2TS
Tel: 01923 331100
Headteacher: Dr Bernard Trafford
Age range: 10–18
No. of pupils: 180
Fees: Day £25,707 FB £32,826
🌐 Ⓐ 🏫 £ ✎ 16

The Royal Masonic School for Girls
Rickmansworth Park, Rickmansworth, Hertfordshire WD3 4HF
Tel: 01923 773168
Headmaster: Mr Kevin Carson M.Phil (Cambridge)
Age range: G4–18
No. of pupils: 930 VIth165
Fees: Day £11,475–£17,475 WB £20,115–£27,495 FB £21,225–£29,835
🚹 🌐 Ⓐ 🏫 £ ✎ 16

Tring Park School for the Performing Arts
Tring Park, Tring, Hertfordshire HP23 5LX
Tel: 01442 824255
Principal: Mr Stefan Anderson MA, ARCM, ARCT
Age range: 8–19
No. of pupils: 354 VIth150
Fees: Day £15,405–£24,510 FB £26,190–£37,050
🌐 Ⓐ 🏫 £ ✎ 16 🐾

Kent

Ashford School
East Hill, Ashford, Kent TN24 8PB
Tel: 01233 739030
Head: Mr Michael Hall
Age range: 3 months–18 years
No. of pupils: 835 VIth170
Fees: Day £10,500–£16,800 WB £24,000 FB £36,000
🌐 Ⓐ 🏫 £ ✎ 16

Ashgrove School
116 Widmore Road, Bromley, Kent BR1 3BE
Tel: 020 8460 4143
Principal: Dr Patricia Ash CertEd, BSc(Hons), PhD, CMath, FIMA
Age range: 3–11 years
🌐

Benenden School
Cranbrook, Kent TN17 4AA
Tel: 01580 240592
Headmistress: Mrs S Price
Age range: G11–18
No. of pupils: 550
Fees: FB £12,650
🚹 🌐 Ⓐ 🏫 £ ✎ 16

Bethany School
Curtisden Green, Goudhurst, Cranbrook, Kent TN17 1LB
Tel: 01580 211273
Headmaster: Mr Francie Healy BSc, HDipEd, NPQH
Age range: 11–18 years
No. of pupils: 352 VIth86
Fees: Day £17,310–£19,110 WB £26,865–£29,670 FB £26,865–£29,670
🌐 Ⓐ 🏫 £ ✎ 16

CATS Canterbury
68 New Dover Road, Canterbury, Kent CT1 3LQ
Tel: +44 (0)1227866540
Principal: Dr Sarah Lockyer
Age range: 14–18
No. of pupils: 400
🌐 16 Ⓐ 🏫 IB 16

COBHAM HALL SCHOOL
For further details see p. 94
Brewers Road, Cobham, Kent DA12 3BL
Tel: 01474 823371
Email: enquiries@cobhamhall.com
Website: www.cobhamhall.com
Headteacher: Mrs Wendy Barrett
Age range: G11–18
No. of pupils: 150
Fees: Day £6,548–£7,936 FB £9,893–£12,349
🚹 🌐 🏫 £ ✎ 16

Dover College
Effingham Crescent,
Dover, Kent CT17 9RH
Tel: 01304 205969
Headmaster: Mr Gareth Doodes MA (Hons)
Age range: 3–18
No. of pupils: 301
Fees: Day £7,725–£16,050 WB £21,000–£25,500 FB £24,750–£31,500

Farringtons School
Perry Street, Chislehurst,
Kent BR7 6LR
Tel: 020 8467 0256
Head: Mr David Jackson
Age range: 3–18
No. of pupils: 700 VIth100
Fees: Day £15,690 WB £30,960 FB £32,880

Kent College Pembury
Old Church Road, Pembury,
Tunbridge Wells, Kent TN2 4AX
Tel: +44 (0)1892 822006
Headmistress: Ms Julie Lodrick
Age range: G3–18
No. of pupils: 500
Fees: Day £21,600 WB £26,994 FB £34,419

Kent College, Canterbury
Whitstable Road, Canterbury,
Kent CT2 9DT
Tel: +44 (0)1227 763 231
Executive Head: Dr David Lamper
Age range: 0–18 years (Boarding from 8)
No. of pupils: 770
Fees: Day £5,598–£6,288 FB £8,748–£11,867

King's Rochester
Satis House, Boley Hill,
Rochester, Kent ME1 1TE
Tel: 01634 888555
Principal: Mr B Charles
Age range: 13–18
No. of pupils: 600 VIth95
Fees: Day £7,440–£20,190 FB £22,950–£33,015

Rochester Independent College
254 St Margaret's Banks,
Rochester, Kent ME1 1HY
Tel: +44 (0)163 482 8115
Head of School: Mr Alistair Brownlow
Age range: 11–18
Fees: Day £13,000–£18,600 WB £12,400 FB £14,100

Sevenoaks School
High Street, Sevenoaks,
Kent TN13 1HU
Tel: +44 (0)1732 455133
Head of School: Mr Jesse R Elzinga AB MSt FCCT
Age range: 11–18
No. of pupils: 1165
Fees: Day £24,291–£27,585 FB £38,790–£42,084

ST EDMUND'S SCHOOL
For further details see p. 106
St Thomas Hill, Canterbury,
Kent CT2 8HU
Tel: 01227 475601
Email: admissions@stedmunds.org.uk
Website: www.stedmunds.org.uk
Head: Mr Edward O'Connor MA (Cantab), MPhil (Oxon), MEd (Cantab)
Age range: 3–18
No. of pupils: 558

St Lawrence College
Ramsgate, Kent CT11 7AE
Tel: 01843 572931
Head of College: Mr Barney Durrant
Age range: 3–18
No. of pupils: 600
Fees: Day £7,845–£16,245 FB £27,765–£36,909

Sutton Valence School
North Street, Sutton
Valence, Kent ME17 3HL
Tel: 01622 845200
Headmaster: Bruce Grindlay MA Cantab, MusB, FRCO, CHM
Age range: 11–18
No. of pupils: 570

The King's School, Canterbury
The Precincts, Canterbury,
Kent CT1 2ES
Tel: 01227 595501
Head: Mr Peter Roberts
Age range: 13–18
No. of pupils: 858 VIth385
Fees: Day £27,495 FB £38,955

TONBRIDGE SCHOOL
For further details see p. 110
High Street, Tonbridge,
Kent TN9 1JP
Tel: 01732 304297
Email: admissions@tonbridge-school.org
Website: www.tonbridge-school.co.uk
Headmaster: Mr James Priory MA (Oxon)
Age range: B13–18
No. of pupils: 802
Fees: Day £31,587 FB £42,105

Middlesex

ACS Hillingdon International School
Hillingdon Court, 108 Vine
Lane, Hillingdon, Uxbridge,
Middlesex UB10 0BE
Tel: +44 (0) 1895 259 771
Head of School: Mr Martin Hall
Age range: 4–18

North London Collegiate School
Canons, Canons Drive,
Edgware, Middlesex HA8 7RJ
Tel: +44 (0)20 8952 0912
Headmistress: Mrs Sarah Clark
Age range: G4–18
No. of pupils: 1080
Fees: Day £5,754–£6,810

RADNOR HOUSE
For further details see p. 90
Pope's Villa, Cross
Deep, Twickenham,
Middlesex TW1 4QG
Tel: 020 8891 6264
Email: admissions@radnorhouse.org
Website: www.radnor-twickenham.org
Head: Mr Darryl Wideman MA Oxon, PGCE
Age range: 9–18

St Helen's School
Eastbury Road, Northwood,
Middlesex HA6 3AS
Tel: +44 (0)1923 843210
Headmistress: Dr Mary Short BA, PhD
Age range: G3–18
No. of pupils: VIth165

Surrey

ACS Cobham International School
Heywood, Portsmouth Road,
Cobham, Surrey KT11 1BL
Tel: +44 (0) 1932 867251
Head of School: Mr Barnaby Sandow
Age range: 2–18

ACS Egham International School
Woodlee, London Road,
Egham, Surrey TW20 0HS
Tel: +44 (0) 1784 430 800
Head of School: Mr Jeremy Lewis
Age range: 4–18
Fees: Day £11,090–£25,870

Box Hill School
London Road, Mickleham,
Dorking, Surrey RH5 6EA
Tel: 01372 373382
Headmaster: Cory Lowde
Age range: 11–18
No. of pupils: 425
Fees: Day £17,985 WB £28,350 FB £34,950

Caterham School
Harestone Valley, Caterham,
Surrey CR3 6YA
Tel: 01883 343028
Head: Mr C. W. Jones MA(Cantab)
Age range: 11–18
No. of pupils: VIth321
Fees: Day £18,735–£19,620 WB £30,936–£33,270 FB £36,795–£38,760

Charterhouse
Godalming, Surrey GU7 2DX
Tel: +44 (0)1483 291501
Headmaster: Dr Alex Peterken
Age range: B13–18 G16–18
No. of pupils: 820

**City of London
Freemen's School**
Ashtead Park, Ashtead,
Surrey KT21 1ET
Tel: 01372 277933
Headmaster: Mr R Martin
Age range: 7–18
No. of pupils: 877 VIth213
Fees: Day £14,067–£19,194 WB
£29,784–£29,841 FB £30,780–£30,816

Cranleigh School
Horseshoe Lane, Cranleigh,
Surrey GU6 8QQ
Tel: +44 (0) 1483 273666
Headmaster: Mr Martin Reader
MA, MPhil, MBA
Age range: 7–18 (including
Prep School)
No. of pupils: 690 VIth252
Fees: Day £32,370 FB £39,330

Duke of Kent School
Peaslake Road, Ewhurst,
Surrey GU6 7NS
Tel: 01483 277313
Head: Mrs Sue Knox
Age range: 3–16
No. of pupils: 234
Fees: Day £7,245–£19,050

Epsom College
Epsom, Surrey KT17 4JQ
Tel: 01372 821000
Headmaster: Mr Jay A Piggot MA
Age range: 11–18
No. of pupils: 884
Fees: Day £19,611–£26,151
WB £35,034 FB £38,568

Frensham Heights
Rowledge, Farnham,
Surrey GU10 4EA
Tel: 01252 792561
Head: Mr Rick Clarke
Age range: 3–18
No. of pupils: 497 VIth105
Fees: Day £7,110–£21,060
FB £27,450–£32,070

KING EDWARD'S WITLEY
For further details see p. 96
Petworth Road, Godalming,
Surrey GU8 5SG
Tel: 01428 686735
Email: admissions@kesw.org
Website: www.kesw.org
Head: Mrs Joanna Wright
Age range: 11–18 years
No. of pupils: 400

MARYMOUNT LONDON
For further details see p. 89
George Road, Kingston upon
Thames, Surrey KT2 7PE
Tel: +44 (0)20 8949 0571
Email: admissions@
marymountlondon.com
Website:
www.marymountlondon.com
Headmistress: Mrs Margaret
Giblin
Age range: G11–18
No. of pupils: 255
Fees: Day £25,985 WB
£42,135 FB £44,000

Prior's Field
Priorsfield Road, Godalming,
Surrey GU7 2RH
Tel: 01483 810551
Head of School: Mrs Tracey Kirnig
Age range: G11–18
No. of pupils: 450
Fees: Day £18,900 FB £30,825

Reed's School
Sandy Lane, Cobham,
Surrey KT11 2ES
Tel: 01932 869001
Headmaster: Mr Mark Hoskins BA
MA MSc
Age range: B11–18 G16–18
No. of pupils: 650 VIth230
Fees: Day £20,430–£25,530
FB £27,225–£32,910

Royal Russell School
Coombe Lane, Croydon,
Surrey CR9 5BX
Tel: 020 8657 3669
Headmaster: Christopher
Hutchinson
Age range: 11–18
No. of pupils: 590 VIth180
Fees: Day £18,480 FB £36,525

St Catherine's, Bramley
Station Road, Bramley,
Guildford, Surrey GU5 0DF
Tel: 01483 899609
Headmistress: Alice Phillips
Age range: G4–18
Fees: Day £9,240–£18,885 FB £31,125

**St James Senior
Boys School**
Church Road, Ashford,
Surrey TW15 3DZ
Tel: 01784 266930
Headmaster: Mr David Brazier
Age range: B11–18
No. of pupils: 403 VIth65
Fees: Day £18,930

St John's School
Epsom Road, Leatherhead,
Surrey KT22 8SP
Tel: 01372 373000
Head of School: Mrs Rowena Cole
Age range: 11–18
No. of pupils: 840
Fees: Day £19,590–£24,555
WB £24,780–£31,035

**St Teresa's Effingham
(Senior School)**
Beech Avenue, Effingham,
Surrey RH5 6ST
Tel: 01372 452037
Executive Director: Mr Mike Farmer
Age range: G11–18
No. of pupils: 640 VIth90
Fees: Day £17,865–£18,465 WB
£28,875–£29,175 FB £30,795–£31,455

**TASIS The American
School in England**
Coldharbour Lane, Thorpe,
Surrey TW20 8TE
Tel: +44 (0)1932 582316
Head of School: Mr Bryan Nixon
Age range: 3–18
No. of pupils: 620
Fees: Day £11,920–
£25,605 FB £47,565

The Royal Junior School
Portsmouth Road, Hindhead,
Surrey GU26 6BW
Tel: 01428 607977
Principal: Mrs Anne J P Lynch
Age range: 6 weeks–11 years
Fees: Day £10,200–£11,955

The Royal School
Farnham Lane, Haslemere,
Surrey GU27 1HQ
Tel: 01428 605805
Head: Mrs Pippa Smithson
Age range: 11–18 years
No. of pupils: 1560
Fees: Day £10,506–£18,507
WB £27,747 FB £31,557

Whitgift School
Haling Park, South Croydon,
Surrey CR2 6YT
Tel: +44 20 8633 9935
Headmaster: Mr Christopher
Ramsey
Age range: B10–18
No. of pupils: 1560
Fees: Day £20,640 WB
£33,081 FB £40,140

WOLDINGHAM SCHOOL
For further details see p. 112
Marden Park, Woldingham,
Surrey CR3 7YA
Tel: 01883 349431
Email: registrar@
woldinghamschool.co.uk
Website:
www.woldinghamschool.co.uk
Head of School: Dr James
Whitehead
Age range: G11–18
No. of pupils: 585
Fees: Day £21,945–£23,910
FB £36,135–£39,330

Yehudi Menuhin School
Stoke Road, Stoke d'Abernon,
Cobham, Surrey KT11 3QQ
Tel: 01932 864739
Interim Head: Richard Tanner
Age range: 7–19
No. of pupils: 80 VIth36
Fees: FB £34,299

West Berkshire

Downe House School
Downe House, Cold Ash,
Thatcham, West Berkshire RG18 9JJ
Tel: +44 (0)1635 200286
Headmistress: Mrs Emma
McKendrick BA(Liverpool)
Age range: G11–18
No. of pupils: 593
Fees: Day £9,705 FB £13,050

West Sussex

Ardingly College
College Road, Ardingly, Haywards
Heath, West Sussex RH17 6SQ
Tel: +44 (0)1444 893320
Headmaster: Mr Ben Figgis
Age range: 13–18
No. of pupils: 559
Fees:–£23,985 FB £35,865–£29,250

Burgess Hill Girls
Keymer Road, Burgess Hill,
West Sussex RH15 0EG
Tel: 01444 241050
Head of School: Liz Laybourn
Age range: B2.5–4 G2.5–18
No. of pupils: 505 VIth70
Fees: Day £8,100–£20,100
FB £31,050–£35,850

Christ's Hospital
Horsham, West Sussex RH13 0LJ
Tel: 01403 211293
Head Teacher: Mr Simon Reid
Age range: 11–18
No. of pupils: 900
Fees: Day £18,510–£23,310
FB £35,850

Farlington School
Strood Park, Horsham,
West Sussex RH12 3PN
Tel: 01403 282573
Headmistress: Ms Louise Higson
BSc, PGCE
Age range: 3–18
No. of pupils: 300
Fees: Day £5,400–£17,670 WB
£23,205–£28,515 FB £24,540–£29,850

Hurstpierpoint College
College Lane, Hurstpierpoint,
West Sussex BN6 9JS
Tel: 01273 833636
Headmaster: Mr. T J Manly BA, MSc
Age range: 4–18
No. of pupils: 1156
Fees: Day £8,790–£22,860
WB £28,800

Lancing College
Lancing, West Sussex BN15 0RW
Tel: 01273 465805
Head Master: Mr Dominic T Oliver
MPhil
Age range: 13–18
No. of pupils: 550 VIth255
Fees: Day £8,190 FB £11,995

Rikkyo School in England
Guildford Road, Rudgwick,
Horsham, West Sussex RH12 3BE
Tel: 01403 822107
Headmaster: Mr Roger Munechika
Age range: 10–18
No. of pupils: 116
Fees: FB £15,000–£21,600

Seaford College
Lavington Park, Petworth,
West Sussex GU28 0NB
Tel: 01798 867392
Headmaster: J P Green MA BA
Age range: 6–18
No. of pupils: 869 VIth219
Fees: Day £10,725–£22,230 WB
£22,350–£30,120 FB £34,380

Slindon College
Slindon House, Slindon, Arundel,
West Sussex BN18 0RH
Tel: 01243 814320
Head Teacher: Mr Mark Birkbeck
Age range: B8–18 years

Worth School
Paddockhurst Road, Turners Hill,
Crawley, West Sussex RH10 4SD
Tel: +44 (0)1342 710200
Head Master: Stuart McPherson
Age range: 11–18
No. of pupils: 580 VIth222
Fees: Day £15,960–£23,730
FB £21,210–£33,690

Specialist schools and sixth form colleges

London

Central London

CATS London
43-45 Bloomsbury Square,
London WC1A 2RA
Tel: 02078 411580
Principal: Mario Di Clemente
Age range: 15–24
(🌐) (A) (🏛) (£) (16+)

City of London School
Queen Victoria Street,
London EC4V 3AL
Tel: 020 3680 6300
Head: Mr A R Bird MSc
Age range: B10–18
No. of pupils: 950 VIth250
Fees: Day £18,939
(🏃) (A) (£) (🖋) (16+)

City of London School for Girls
St Giles' Terrace, Barbican,
London EC2Y 8BB
Tel: 020 7847 5500
Headmistress: Mrs E Harrop
Age range: G7–18
No. of pupils: 725
(🏃) (A) (£) (🖋) (16+)

Italia Conti Academy of Theatre Arts
Italia Conti House, 23 Goswell
Road, London EC1M 7AJ
Tel: 020 7608 0047
Director: Chris White
Age range: 10 21
(16+) (A) (16+)

The College of Central London
Tower Bridge Business Centre, 46-48
East Smithfield, London E1W 1AW
Tel: +44 (0) 20 3667 7607
(16+) (16+)

East London

Forest School
College Place, Snaresbrook,
London E17 3PY
Tel: 020 8520 1744
Warden: Mr Cliff Hodges
Age range: 4–18
No. of pupils: 1355 VIth260
Fees: Day £13,095–£18,681
(A) (£) (🖋) (16+)

North London

Channing School
The Bank, Highgate, London N6 5HF
Tel: 020 8340 2328
Head: Mrs B M Elliott
Age range: G4–18
No. of pupils: 746 VIth108
Fees: Day £17,610–£19,410
(🏃) (A) (£) (🖋) (16+)

Dwight School London
6 Friern Barnet Lane,
London N11 3LX
Tel: +44 (0)20 8920 0637
Head: Mrs Alison Cobbin BA, Dip
Ed, MBA
Age range: 3–18
(🌐) (£) (IB) (🖋) (16+)

Greek Secondary School of London
22 Trinity Road, London N22 8LB
Tel: +44 (0)20 8881 9320
Headteacher: Nikos Kazantzakis
Age range: 13–18
(A) (16+)

Highgate
North Road, Highgate,
London N6 4AY
Tel: 020 8340 1524
Head Master: Mr A S Pettitt MA
Age range: 3–18
No. of pupils: 1541 VIth312
Fees: Day £18,165–£20,970
(A) (£) (🖋) (16+)

North-West London

Francis Holland School, Regent's Park, NW1
Clarence Gate, Ivor Place,
Regent's Park, London NW1 6XR
Tel: 020 7723 0176
Head: Mr C B Fillingham MA (King's
College London)
Age range: G11–18
No. of pupils: 495 VIth120
Fees: Day £19,260
(🏃) (A) (£) (16+)

ICS London
7B Wyndham Place,
London W1H 1PN
Tel: +44 (0) 20 7298 8817
Head of School: Mr. Rod Jackson
Age range: 3–18 years
No. of pupils: 205
(🌐) (IB) (🖋) (16+)

Lakefield Catering & Educational Centre
Maresfield Gardens,
Hampstead, London NW3 5RY
Tel: 020 7794 5669
Course Director: Mrs Maria Brown
Age range: G16–24
No. of pupils: 16
Fees: FB £1,160
(🏃) (16+) (🏛) (£) (🖋) (16+) (🐾)

London Academy of Dressmaking and Design
18 Dobree Avenue, Willesden,
London NW10 2AE
Tel: 020 8451 7174
Principal: Mrs P A Parkinson MA
Age range: 13+
Fees: Day £2,650
(16+) (🖋) (16+) (🐾)

Mill Hill School
The Ridgeway, Mill Hill
Village, London NW7 1QS
Tel: 020 8959 1176
Head: Mrs Jane Sanchez BSc (Hons)
PGCE
Age range: 13–18
No. of pupils: 689 VIth259
Fees: Day £21,987 WB
£28,524 FB £33,717
(🌐) (A) (🏛) (£) (🖋) (16+)

NW5 Theatre School
14 Fortess Road, London NW5 2EU
Tel: 020 8340 1498
Age range: 16–30
(16+) (16+)

South Hampstead High School GDST
3 Maresfield Gardens,
London NW3 5SS
Tel: 020 7435 2899
Head of School: Mrs V Bingham
Age range: G4–18
No. of pupils: 900
Fees: Day £15,327–£18,654
(🏃) (A) (£) (🖋) (16+)

The American School in London
One Waverley Place,
London NW8 0NP
Tel: 020 7449 1221
Head: Robin Appleby
Age range: 4–18
No. of pupils: 1350
Fees: Day £27,050–£31,200
(🌐) (16+)

The King Alfred School
Manor Wood, North End
Road, London NW11 7HY
Tel: 020 8457 5200
Head: Robert Lobatto MA (Oxon)
Age range: 4–18
No. of pupils: 650 VIth100
Fees: Day £15,531–£18,723
(A) (£) (🖋) (16+)

University College School Hampstead (UCS)
Frognal, Hampstead,
London NW3 6XH
Tel: 020 7435 2215
Headteacher: Mr Mark J Beard
Age range: B11–18 G16–18
(🏃) (A) (£) (🖋) (16+)

Wentworth College
6-10 Brentmead Place,
London NW11 9LH
Tel: 020 8458 8524/5
Principal: Manuel Guimaraes
Age range: 14–19
No. of pupils: 115
(16+) (A) (16+)

South-East London

Alleyn's School
Townley Road, Dulwich,
London SE22 8SU
Tel: 020 8557 1500
Head of School: Jane Lunnon
Age range: 4–18 years
(A) (£) (🖋) (16+)

Blackheath High School GDST
Vanbrugh Park, Blackheath,
London SE3 7AG
Tel: 020 8853 2929
Head: Mrs Carol Chandler-
Thompson BA (Hons) Exeter, PGCE
Exeter
Age range: G3–18
No. of pupils: 780
(🏃) (A) (£) (🖋) (16+)

Colfe's School
Horn Park Lane, Lee,
London SE12 8AW
Tel: 020 8852 2283
Head: Mr R F Russell MA(Cantab)
Age range: 3–18
No. of pupils: 1120
(A) (£) (🖋) (16+)

Dulwich College
Dulwich Common, ,
London SE21 7LD
Tel: 020 8693 3601
Master: Dr J A F Spence
Age range: B0–18
No. of pupils: 1589 VIth470
Fees: Day £21,246 WB
£41,557 FB £44,346
(🏃) (🌐) (A) (🏛) (£) (🖋) (16+)

Eltham College
Grove Park Road, Mottingham,
London SE9 4QF
Tel: 0208 857 1455
Headmaster: Guy Sanderson
Age range: 7–18
No. of pupils: 911 VIth199
(A) (£) (🖋) (16+)

James Allen's Girls' School
144 East Dulwich Grove,
Dulwich, London SE22 8TE
Tel: 020 8693 1181
Head of School: Mrs Sally-Anne
Huang MA, MSc
Age range: G4–18
No. of pupils: 1075
(🏃) (A) (£) (🖋) (16+)

Riverston School
63-69 Eltham Road, Lee
Green, London SE12 8UF
Tel: 020 8318 4327
Principal: Michael Lewis
Age range: 9 months–19 years
(£) (🖋) (16+) (🐾)

St Dunstan's College
Stanstead Road, London SE6 4TY
Tel: 020 8516 7200
Headmaster: Mr Nicholas Hewlett
Age range: 3–18
No. of pupils: 870
🌐 Ⓐ £ 16+

SYDENHAM HIGH SCHOOL GDST
For further details see p. 80
15 & 19 Westwood Hill,
London SE26 6BL
Tel: 020 8557 7004
Email: admissions@syd.gdst.net
Website: www.sydenhamhigh
school.gdst.net
Headmistress: Mrs Katharine
Woodcock
Age range: G4–18
No. of pupils: 665
Ⓐ £ 16+

South-West London

Centre Academy London
92 St John's Hill, Battersea,
London SW11 1SH
Tel: 020 7738 2344
Headteacher: Rachel Maddison
Age range: 9–19
£ 16+

Emanuel School
Battersea Rise, London SW11 1HS
Tel: 020 8870 4171
Headmaster: Mr Robert Milne
Age range: 10–18
No. of pupils: 930
Fees: Day £18,372
Ⓐ £ 16+

Francis Holland School, Sloane Square, SW1
39 Graham Terrace,
London SW1W 8JF
Tel: 020 7730 2971
Head: Mrs Lucy Elphinstone
MA(Cantab)
Age range: G4–18
No. of pupils: 520 VIth70
Fees: Day £17,760–£20,085
Ⓐ £ 16+

Harrodian School
Lonsdale Road, London SW13 9QN
Tel: 020 8748 6117
Headmaster: James R Hooke
Age range: 4–18
No. of pupils: 890 VIth95
Fees: Day £15,000–£23,040
Ⓐ 16+

Ibstock Place School
Clarence Lane, London SW15 5PY
Tel: 020 8876 9991
Head of School: Mr Chris Wolsey
Age range: 4–18
No. of pupils: 1000
Fees: Day £17,115–£21,735
Ⓐ £ 16+

King's College School
Southside, Wimbledon
Common, London SW19 4TT
Tel: 020 8255 5300
Head Master: Mr A D Halls OBE
Age range: B7–18 G16–18
No. of pupils: 1475
Ⓐ £ IB 16+

Lycée Français Charles de Gaulle
35 Cromwell Road,
London SW7 2DG
Tel: 020 7584 6322
Head of School: Mr Olivier Rauch
Age range: 5–19
No. of pupils: 4000
Ⓐ £ 16+

MORE HOUSE SCHOOL
For further details see p. 69
22-24 Pont Street, Knightsbridge,
London SW1X 0AA
Tel: 020 7235 2855
Email: office@
morehousemail.org.uk
Website:
www.morehouse.org.uk
Head: Ms Faith Hagerty
Age range: G11–18
No. of pupils: 200
Fees: Day £6,950
Ⓐ £ 16+

Putney High School GDST
35 Putney Hill, London SW15 6BH
Tel: 020 8788 4886
Headmistress: Mrs Suzie Longstaff
BA, MA, PGCE
Age range: G4–18
No. of pupils: 976 VIth150
Ⓐ £ 16+

Queen's Gate School
133 Queen's Gate, London SW7 5LE
Tel: 020 7589 3587
Principal: Mrs R M Kamaryc BA,
MSc, PGCE
Age range: G4–18
No. of pupils: 529 VIth94
Ⓐ £ 16+

St Paul's School
Lonsdale Road, Barnes,
London SW13 9JT
Tel: 020 8748 9162
High Master: Prof Mark Bailey
Age range: B13–18
No. of pupils: 897
Fees: Day £25,032 FB £37,611
Ⓐ £ 16+

Streatham & Clapham High School GDST
42 Abbotswood Road,
London SW16 1AW
Tel: 020 8677 8400
Headmaster: Dr Millan Sachania
Age range: G3–18
No. of pupils: 603 VIth70
Fees: Day £10,431–£19,743
Ⓐ £ 16+

Swedish School
82 Lonsdale Road, London SW13 9JS
Tel: 020 8741 1751
Head of School: Ms. Annika
Simonsson Bergqvist
Age range: 3–18
No. of pupils: 300 VIth145
Fees: Day £8,600–£9,100
16+

Westminster School
Little Dean's Yard, Westminster,
London SW1P 3PF
Tel: 020 7963 1003
Headmaster: Mr Patrick Derham
Age range: B13–18 G16–18
No. of pupils: 744
Fees: Day £26,130–
£28,566 FB £37,740
Ⓐ £ 16+

Wimbledon High School GDST
Mansel Road, Wimbledon,
London SW19 4AB
Tel: 020 8971 0900
Headmistress: Mrs Jane Lunnon
Age range: G4–18
No. of pupils: 900 VIth155
Fees: Day £14,622–£18,810
Ⓐ £ 16+

West London

Alan D Hairdressing Education
4 West Smithfield, London EC1A 9JX
Tel: 020 7580 1030
Director of Education: Alan
Hemmings
Fees: Day £200 FB £12,400
16+ 16+

Blake College
162 New Cavendish Street,
London W1W 6YS
Tel: 020 7636 0658
Course Director: D A J Cluckie
BA, BSc
Fees: Day £4,720–£5,310
16+ 16+

David Game College
31 Jewry Street, London EC3N 2ET
Tel: 020 7221 6665
Principal: D T P Game MA, MPhil
Age range: 14–19
No. of pupils: 200 VIth150
Fees: Day £3,680–£30,630
16+ Ⓐ £ 16+

Ealing Independent College
83 New Broadway, Ealing,
London W5 5AL
Tel: 020 8579 6668
Principal: Dr Ian Moores
Age range: 13–19
No. of pupils: 100 VIth70
Fees: Day £2,910–£18,120
16+ Ⓐ 16+

Godolphin and Latymer School
Iffley Road, Hammersmith,
London W6 0PG
Tel: +44 (0)20 8741 1936
Head Mistress: Dr Frances Ramsey
Age range: G11–18
No. of pupils: 800
Fees: Day £23,085
Ⓐ £ IB 16+

International School of London (ISL)
139 Gunnersbury Avenue,
London W3 8LG
Tel: +44 (0)20 8992 5823
Principal: Mr Richard Parker
Age range: 3–18 years
No. of pupils: 500
Fees: Day £19,000–£26,300
IB 16+

King Fahad Academy
Bromyard Avenue, Acton,
London W3 7HD
Tel: 020 8743 0131
Director General: Dr Tahani Aljafari
Age range: 3–19
Ⓐ £ IB 16+

Latymer Upper School
King Street, Hammersmith,
London W6 9LR
Tel: 020862 92024
Head: Mr D Goodhew MA(Oxon)
Age range: 11–18
No. of pupils: 1400
Fees: Day £6,945
Ⓐ £ 16+

Notting Hill & Ealing High School GDST
2 Cleveland Road, West
Ealing, London W13 8AX
Tel: (020) 8799 8400
Headmaster: Mr Matthew Shoults
Age range: G4–18
No. of pupils: 903 VIth150
Fees: Day £14,313–£18,561
Ⓐ £ 16+

Queen's College
43-49 Harley Street,
London W1G 8BT
Tel: 020 7291 7000
Principal: Mr Richard Tillet
Age range: G11–18
No. of pupils: 360 VIth90
Ⓐ £ 16+

Ray Cochrane Beauty School
118 Baker Street, London W1U 6TT
Tel: 02033224738
Principal: Miss Baljeet Suri
Age range: 16–50
No. of pupils: 30
Fees: Day £650–£8,495
16+ 16+

Southbank International School - Westminster
63-65 Portland Place,
London W1B 1QR
Tel: 020 7243 3803
Principal: Dr Paul Wood
Age range: 11–19
IB 16+

St Augustine's Priory
Hillcrest Road, Ealing,
London W5 2JL
Tel: 020 8997 2022
Headteacher: Mrs Sarah Raffray
M.A., N.P.Q.H
Age range: B3–4 G3–18
No. of pupils: 485
Fees: Day £11,529–£16,398

ST BENEDICT'S SCHOOL
For further details see p. 76
54 Eaton Rise, Ealing,
London W5 2ES
Tel: 020 8862 2000
Email: admissions@
stbenedicts.org.uk
Website:
www.stbenedicts.org.uk
Headmaster: Mr A Johnson BA
Age range: 3–18
No. of pupils: 1073 VIth203
Fees: Day £13,485–£17,655

**St James Senior
Girls' School**
Earsby Street, London W14 8SH
Tel: 020 7348 1777
Headmistress: Mrs Sarah Labram BA
Age range: G11–18
No. of pupils: 295 VIth67
Fees: Day £20,100

St Paul's Girls' School
Brook Green, London W6 7BS
Tel: 020 7603 2288
High Mistress: Mrs Sarah Fletcher
Age range: G11–18 years
No. of pupils: 750 VIth200
Fees: Day £24,891–£26,760

Berkshire

Bradfield College
Bradfield, Berkshire RG7 6AU
Tel: 0118 964 4516
Headmaster: Dr Christopher
Stevens
Age range: 13–18
No. of pupils: 815
Fees: Day £31,080 FB £38,850

**Claires Court Nursery,
Girls and Sixth Form**
1 College Avenue, Maidenhead,
Berkshire SL6 6AW
Tel: 01628 327700
Head of School: Mrs M Heywood
Age range: B16–18 G3–18
No. of pupils: 495 VIth111
Fees: Day £9,270–£16,740

Claires Court Senior Boys
Ray Mill Road East, Maidenhead,
Berkshire SL6 8TE
Tel: 01628 327700
Headmaster: Mr J M Rayer BSc,
PGCE
Age range: B11–16
No. of pupils: 335 VIth112
Fees: Day £15,930–£16,740

Eton College
Windsor, Berkshire SL4 6DW
Tel: 01753 671249
Head Master: Simon Henderson MA
Age range: B13–18
No. of pupils: 1300 VIth520
Fees: FB £40,668

Heathfield School
London Road, Ascot,
Berkshire SL5 8BQ
Tel: 01344 898342
Head of School: Ms Sarah Wilson
Age range: G11–18
No. of pupils: 200
Fees: Day £7,690–£7,900
FB £12,400–£12,700

LEIGHTON PARK SCHOOL
For further details see p. 98
Shinfield Road, Reading,
Berkshire RG2 7ED
Tel: 0118 987 9600
Email: admissions@
leightonpark.com
Website:
www.leightonpark.com
Head: Mr Matthew L S Judd BA,
PGCE
Age range: 11–18
No. of pupils: 520

Luckley House School
Luckley Road, Wokingham,
Berkshire RG40 3EU
Tel: 0118 978 4175
Head: Mrs Jane Tudor
Age range: 11–18
No. of pupils: 300
Fees: Day £5,662 WB £9,183 FB £9,907

LVS ASCOT
For further details see p. 100
London Road, Ascot,
Berkshire SL5 8DR
Tel: 01344 882770
Email: enquiries@lvs.
ascot.sch.uk
Website: www.lvs.ascot.sch.uk
Principal: Mrs Christine Cunniffe
BA (Hons), MMus, MBA
Age range: 4–18
No. of pupils: 800
Fees: Day £10,785–£19,335
FB £27,585–£33,975

Padworth College
Padworth, Reading,
Berkshire RG7 4NR
Tel: 0118 983 2644
Acting Principal: Mr Chris Randell
Age range: 13–19
No. of pupils: 116 VIth50
Fees: Day £14,400 FB £29,400

Pangbourne College
Pangbourne, Reading,
Berkshire RG8 8LA
Tel: 0118 984 2101
Headmaster: Thomas J C Garnier
Age range: 11–18
No. of pupils: 450 VIth134
Fees: Day £18,000–£25,380
FB £25,860–£36,660

Queen Anne's School
6 Henley Road, Caversham,
Reading, Berkshire RG4 6DX
Tel: 0118 918 7300
Headmistress: Mrs Julia Harrington
BA(Hons), PGCE, NPQH
Age range: G11–18

Reading Blue Coat School
Holme Park, Sonning Lane, Sonning,
Reading, Berkshire RG4 6SU
Tel: 0118 944 1005
Headmaster: Mr Jesse Elzinga
Age range: B11–18 G16–18
No. of pupils: 710 VIth230
Fees: Day £16,695

**REDDAM HOUSE
BERKSHIRE**
For further details see p. 102
Bearwood Road, Sindlesham,
Wokingham, Berkshire RG41 5BG
Tel: 0118 467 8731
Email: registrar@
reddamhouse.org.uk
Website:
http://reddamhouse.org.uk
Principal: Mrs Tammy Howard
Age range: 3 months–18 years
No. of pupils: 650
Fees: Day £11,490–£18,330
WB £27,981–£32,244 FB
£29,526–£33,789

**Redroofs School for the
Performing Arts (Redroofs
Theatre School)**
26 Bath Road, Maidenhead,
Berkshire SL6 4JT
Tel: 01628 674092
Principal: June Rose
Age range: 8–18
No. of pupils: 100
Fees: Day £4,882–£5,527

St George's Ascot
Wells Lane, Ascot, Berkshire SL5 7DZ
Tel: 01344 629920
Headmistress: Mrs Liz Hewer MA
(Hons) (Cantab) PGCE
Age range: G11–18
No. of pupils: 270 VIth70
Fees: Day £22,800 WB
£34,050–£34,680 FB £35,460

St Joseph's College
Upper Redlands Road,
Reading, Berkshire RG1 5JT
Tel: 0118 966 1000
Headmaster: Mr Andrew Colpus
Age range: 3–18
No. of pupils: VIth65
Fees: Day £6,672–£11,406

St Mary's School Ascot
St Mary's Road, Ascot,
Berkshire SL5 9JF
Tel: 01344 296614
Headmistress: Mrs Danuta Staunton
Age range: G11–18
No. of pupils: 386 VIth120
Fees: Day £27,630 FB £38,790

The Abbey School
Kendrick Road, Reading,
Berkshire RG1 5DZ
Tel: 0118 987 2256
Head: Mr Will le Fleming
Age range: G3–18
No. of pupils: 1000
Fees: Day £10,860–£18,000

The Marist School
King's Road, Sunninghill,
Ascot, Berkshire SL5 7PS
Tel: 01344 624291
Principal: Mr Karl McCloskey
Age range: G3–18

The Oratory School
Woodcote, Reading,
Berkshire RG8 0PJ
Tel: 01491 683500
Head Master: Mr J J Smith BA(Hons),
MEd, PGCE
Age range: B11–18
No. of pupils: 380 VIth120
Fees: Day £24,966 FB £34,299

Wellington College
Duke's Ride, Crowthorne,
Berkshire RG45 7PU
Tel: +44 (0)1344 444000
Master: Mr James Dahl
Age range: 13–18
No. of pupils: 1080 VIth485
Fees: Day £30,375–
£34,890 FB £41,580

Buckinghamshire

Pipers Corner School
Pipers Lane, Great
Kingshill, High Wycombe,
Buckinghamshire HP15 6LP
Tel: 01494 718 255
Headmistress: Mrs H J Ness-Gifford
BA(Hons), PGCE
Age range: G4–18
No. of pupils: VIth72
Fees: Day £8,880–18,390

St Mary's School
94 Packhorse Road, Gerrards
Cross, Buckinghamshire SL9 8JQ
Tel: 01753 883370
Head of School: Mrs P Adams
Age range: G3–18
No. of pupils: 350 VIth50
Fees: Day £5,670–£16,980

Stowe School
Buckingham, Buckinghamshire
MK18 5EH
Tel: 01280 818000
Headmaster: Dr Anthony
Wallersteiner
Age range: 13–18
No. of pupils: 769 VIth318
Fees: Day £26,355 FB £36,660

**The Webber
Independent School**
Soskin Drive, Stantonbury
Fields, Milton Keynes,
Buckinghamshire MK14 6DP
Tel: 01908 574740
Principal: Mrs Hilary Marsden
Age range: 3–18
No. of pupils: 300 VIth15
Fees: Day £9,030–£12,705

Wycombe Abbey
High Wycombe,
Buckinghamshire HP11 1PE
Tel: +44 (0)1494 897008
Headmistress: Mrs Jo Duncan MA
(St Andrews), PGCE (Cantab)
Age range: G11–18
No. of pupils: 649
Fees: Day £30,270 FB £40,350

East Sussex

Battle Abbey School
Battle, East Sussex TN33 0AD
Tel: 01424 772385
Headmaster: Mr D Clark BA(Hons)
Age range: 2–18
No. of pupils: 286 VIth48
Fees: Day £6,939–£16,914
FB £26,649–£31,932

Bede's School
The Dicker, Upper Dicker,
Hailsham, East Sussex BN27 3QH
Tel: +44 (0)1323843252
Head: Mr Peter Goodyer
Age range: 3 months–18
No. of pupils: 800 VIth295
Fees: Day £10,230–£17,400
FB £22,290–£25,650

Brighton College
Eastern Road, Brighton,
East Sussex BN2 0AL
Tel: 01273 704200
Head Master: Richard Cairns MA
Age range: 3–18
No. of pupils: 950
Fees: Day £10,050–£24,540 WB
£33,390–£34,410 FB £37,470–£45,210

Brighton Girls GDST
Montpelier Road, Brighton,
East Sussex BN1 3AT
Tel: 01273 280280
Head: Jennifer Smith
Age range: G3–18
No. of pupils: 680 VIth70
Fees: Day £7,191–£14,421

Buckswood School
Broomham Hall, Rye
Road, Guestling, Hastings,
East Sussex TN35 4LT
Tel: 01424 813 813
School Director: Mr Giles Sutton
Age range: 10–19
No. of pupils: 420

Eastbourne College
Old Wish Road, Eastbourne,
East Sussex BN21 4JX
Tel: 01323 452323 (Admissions)
Headmaster: Mr Tom Lawson MA
(Oxon)
Age range: 13–18
No. of pupils: 650 VIth312
Fees: Day £23,895–£24,375
FB £36,420–£36,975

**Greenfields Independent
Day & Boarding School**
Priory Road, Forest Row,
East Sussex RH18 5JD
Tel: +44 (0)1342 822189
Executive Head: Mr. Jeff Smith
Age range: 2–19

**Lewes Old Grammar
School**
High Street, Lewes, East
Sussex BN7 1XS
Tel: 01273 472634
Headmaster: Mr Robert Blewitt
Age range: 3–18
No. of pupils: 463 VIth50
Fees: Day £8,760–£14,625

MAYFIELD SCHOOL
For further details see p. 101
The Old Palace, Mayfield,
East Sussex TN20 6PH
Tel: 01435 874642
Email: registrar@
mayfieldgirls.org
Website: www.mayfieldgirls.org
Head: Ms Antonia Beary MA,
MPhil (Cantab), PGCE
Age range: G11–18
No. of pupils: 385
Fees: Day £7,280 FB £11,750

Michael Hall School
Kidbrooke Park, Priory Road,
Forest Row, East Sussex RH18 5JA
Tel: 01342 822275
Age range: 0 years–18 years
No. of pupils: VIth102
Fees: Day £9,245–£12,670

Roedean Moira House
Upper Carlisle Road, Eastbourne,
East Sussex BN20 7TE
Tel: 01323 644144
Headmaster: Mr Andrew Wood
Age range: G0–18
No. of pupils: 289

ROEDEAN SCHOOL
For further details see p. 104
Roedean Way, Brighton,
East Sussex BN2 5RQ
Tel: 01273 667500
Email: info@roedean.co.uk
Website: www.roedean.co.uk
Headmaster: Mr. Oliver Bond
BA(Essex), PGCE, NPQH
Age range: G11–18
No. of pupils: 630 VIth155
Fees: Day £5,670–£7,415
WB £10,030–£11,185 FB
£10,990–£13,305

Essex

Bancroft's School
High Road, Woodford
Green, Essex IG8 0RF
Tel: 020 8505 4821
Head: Mr Simon Marshall MA, PGCE
(Cantab), MA, MPhil (Oxon)
Age range: 7–18
No. of pupils: 1120 VIth247
Ⓐ Ⓔ 🖉 16•

Brentwood School
Middleton Hall Lane,
Brentwood, Essex CM15 8EE
Tel: 01277 243243
Headmaster: Mr Michael Bond
Age range: 3–18
No. of pupils: 1800
Fees: Day £20,097 FB £39,381
Ⓦ Ⓐ Ⓐ Ⓔ Ⓘ🅑 🖉 16•

Chigwell School
High Road, Chigwell, Essex IG7 6QF
Tel: 020 8501 5700
Headmaster: Mr M E Punt M.A.
M.Sc. P.G.C.E.
Age range: 4–18
Fees: Day £4,250–£6,295 FB £10,995
Ⓦ Ⓐ Ⓐ Ⓔ 🖉 16•

Felsted School
Felsted, Great Dunmow,
Essex CM6 3LL
Tel: +44 (0)1371 822608
Headmaster: Mr Chris Townsend
Age range: 4–18
Ⓦ Ⓐ Ⓐ Ⓔ Ⓘ🅑 🖉 16•

Gosfield School
Cut Hedge Park, Halstead Road,
Gosfield, Halstead, Essex CO9 1PF
Tel: 01787 474040
Headteacher: Mr Guy Martyn
Age range: 4–18
No. of pupils: VIth21
Fees: Day £6,690–£15,525
Ⓦ Ⓐ Ⓐ Ⓔ 🖉 16•

Park School for Girls
20-22 Park Avenue,
Ilford, Essex IG1 4RS
Tel: 020 8554 2466
Head Teacher: Mrs Androulla
Nicholas BSc Hons (Econ) PGCE
Age range: G4–16
No. of pupils: 160
Fees: Day £2,375–£3,580
Ⓐ Ⓐ 16•

New Hall School
The Avenue, Boreham,
Chelmsford, Essex CM3 3HS
Tel: 01245 467588
Principal: Mrs Katherine Jeffrey MA,
BA, PGCE, MA(Ed Mg), NPQH
Age range: 1–18
No. of pupils: 1400
Fees: Day £3,096–£6,597 WB
£8,076–£9,735 FB £2,142–£10,233
Ⓦ Ⓐ Ⓐ Ⓔ 🖉 16•

Hampshire

Alton School
Anstey Lane, Alton,
Hampshire GU34 2NG
Tel: 01420 82070
Head: Karl Guest
Age range: 0–18 years
No. of pupils: 420
Ⓐ Ⓔ 16•

Bedales School
Church Road, Steep, Petersfield,
Hampshire GU32 2DG
Tel: 01730 711733
Head of School: Magnus Bashaarat
Age range: 13–18
No. of pupils: 463
Fees: Day £28,515 FB £36,285
Ⓦ Ⓐ Ⓐ Ⓔ 🖉 16•

Brockwood Park & Inwoods School
Brockwood Park, Bramdean,
Hampshire SO24 0LQ
Tel: +44 (0)1962 771744
Principal: Mr Antonio Autor
Age range: 14–19
No. of pupils: 112 VIth39
Fees: Day £5,630–£6,400 FB £21,400
Ⓦ Ⓐ Ⓐ Ⓔ 🖉 16•

Churcher's College
Petersfield, Hampshire GU31 4AS
Tel: 01730 263033
Headmaster: Mr Simon Williams
MA, BSc
Age range: 3–18 years
Fees: Day £10,320–£16,035
Ⓐ Ⓔ 🖉 16•

Embley
Embley Park, Romsey,
Hampshire SO51 6ZE
Tel: 01794 512206
Headteacher: Mr Cliff Canning
Age range: 2–18
No. of pupils: 500
Fees: Day £8,754–£31,338
Ⓦ Ⓐ Ⓐ Ⓔ 🖉 16•

Farnborough Hill
Farnborough Road, Farnborough,
Hampshire GU14 8AT
Tel: 01252 545197
Head: Mrs A Neil BA, MEd, PGCE
Age range: G11–18
No. of pupils: 550 VIth90
Fees: Day £14,796
Ⓐ Ⓐ Ⓔ 🖉 16•

King Edward VI School
Wilton Road, Southampton,
Hampshire SO15 5UQ
Tel: 023 8070 4561
Head Master: Mr N T Parker
Age range: 11–18
No. of pupils: 961
Fees: Day £17,130
Ⓐ Ⓔ 🖉 16•

Lord Wandsworth College
Long Sutton, Hook,
Hampshire RG29 1TB
Tel: 01256 862201
Head of School: Mr Adam Williams
Age range: 11–18 years
No. of pupils: 615
Fees: Day £21,240–£24,390
WB £29,400–£33,000 FB
£30,345–£34,650
Ⓦ Ⓐ Ⓐ Ⓔ 🖉 16•

Portsmouth High School GDST
Kent Road, Southsea, Portsmouth,
Hampshire PO5 3EQ
Tel: 023 9282 6714
Headmistress: Mrs Jane Prescott
BSc NPQH
Age range: G3–18
No. of pupils: 500
Fees: Day £2,574–£4,800
Ⓐ Ⓐ Ⓔ 🖉 16•

Salesian College
Reading Road, Farnborough,
Hampshire GU14 6PA
Tel: 01252 893000
Headmaster: Mr Gerard Owens
Age range: B11–18 G16–18
No. of pupils: 650 VIth140
Fees: Day £11,961
Ⓐ Ⓐ Ⓔ 🖉 16•

Sherfield School
South Drive, Sherfield-on-Loddon,
Hook, Hampshire RG27 0HU
Tel: 01256 884800
Headmaster: Mr Nick Brain
BA(Hons), PGCE, MA, NPQH
Age range: 3 months–18 years
No. of pupils: 450
Fees: Day £10,320–£17,085 WB
£18,960–£26,130 FB £22,125–£30,495
Ⓦ Ⓐ Ⓐ Ⓔ 🖉 16• 🐾

St John's College
Grove Road South, Southsea,
Portsmouth, Hampshire PO5 3QW
Tel: 023 9281 5118
Head of School: Mrs Mary Maguire
Age range: 4–18
No. of pupils: 560 VIth86
Fees: Day £9,975–£13,125
FB £28,500–£32,250
Ⓦ Ⓐ Ⓐ Ⓔ 🖉 16• 🐾

ST SWITHUN'S SCHOOL
For further details see p. 114
Alresford Road, Winchester,
Hampshire SO21 1HA
Tel: 01962 835700
Email: office@stswithuns.com
Website: www.stswithuns.com
Head of School: Jane Gandee
MA(Cantab)
Age range: G11–18
No. of pupils: 510
Fees: Day £20,976 FB £34,776
Ⓐ Ⓦ Ⓐ Ⓐ Ⓔ 🖉 16•

The Portsmouth Grammar School
High Street, Portsmouth,
Hampshire PO1 2LN
Tel: +44 (0)23 9236 0036
Headmistress: Dr Anne Cotton
Age range: 2–18
No. of pupils: 1556 VIth336
Fees: Day £10,233–£15,951
Ⓦ Ⓐ Ⓔ Ⓘ🅑 🖉 16•

Winchester College
College Street, Winchester,
Hampshire SO23 9NA
Tel: 01962 621247
Headmaster: Dr. T R Hands
Age range: B13–18
No. of pupils: 690 VIth280
Fees: FB £39,912
Ⓐ Ⓦ Ⓐ Ⓔ 🖉 16•

Hertfordshire

Aldenham School
Elstree, Hertfordshire WD6 3AJ
Tel: 01923 858122
Head of School: Mr Andrew Williams
Age range: 3–18

BERKHAMSTED SCHOOL
For further details see p. 93
Overton House, 131 High Street, Berkhamsted, Hertfordshire HP4 2DJ
Tel: 01442 358001
Email: admissions@berkhamsted.com
Website: www.berkhamsted.com
Principal: Mr Richard Backhouse MA(Cantab)
Age range: 3–18
No. of pupils: 1852 VIth406
Fees: Day £10,725–£21,636 WB £29,061 FB £34,620

Bishop's Stortford College
10 Maze Green Road, Bishop's Stortford, Hertfordshire CM23 2PJ
Tel: 01279 838575
Headmaster: Mr Jeremy Gladwin
Age range: 13–18
No. of pupils: VIth249
Fees: Day £20,349–£20,532 WB £31,569–£31,917 FB £33,402–£33,930

Champneys International College of Health & Beauty
Chesham Road, Wigginton, Tring, Hertfordshire HP23 6HY
Tel: 01442 291333
College Principal: Ms Pam Clegg
Age range: 16+
No. of pupils: 61
Fees: Day £3,000–£9,050

Haberdashers' Aske's School for Girls
Aldenham Road, Elstree, Borehamwood, Hertfordshire WD6 3BT
Tel: 020 8266 2300
Head of School: Ms Rose Hardy
Age range: G4–18
No. of pupils: 1190
Fees: Day £17,826–£19,311

Haileybury
Haileybury, Hertford, Hertfordshire SG13 7NU
Tel: +44 (0)1992 706353
The Master: Mr Martin Collier MA BA PGCE
Age range: 11–18
No. of pupils: 880 VIth319
Fees: Day £17,712–£26,646 FB £22,929–£36,141

Immanuel College
87/91 Elstree Road, Bushey, Hertfordshire WD23 4EB
Tel: 020 8950 0604
Headmaster: Mr Gary Griffin
Age range: 4–18
No. of pupils: 520 VIth127
Fees: Day £10,995

Mount House School
Camlet Way, Hadley Wood, Barnet, Hertfordshire EN4 0NJ
Tel: 020 8449 6889
Principal: Mr Toby Mullins
Age range: 11–18
No. of pupils: 190
Fees: Day £16,560

Queenswood
Shepherd's Way, Brookmans Park, Hatfield, Hertfordshire AL9 6NS
Tel: 01707 602500
Principal: Mrs Jo Cameron
Age range: G11–18
No. of pupils: 418
Fees: Day £7,115–£8,440 WB 7,325–10,615 FB £8,395–£11,810

Sherrardswood School
Lockleys, Welwyn, Hertfordshire AL6 0BJ
Tel: 01438 714282
Headmistress: Mrs Anna Wright
Age range: 2–18
No. of pupils: 357
Fees: Day £10,383–£16,113

St Albans High School for Girls
Townsend Avenue, St Albans, Hertfordshire AL1 3SJ
Tel: 01727 853800
Headmistress: Amber Waite
Age range: G4–18
No. of pupils: 940 VIth170

St Albans School
Abbey Gateway, St Albans, Hertfordshire AL3 4HB
Tel: 01727 855521
Headmaster: Mr JWJ Gillespie MA(Cantab), FRSA
Age range: B11–18 G16–18
No. of pupils: 870
Fees: Day £18,600

St Christopher School
Barrington Road, Letchworth, Hertfordshire SG6 3JZ
Tel: 01462 650 850
Head: Richard Palmer
Age range: 3–18
No. of pupils: 511 VIth78
Fees: Day £4,590–£18,075 WB £19,950–£24,675 FB £31,650

St Columba's College
King Harry Lane, St Albans, Hertfordshire AL3 4AW
Tel: 01727 892040
Head: Mr David Buxton
Age range: B4–18
No. of pupils: 760

St Edmund's College & Prep School
Old Hall Green, Nr Ware, Hertfordshire SG11 1DS
Tel: 01920 824247
Headmaster: Mr Matthew Mostyn BA (Hons) MA (Ed)
Age range: 3–18
No. of pupils: 852
Fees: Day £9,882–£18,345 WB £24,165–£27,630 FB £28,302–£32,460

St Francis' College
Broadway, Letchworth Garden City, Hertfordshire SG6 3PJ
Tel: 01462 670511
Headmistress: Mrs B Goulding
Age range: G3–18
No. of pupils: 460 VIth75
Fees: Day £9,990–£16,980 WB £22,350–£26,475 FB £27,990–£31,995

St Margaret's School, Bushey
Merry Hill Road, Bushey, Hertfordshire WD23 1DT
Tel: +44 (0)20 8416 4400
Headteacher: Lara Péchard
Age range: 3–18 years
No. of pupils: 445

Stanborough School
Stanborough Park, Garston, Watford, Hertfordshire WD25 9JT
Tel: 01923 673268
Acting Head Teacher: Ms Eileen Hussey
Age range: 3–17
No. of pupils: 300
Fees: Day £6,630–£10,224 WB £10,350–£13,995

The Haberdashers' Aske's Boys' School
Butterfly Lane, Elstree, Borehamwood, Hertfordshire WD6 3AF
Tel: 020 8266 1700
Headmaster: Gus Lock MA (Oxon)
Age range: B5–18 years
No. of pupils: 1428
Fees: Day £15,339–£20,346

The Purcell School, London
Aldenham Road, Bushey, Hertfordshire WD23 2TS
Tel: 01923 331100
Headteacher: Dr Bernard Trafford
Age range: 10–18
No. of pupils: 180
Fees: Day £25,707 FB £32,826

The Royal Masonic School for Girls
Rickmansworth Park, Rickmansworth, Hertfordshire WD3 4HF
Tel: 01923 773168
Headmaster: Mr Kevin Carson M.Phil (Cambridge)
Age range: G4–18
No. of pupils: 930 VIth165
Fees: Day £11,475–£17,475 WB £20,115–£27,495 FB £21,225–£29,835

Tring Park School for the Performing Arts
Tring Park, Tring, Hertfordshire HP23 5LX
Tel: 01442 824255
Principal: Mr Stefan Anderson MA, ARCM, ARCT
Age range: 8–19
No. of pupils: 354 VIth150
Fees: Day £15,405–£24,510 FB £26,190–£37,050

Kent

Ashford School
East Hill, Ashford, Kent TN24 8PB
Tel: 01233 739030
Head: Mr Michael Hall
Age range: 3 months–18 years
No. of pupils: 835 VIth170
Fees: Day £10,500–£16,800
WB £24,000 FB £36,000

Beckenham College
The Clockhouse Business Centre,
Unit 2, Thayers Farm Road,
Beckenham, Kent BR3 4LZ
Tel: 020 8650 3321
Principal: Mrs E Wakeling
Age range: 16+
Fees: Day £100–£3,500

Beechwood Sacred Heart
12 Pembury Road, Tunbridge
Wells, Kent TN2 3QD
Tel: 01892 532747
Acting Head: Mrs Helen Rowe
Age range: 3–18
No. of pupils: 400 VIth70
Fees: Day £8,685–£17,385
WB £26,850 FB £29,850

Benenden School
Cranbrook, Kent TN17 4AA
Tel: 01580 240592
Headmistress: Mrs S Price
Age range: G11–18
No. of pupils: 550
Fees: FB £12,650

Bethany School
Curtisden Green, Goudhurst,
Cranbrook, Kent TN17 1LB
Tel: 01580 211273
Headmaster: Mr Francie Healy BSc,
HDipEd, NPQH
Age range: 11–18 years
No. of pupils: 352 VIth86
Fees: Day £17,310–£19,110 WB
£26,865–£29,670 FB £26,865–£29,670

Bishop Challoner School
228 Bromley Road, Shortlands,
Bromley, Kent BR2 0BS
Tel: 020 8460 3546
Headteacher: Mrs Paula Anderson
Age range: 3–18
No. of pupils: 340
Fees: Day £3,150–£4,500

Bromley High School GDST
Blackbrook Lane, Bickley,
Bromley, Kent BR1 2TW
Tel: 020 8781 7000/1
Head: Mrs A M Drew BA(Hons), MBA
(Dunelm)
Age range: G4–18

CATS Canterbury
68 New Dover Road,
Canterbury, Kent CT1 3LQ
Tel: +44 (0)1227866540
Principal: Dr Sarah Lockyer
Age range: 14–18
No. of pupils: 400

COBHAM HALL SCHOOL
For further details see p. 94
Brewers Road, Cobham,
Kent DA12 3BL
Tel: 01474 823371
Email: enquiries@
cobhamhall.com
Website: www.cobhamhall.com
Headteacher: Mrs Wendy
Barrett
Age range: G11–18
No. of pupils: 150
Fees: Day £6,548–£7,936
FB £9,893–£12,349

Darul Uloom London
Foxbury Avenue, Perry Street,
Chislehurst, Kent BR7 6SD
Tel: 020 8295 0637
Principal: Mufti Mustafa
Age range: B11–18
No. of pupils: 160
Fees: FB £2,400

Dover College
Effingham Crescent,
Dover, Kent CT17 9RH
Tel: 01304 205969
Headmaster: Mr Gareth Doodes
MA (Hons)
Age range: 3–18
No. of pupils: 301
Fees: Day £7,725–£16,050 WB
£21,000–£25,500 FB £24,750–£31,500

Farringtons School
Perry Street, Chislehurst,
Kent BR7 6LR
Tel: 020 8467 0256
Head: Mr David Jackson
Age range: 3–18
No. of pupils: 700 VIth100
Fees: Day £15,690 WB
£30,960 FB £32,880

Kent College Pembury
Old Church Road, Pembury,
Tunbridge Wells, Kent TN2 4AX
Tel: +44 (0)1892 822006
Headmistress: Ms Julie Lodrick
Age range: G3–18
No. of pupils: 500
Fees: Day £21,600 WB
£26,994 FB £34,419

Kent College, Canterbury
Whitstable Road, Canterbury,
Kent CT2 9DT
Tel: +44 (0)1227 763 231
Executive Head: Dr David Lamper
Age range: 0–18 years
(Boarding from 8)
No. of pupils: 770
Fees: Day £5,598–£6,288
FB £8,748–£11,867

King's Rochester
Satis House, Boley Hill,
Rochester, Kent ME1 1TE
Tel: 01634 888555
Principal: Mr B Charles
Age range: 13–18
No. of pupils: 600 VIth95
Fees: Day £7,440–£20,190
FB £22,950–£33,015

Radnor House, Sevenoaks
Combe Bank Drive,
Sevenoaks, Kent TN14 6AE
Tel: 01959 563720
Head: Mr David Paton BComm
(Hons) PGCE MA
Age range: 2.5–18
No. of pupils: 250

Sackville School
Tonbridge Rd, Hildenborough,
Tonbridge, Kent TN11 9HN
Tel: 01732 838888
Headmaster: Mr Justin Foster-
Gandey BSc (hons)
Age range: 11–18
No. of pupils: 160 VIth29
Fees: Day £15,750

Sevenoaks School
High Street, Sevenoaks,
Kent TN13 1HU
Tel: +44 (0)1732 455133
Head of School: Mr Jesse R Elzinga
AB MSt FCCT
Age range: 11–18
No. of pupils: 1165
Fees: Day £24,291–£27,585
FB £38,790–£42,084

ST EDMUND'S SCHOOL
For further details see p. 106
St Thomas Hill, Canterbury,
Kent CT2 8HU
Tel: 01227 475601
Email: admissions@
stedmunds.org.uk
Website: www.stedmunds.org.uk
Head: Mr Edward O'Connor MA
(Cantab), MPhil (Oxon), MEd
(Cantab)
Age range: 3–18
No. of pupils: 558

St Lawrence College
Ramsgate, Kent CT11 7AE
Tel: 01843 572931
Head of College: Mr Barney Durrant
Age range: 3–18
No. of pupils: 600
Fees: Day £7,845–£16,245
FB £27,765–£36,909

Sutton Valence School
North Street, Sutton
Valence, Kent ME17 3HL
Tel: 01622 845200
Headmaster: Bruce Grindlay MA
Cantab, MusB, FRCO, CHM
Age range: 11–18
No. of pupils: 570

The King's School, Canterbury
The Precincts, Canterbury,
Kent CT1 2ES
Tel: 01227 595501
Head: Mr Peter Roberts
Age range: 13–18
No. of pupils: 858 VIth385
Fees: Day £27,495 FB £38,955

TONBRIDGE SCHOOL
For further details see p. 110
High Street, Tonbridge,
Kent TN9 1JP
Tel: 01732 304297
Email: admissions@
tonbridge-school.org
Website:
www.tonbridge-school.co.uk
Headmaster: Mr James Priory
MA (Oxon)
Age range: B13–18
No. of pupils: 802
Fees: Day £31,587 FB £42,105

Walthamstow Hall School
Sevenoaks, Kent TN13 3UL
Tel: 01732 451334
Headmistress: Miss S Ferro
Age range: G2–18
No. of pupils: 500 VIth80

Middlesex

ACS Hillingdon International School
Hillingdon Court, 108 Vine Lane, Hillingdon, Uxbridge, Middlesex UB10 0BE
Tel: +44 (0) 1895 259 771
Head of School: Mr Martin Hall
Age range: 4–18
Ⓧ Ⓔ ⒾⒷ ✎ 16+

Halliford School
Russell Road, Shepperton, Middlesex TW17 9HX
Tel: 01932 223593
Head: Mr James Davies BMus (Hons) LGSM FASC ACertCM PGCE
Age range: B11–18 G16–18
No. of pupils: 435
Fees: Day £16,590
Ⓕ Ⓐ Ⓔ ✎ 16+

Hampton School
Hanworth Road, Hampton, Middlesex TW12 3HD
Tel: 020 8979 9273
Headmaster: Mr Kevin Knibbs MA (Oxon)
Age range: B11–18
No. of pupils: 1200
Fees: Day £6,390
Ⓕ Ⓐ Ⓔ ✎ 16+

Harrow School
5 High Street, Harrow on the Hill, Middlesex HA1 3HT
Tel: 020 8872 8000
Head Master: Mr Alastair Land
Age range: B13–18
No. of pupils: 830 VIth320
Fees: FB £40,050
Ⓕ Ⓐ Ⓐ Ⓔ ✎ 16+

KEW HOUSE SCHOOL
For further details see p. 88
Kew House, 6 Capital Interchange Way, London, Middlesex TW8 0EX
Tel: 0208 742 2038
Email: admissions@ kewhouseschool.com
Website: www.kewhouseschool.com
Headmaster: Mr Will Williams
Age range: 11–18
No. of pupils: 550
Fees: Day £7,450
Ⓐ ✎ 16+

Lady Eleanor Holles
Hanworth Road, Hampton, Middlesex TW12 3HF
Tel: 020 8979 1601
Head of School: Mrs Heather Hanbury
Age range: G7–18
No. of pupils: 930
Fees: Day £20,802
Ⓧ Ⓐ Ⓔ ✎ 16+

Merchant Taylors' School
Sandy Lodge, Northwood, Middlesex HA6 2HT
Tel: 01923 820644
Head: Mr S J Everson MA (Cantab)
Age range: B11–18
No. of pupils: 865 VIth282
Fees: Day £19,998
Ⓕ Ⓐ Ⓔ ✎ 16+

North London Collegiate School
Canons, Canons Drive, Edgware, Middlesex HA8 7RJ
Tel: +44 (0)20 8952 0912
Headmistress: Mrs Sarah Clark
Age range: G4–18
No. of pupils: 1080
Fees: Day £5,754–£6,810
Ⓧ Ⓖ Ⓐ Ⓔ ⒾⒷ 16+

Northwood College for Girls GDST
Maxwell Road, Northwood, Middlesex HA6 2YE
Tel: 01923 825446
Head: Ms Zara Hubble
Age range: G3–18
Ⓧ Ⓐ Ⓔ ✎ 16+

Regent College
Sai House, 167 Imperial Drive, Harrow, Middlesex HA2 7HD
Tel: 020 8966 9900
Principal: Mrs Tharshiny Pankaj
Age range: 11–19
No. of pupils: 167
Fees: Day £4,100–£15,525
16+ Ⓐ 16+

St Catherine's School
Cross Deep, Twickenham, Middlesex TW1 4QJ
Tel: 020 8891 2898
Headmistress: Mrs Johneen McPherson MA
Age range: G3–18
No. of pupils: 449
Fees: Day £11,205–£15,585
Ⓧ Ⓐ Ⓔ ✎ 16+

St Helen's School
Eastbury Road, Northwood, Middlesex HA6 3AS
Tel: +44 (0)1923 843210
Headmistress: Dr Mary Short BA, PhD
Age range: G3–18
No. of pupils: VIth165
Ⓧ Ⓖ Ⓐ Ⓔ 16+

St. John's Senior School
North Lodge, The Ridgeway, Enfield, Middlesex EN2 8BE
Tel: +44 (0)20 8366 0035
Head Teacher: Mr A Tardios
Age range: 11–18 years
Ⓐ 16+

The John Lyon School
Middle Road, Harrow on the Hill, Middlesex HA2 0HN
Tel: 020 8515 9443
Head: Miss Katherine Haynes BA, MEd, NPQH
Age range: B11–18
No. of pupils: 600
Ⓕ Ⓐ Ⓔ ✎ 16+

Surrey

ACS Cobham International School
Heywood, Portsmouth Road, Cobham, Surrey KT11 1BL
Tel: +44 (0) 1932 867251
Head of School: Mr Barnaby Sandow
Age range: 2–18
Ⓖ Ⓐ Ⓔ ⒾⒷ ✎ 16+

ACS Egham International School
Woodlee, London Road, Egham, Surrey TW20 0HS
Tel: +44 (0) 1784 430 800
Head of School: Mr Jeremy Lewis
Age range: 4–18
Fees: Day £11,090–£25,870
Ⓖ Ⓔ ⒾⒷ ✎ 16+

Box Hill School
London Road, Mickleham, Dorking, Surrey RH5 6EA
Tel: 01372 373382
Headmaster: Cory Lowde
Age range: 11–18
No. of pupils: 425
Fees: Day £17,985 WB £28,350 FB £34,950
Ⓖ Ⓐ Ⓔ ⒾⒷ ✎ 16+

Cambridge Tutors College
Water Tower Hill, Croydon, Surrey CR0 5SX
Tel: 020 8688 5284/7363
Principal: Dr Chris Drew
Age range: 15–19
No. of pupils: 215 VIth200
Fees: Day £10,400–£22,995
16+ Ⓐ Ⓐ Ⓔ 16+

Caterham School
Harestone Valley, Caterham, Surrey CR3 6YA
Tel: 01883 343028
Head: Mr C. W. Jones MA(Cantab)
Age range: 11–18
No. of pupils: VIth321
Fees: Day £18,735–£19,620 WB £30,936–£33,270 FB £36,795–£38,760
Ⓖ Ⓐ Ⓐ Ⓔ ✎ 16+

Charterhouse
Godalming, Surrey GU7 2DX
Tel: +44 (0)1483 291501
Headmaster: Dr Alex Peterken
Age range: B13–18 G16–18
No. of pupils: 820
Ⓖ Ⓐ Ⓐ Ⓔ ⒾⒷ ✎ 16+

City of London Freemen's School
Ashtead Park, Ashtead, Surrey KT21 1ET
Tel: 01372 277933
Headmaster: Mr R Martin
Age range: 7–18
No. of pupils: 877 VIth213
Fees: Day £14,067–£19,194 WB £29,784–£29,841 FB £30,780–£30,816
Ⓖ Ⓐ Ⓐ Ⓔ ✎ 16+

Claremont Fan Court School
Claremont Drive, Esher, Surrey KT10 9LY
Tel: 01372 473780
Head: Mr William Brierly
Age range: 2 1/2–18
No. of pupils: 890
Fees: Day £790–£6,125
Ⓐ Ⓔ ✎ 16+

Cranleigh School
Horseshoe Lane, Cranleigh,
Surrey GU6 8QQ
Tel: +44 (0) 1483 273666
Headmaster: Mr Martin Reader
MA, MPhil, MBA
Age range: 7–18 (including
Prep School)
No. of pupils: 690 VIth252
Fees: Day £32,370 FB £39,330

Croydon High School GDST
Old Farleigh Road, Selsdon,
South Croydon, Surrey CR2 8YB
Tel: 020 8260 7500
Headmistress: Mrs Emma Pattison
Age range: G3–18
No. of pupils: 580 VIth75

Dunottar School
High Trees Road, Reigate,
Surrey RH2 7EL
Tel: 01737 761945
Head of School: Mr Mark Tottman
Age range: 11–18
No. of pupils: 423
Fees: Day £17,739

Epsom College
Epsom, Surrey KT17 4JQ
Tel: 01372 821000
Headmaster: Mr Jay A Piggot MA
Age range: 11–18
No. of pupils: 884
Fees: Day £19,611–£26,151
WB £35,034 FB £38,568

Ewell Castle School
Church Street, Ewell, Epsom,
Surrey KT17 2AW
Tel: 020 8393 1413
Principal: Mr Silas Edmonds
Age range: 3–18
No. of pupils: 644
Fees: Day £5,175–£17,442

Frensham Heights
Rowledge, Farnham,
Surrey GU10 4EA
Tel: 01252 792561
Head: Mr Rick Clarke
Age range: 3–18
No. of pupils: 497 VIth105
Fees: Day £7,110–£21,060
FB £27,450–£32,070

Guildford High School
London Road, Guildford,
Surrey GU1 1SJ
Tel: 01483 561440
Headmistress: Mrs F J Boulton BSc,
MA
Age range: G4–18
No. of pupils: 1000
Fees: Day £11,175–£17,940

KING EDWARD'S WITLEY
For further details see p. 96
Petworth Road, Godalming,
Surrey GU8 5SG
Tel: 01428 686735
Email: admissions@kesw.org
Website: www.kesw.org
Head: Mrs Joanna Wright
Age range: 11–18 years
No. of pupils: 400

Kingston Grammar School
70 London Rd, Kingston upon
Thames, Surrey KT2 6PY
Tel: 020 8546 5875
Head: Mr Stephen Lehec
Age range: 11–18

Lingfield College
Racecourse Road, Lingfield,
Surrey RH7 6PH
Tel: 01342 832407
Headmaster: Mr R Bool B.A. Hons,
MBA
Age range: 2–18
No. of pupils: 935
Fees: Day £11,250–£21,801

MARYMOUNT LONDON
For further details see p. 89
George Road, Kingston upon
Thames, Surrey KT2 7PE
Tel: +44 (0)20 8949 0571
Email: admissions@
marymountlondon.com
Website:
www.marymountlondon.com
Headmistress: Mrs Margaret
Giblin
Age range: G11–18
No. of pupils: 255
Fees: Day £25,985 WB
£42,135 FB £44,000

Notre Dame School
Cobham, Surrey KT11 1HA
Tel: 01932 869990
Head of Seniors: Mrs Anna King
MEd, MA (Cantab), PGCE
Age range: 2–18
No. of pupils: 600

Old Palace of John Whitgift School
Old Palace Road, Croydon,
Surrey CR0 1AX
Tel: 020 8686 7347
Head: Mrs. C Jewell
Age range: B3 months–4
years G3 months–19 years
No. of pupils: 740 VIth120
Fees: Day £11,316–£15,366

Prior's Field
Priorsfield Road, Godalming,
Surrey GU7 2RH
Tel: 01483 810551
Head of School: Mrs Tracey Kirnig
Age range: G11–18
No. of pupils: 450
Fees: Day £18,900 FB £30,825

Reed's School
Sandy Lane, Cobham,
Surrey KT11 2ES
Tel: 01932 869001
Headmaster: Mr Mark Hoskins BA
MA MSc
Age range: B11–18 G16–18
No. of pupils: 650 VIth230
Fees: Day £20,430–£25,530
FB £27,225–£32,910

Reigate Grammar School
Reigate Road, Reigate,
Surrey RH2 0QS
Tel: 01737 222231
Headmaster: Mr Shaun Fenton MA
(Oxon) MEd (Oxon)
Age range: 11–18
No. of pupils: 969 VIth262
Fees: Day £19,140–£19,350

Royal Grammar School, Guildford
High Street, Guildford,
Surrey GU1 3BB
Tel: 01483 880600
Headmaster: Dr J M Cox BSc, PhD
Age range: B11–18
No. of pupils: 940
Fees: Day £19,035

Royal Russell School
Coombe Lane, Croydon,
Surrey CR9 5BX
Tel: 020 8657 3669
Headmaster: Christopher
Hutchinson
Age range: 11–18
No. of pupils: 590 VIth180
Fees: Day £18,480 FB £36,525

Sir William Perkins's School
Guildford Road, Chertsey,
Surrey KT16 9BN
Tel: 01932 574900
Head: Mr C C Muller
Age range: G11–18 years
No. of pupils: 600
Fees: Day £5,618

St Catherine's, Bramley
Station Road, Bramley,
Guildford, Surrey GU5 0DF
Tel: 01483 899609
Headmistress: Alice Phillips
Age range: G4–18
Fees: Day £9,240–£18,885 FB £31,125

St George's College
Weybridge Road, Addlestone,
Weybridge, Surrey KT15 2QS
Tel: 01932 839300
Headmistress: Mrs Rachel Owens
Age range: 11–18
No. of pupils: 909 VIth250
Fees: Day £17,655–£20,100

St James Senior Boys School
Church Road, Ashford,
Surrey TW15 3DZ
Tel: 01784 266930
Headmaster: Mr David Brazier
Age range: B11–18
No. of pupils: 403 VIth65
Fees: Day £18,930

St John's School
Epsom Road, Leatherhead,
Surrey KT22 8SP
Tel: 01372 373000
Head of School: Mrs Rowena Cole
Age range: 11–18
No. of pupils: 840
Fees: Day £19,590–£24,555
WB £24,780–£31,035

St Teresa's Effingham (Senior School)
Beech Avenue, Effingham,
Surrey RH5 6ST
Tel: 01372 452037
Executive Director: Mr Mike Farmer
Age range: G11–18
No. of pupils: 640 VIth90
Fees: Day £17,865–£18,465 WB
£28,875–£29,175 FB £30,795–£31,455

Surbiton High School
13-15 Surbiton Crescent, Kingston
upon Thames, Surrey KT1 2JT
Tel: 020 8546 5245
Principal: Mrs Rebecca Glover
Age range: B4–11 G4–18
No. of pupils: 1210 VIth186
Fees: Day £10,857–£17,142

Sutton High School GDST
55 Cheam Road, Sutton,
Surrey SM1 2AX
Tel: 020 8642 0594
Headmistress: Mrs Katharine
Crouch
Age range: G3–18
No. of pupils: 600 VIth60
Fees: Day £10,095–£17,043

Tante Marie Culinary Academy
Woodham House, Carlton Road,
Woking, Surrey GU21 4HF
Tel: 01483 726957
Principal: Mr Andrew Maxwell
Age range: 16–60
No. of pupils: 72
Fees: Day £20,750

TASIS The American School in England
Coldharbour Lane, Thorpe, Surrey TW20 8TE
Tel: +44 (0)1932 582316
Head of School: Mr Bryan Nixon
Age range: 3–18
No. of pupils: 620
Fees: Day £11,920–£25,605 FB £47,565

The Royal School
Farnham Lane, Haslemere, Surrey GU27 1HQ
Tel: 01428 605805
Head: Mrs Pippa Smithson
Age range: 11–18 years
Fees: Day £10,506–£18,507 WB £27,747 FB £31,557

Tormead School
27 Cranley Road, Guildford, Surrey GU1 2JD
Tel: 01483 575101
Headmistress: Mrs Christina Foord
Age range: G4–18
No. of pupils: 760 VIth120
Fees: Day £8,385–£15,915

Trinity School
Shirley Park, Croydon, Surrey CR9 7AT
Tel: 020 8656 9541
Head: Alasdair Kennedy MA (Cantab)
Age range: B10–18 G16–18
No. of pupils: 1007
Fees: Day £16,656

Whitgift School
Haling Park, South Croydon, Surrey CR2 6YT
Tel: +44 20 8633 9935
Headmaster: Mr Christopher Ramsey
Age range: B10–18
No. of pupils: 1560
Fees: Day £20,640 WB £33,081 FB £40,140

WOLDINGHAM SCHOOL
For further details see p. 112
Marden Park, Woldingham, Surrey CR3 7YA
Tel: 01883 349431
Email: registrar@woldinghamschool.co.uk
Website: www.woldinghamschool.co.uk
Head of School: Dr James Whitehead
Age range: G11–18
No. of pupils: 585
Fees: Day £21,945–£23,910 FB £36,135–£39,330

Yehudi Menuhin School
Stoke Road, Stoke d'Abernon, Cobham, Surrey KT11 3QQ
Tel: 01932 864739
Interim Head: Richard Tanner
Age range: 7–19
No. of pupils: 80 VIth36
Fees: FB £34,299

West Berkshire

Downe House School
Downe House, Cold Ash, Thatcham, West Berkshire RG18 9JJ
Tel: +44 (0)1635 200286
Headmistress: Mrs Emma McKendrick BA(Liverpool)
Age range: G11–18
No. of pupils: 593
Fees: Day £9,705 FB £13,050

St Gabriel's
Sandleford Priory, Newbury, West Berkshire RG20 9BD
Tel: 01635 555680
Principal: Mr Richard Smith MA (Hons), MEd, PGCE
Age range: B6 months–11 G6 months–18
No. of pupils: 469 VIth40
Fees: Day £10,668–£17,418

West Sussex

Ardingly College
College Road, Ardingly, Haywards Heath, West Sussex RH17 6SQ
Tel: +44 (0)1444 893320
Headmaster: Mr Ben Figgis
Age range: 13–18
No. of pupils: 559
Fees:–£23,985 FB £35,865–£29,250

Burgess Hill Girls
Keymer Road, Burgess Hill, West Sussex RH15 0EG
Tel: 01444 241050
Head of School: Liz Laybourn
Age range: B2.5–4 G2.5–18
No. of pupils: 505 VIth70
Fees: Day £8,100–£20,100 FB £31,050–£35,850

Christ's Hospital
Horsham, West Sussex RH13 0LJ
Tel: 01403 211293
Head Teacher: Mr Simon Reid
Age range: 11–18
No. of pupils: 900
Fees: Day £18,510–£23,310 FB £35,850

Farlington School
Strood Park, Horsham, West Sussex RH12 3PN
Tel: 01403 282573
Headmistress: Ms Louise Higson BSc, PGCE
Age range: 3–18
No. of pupils: 300
Fees: Day £5,400–£17,670 WB £23,205–£28,515 FB £24,540–£29,850

Hurstpierpoint College
College Lane, Hurstpierpoint, West Sussex BN6 9JS
Tel: 01273 833636
Headmaster: Mr. T J Manly BA, MSc
Age range: 4–18
No. of pupils: 1156
Fees: Day £8,790–£22,860 WB £28,800

Lancing College
Lancing, West Sussex BN15 0RW
Tel: 01273 465805
Head Master: Mr Dominic T Oliver MPhil
Age range: 13–18
No. of pupils: 550 VIth255
Fees: Day £8,190 FB £11,995

Our Lady of Sion School
Gratwicke Road, Worthing, West Sussex BN11 4BL
Tel: 01903 204063
Headmaster: Dr Simon Orchard
Age range: 3–18
No. of pupils: 410
Fees: Day £8,640–£13,575

Seaford College
Lavington Park, Petworth, West Sussex GU28 0NB
Tel: 01798 867392
Headmaster: J P Green MA BA
Age range: 6–18
No. of pupils: 869 VIth219
Fees: Day £10,725–£22,230 WB £22,350–£30,120 FB £34,380

Worth School
Paddockhurst Road, Turners Hill, Crawley, West Sussex RH10 4SD
Tel: +44 (0)1342 710200
Head Master: Stuart McPherson
Age range: 11–18
No. of pupils: 580 VIth222
Fees: Day £15,960–£23,730 FB £21,210–£33,690

Examinations and qualifications

Qualifications

Common Entrance

What is Common Entrance?

The Common Entrance examinations are used in UK independent schools (and some independent schools overseas) for transfer from junior to senior schools at the ages of 11+ and 13+. They were first introduced in 1904 and are internationally recognised as being a rigorous form of assessment following a thorough course of study. The examinations are produced by the Independent Schools Examinations Board and backed by HMC (Headmasters' and Headmistresses' Conference), GSA (Girls' Schools Association), and IAPS (Independent Association of Prep Schools) which together represent the leading independent schools in the UK, and many overseas.

Common Entrance is not a public examination as, for example, GCSE, and candidates may normally be entered only in one of the following circumstances:

a)   they have been offered a place at a senior school subject to their passing the examination, or

b)   they are entered as a 'trial run', in which case the papers are marked by the junior school concerned

Candidates normally take the examination in their own junior or preparatory schools, either in the UK or overseas.

How does Common Entrance fit into the progression to GCSEs?

Rapid changes in education nationally and internationally have resulted in regular reviews of the syllabuses for all the Common Entrance examinations. Reviews of the National Curriculum, in particular, have brought about a number of changes, with the Board wishing to ensure that it continues to set high standards. It is also a guiding principle that Common Entrance should be part of the natural progression from 11-16, and not a diversion from it.

Common Entrance at 11+

At 11+, the examination consists of papers in English, mathematics and science. It is designed so that it can be taken by candidates either from independent preparatory schools or by candidates from schools in the maintained sector or overseas who have had no special preparation. The examination is normally taken in January for entrance to senior schools in the following September.

Common Entrance at 13+

At 13+, most candidates come from independent preparatory schools. The compulsory subjects are English, mathematics and science. Papers in French, geography, German, Classical Greek, history, Latin, religious studies and Spanish are also available and candidates usually offer as many subjects as they can. In most subjects, papers are available at more than one level to cater for candidates of different abilities. There are three examination sessions each year, with the majority of candidates sitting in the summer prior to entry to their senior schools in September.

Marking and grading

The papers are set centrally but the answers are marked by the senior school for which a candidate is entered. Mark schemes are provided by the Board but senior schools are free to set their own grade boundaries. Results are available within two weeks of the examinations taking place.

Pre-Testing and the ISEB Common Pre-Tests

A number of senior independent schools 'pre-test' pupils for entry, prior to them taking their main entrance examinations at a later date. Usually, these pre-tests take place when a pupil is in Year 6 or Year 7 of his or her junior school and will then be going on to sit Common Entrance in Year 8. The tests are designed to assess a pupil's academic potential and suitability for a particular senior school so that the child, the parents and the school know well in advance whether he/she is going to be offered a place at the school, subject to a satisfactory performance in the entrance examinations. The tests enable senior schools to manage their lists and help to ensure that pupils are not entered for examinations in which they are unlikely to be successful. In short, it reduces uncertainty for all concerned.

Pre-tests may be written specifically for the senior school for which the candidate is entered but a growing number of schools are choosing to use the Common Pre-Tests provided by the Independent Schools Examinations Board. These online tests are usually taken in the candidate's own junior school and one of their main advantages is that a pupil need sit the tests only once, with the results then made available to any senior school which wishes to use them. The multiple-choice tests cover verbal reasoning, non-verbal reasoning, English and mathematics, with the results standardised according to the pupil's age when they are taken. Further information is available on the ISEB website at www.iseb.co.uk.

Parents are advised to check the entrance requirements for senior schools to see if their child will be required to sit a pre-test.

Further information
Details of the Common Entrance examinations and how to register candidates are available on the ISEB website www.iseb.co.uk. Copies of past papers and a wide range of textbooks and other resources can be purchased from Galore Park Publishing Ltd at www.galorepark.co.uk. Support materials are also available from Hodder Education and other publishers; see the Resources section of the ISEB website for details.

Independent Schools Examinations Board
Endeavour House, Crow Arch Lane,
Ringwood, Hampshire BH24 1HP
Telephone: 01425 470555
Email: enquiries@iseb.co.uk
Web: www.iseb.co.uk

7+ Entrance Exams

What is the 7+?
The 7+ is the descriptive name given to the entrance exams set by an increasing number of independent schools for pupils wishing to gain admission into their Year 3.

7+ entrance exams may be simply for admission into a selective preparatory school, which will then prepare the child for Common Entrance exams to gain a place at senior school. Alternatively, the 7+ can be a route into a school with both prep and senior departments, therefore often effectively bypassing the 11+ or 13+ Common Entrance exams.

The Independent Schools Examinations Board provides Common Entrance examinations and assessments for pupils seeking entry to independent senior schools at 11+ and 13+, but there is as yet no equivalent for the 7+. The testing is largely undertaken by the individual schools, although some schools might commission the test from external agencies. Many schools in the incredibly competitive London area offer entrance exams at 7+ and some share specimen papers on their website to clarify what 7+ children will face.

Who sits the 7+?
The 7+ is sat by Year 2 children, who may be moving from a state primary school or a stand-alone pre-prep school to an independent prep school (although many prep schools now have their own pre-prep department, with a cohort of children poised to pass into Year 3 there).

Registration for 7+ entrance exams usually closes in the November of Year 2, with the exams then sat in January or February, for entry that September.

How is the 7+ assessed?
Written exam content will be primarily English and maths based, whilst spelling, dictation, mental arithmetic and more creative skills may be assessed verbally on a one-to-one basis. Group exercises are also sometimes used to look at a child's initiative and their ability to work with others.

Schools will not only be looking for academic potential, but also good citizens and a mixture of personalities to produce a well-rounded year group. For this reason, children are often asked to attend an interview. Some schools interview all candidates, whilst others may call back a limited number with good test results. They will be looking for a child's ability to look an adult in the eye and think on their feet, but also simply to show some spark and personality.

After the assessments, children will be told if they have been successful in gaining a firm place, or a place on a waiting list.

Further Information
As the 7+ is not centrally regulated, it is best for parents to seek accurate admissions and testing information direct from the schools in which they are interested. In addition to a school's facilities and ethos, choosing a school for admission at 7+ will probably also involve whether the school has a senior department and if not, the prep school's record in gaining its students places at target senior schools.

Experienced educational consultants may be able to help parents decide which independent prep school is best suited for their child, based on their personality, senior school ambitions and academic potential. Many parents enlist the help of tutors to prepare children for the 7+, if only to reduce the fear of the unknown in these very young children. This is achieved by teaching them the required curriculum, what to expect on their test and interview days, and giving them the opportunity to practice tackling the type of assessments they will face.

PSB

The Pre-Senior Baccalaureate (PSB) is a framework of study for children in junior and preparatory schools that was introduced in 2012, and focuses on the active development and assessment of 6 core skills: Communication, Collaboration, Leadership, Independence, Reviewing and Improving and Thinking and Learning. Member schools promote the core skills across all areas of school life, and provide guidance for pupils in progressing these skills, which are seen as essential for developing capable and balanced adults able to make the most of the opportunities of a fast-changing world. A strong but appropriate knowledge base compliments this, with the use of focused tutoring, pastoral care and Well Being programmes.

Schools do not work to a prescribed curriculum and the emphasis is upon promoting an independent approach which works for each individual school. There are subject INSET days for PSB school staff annually and these are supported by senior school colleagues, to ensure that work done in PSB schools compliments the demands of education at higher levels.

The PSB is a whole school initiative from Early Years to either Year 6 or Year 8, at which point the certificate is awarded at the time of matriculation to senior schools. An additional PSB Year 9 framework is being developed together with international membership.

The development of skills is now recognised as essential by the Independent Schools Inspectorate (ISI), and recent ISI reports on PSB schools highlight the excellent contribution the PSB has in schools achieving excellence.

Assessment

The PSB has a 10 point scale for all subjects studied with a compulsory spine covering: English, Maths, Science, Modern Languages, The Humanities, Art, Design Technology, Music, Sport and PE with each pupil additionally completing a cross curricular project. Optional subjects are agreed with schools but these must be supported by a scheme of work clearly identifying appropriate core skills which are assessed on a 5 point scale. There are distinction levels on both scales and the 10 point scale cross references both ISEB and National Curriculum assessment levels.

Pupils moving on to senior school do so via individual senior school pre-testing arrangements, the award of the PSB certificate, core ISEB papers or a combination of the above.

Membership categories

Partner membership is available to schools developing the PSB with support given from existing schools and the Communications director.

Full membership entitles schools to use the PSB matriculation certificate and join the PSB committee as voting members.

Affiliated membership is for schools that have developed their own skills based approach, in line with PSB principles; staff can participate in all training opportunities and the Heads of Affiliated Schools join committee meetings as non-voting guests.

Membership of the above categories is dependent upon strong ISI reports, the development of a skills based curriculum, with skills clearly identified in schemes of work and excellent teaching.

Associate membership is for senior schools that actively support the PSB in providing staff for subject meetings, hosting meetings, conferences and committee meetings and offer a valuable perspective on the demands of GCSE, A Level and the International Baccalaureate.

Further details

The PSB is an entirely independent charity overseen by a Board of Trustees who have expertise in both primary and secondary education. Details of the PSB can be found on the website – psbacc.org – and you can contact the PSB Administrator at rebecca.morris@psbacc.org and she will answer any questions you may have.

General Certificate of Secondary Education (GCSE)

What are the GCSE qualifications?

GCSE qualifications were first introduced in 1986 and are the principal means of assessment at Key Stage 4 across a range of academic subject areas. They command respect and have status not only in the UK but worldwide.

Main features of the GCSE

There are four unitary awarding organisations for GCSEs in England (see 'Awarding organisations and examination dates' section, p435). WJEC and CCEA also offer GCSE qualifications in Wales and Northern Ireland. Each examining group designs its own specifications but they are required to conform to set criteria. For some aspects of the qualification system, the exam boards adopt common ways of working. When the exam boards work together in this way they generally do so through the Joint Council of Qualifications (JCQ). The award of a grade is intended to indicate that a candidate has met the required level of skills, knowledge and understanding.

In 2015 GCSEs began a series of reform starting with English Language, English literature, and mathematics. New GCSEs in ancient languages (classical Greek, Latin), art and design, biology, chemistry, citizenship studies, combined science (double award), computer science, dance, drama, food preparation and nutrition, geography, history, modern foreign languages (French, German, Spanish), music, physics, physical education and religious studies were first taught in September 2016, with first results in summer 2018. Assessment in these reformed GCSEs consists primarily of formal examinations taken at the end of the student's two-year course. Other types of assessment, non-exam assessment (NEA), is used where there are skills and knowledge which cannot be assessed through exams. Ofqual have set the percentage of the total marks that will come from NEA.

The reformed GCSEs feature new and more demanding content, as required by the government and developed by the exam boards. Courses are designed for two years of study (linear assessment) and no longer divided into different modules.

Exams can only be split into 'foundation tier' and 'higher tier' if one exam paper does not give all students the opportunity to show their knowledge and their abilities. Such tiering is only available in maths, science and modern foreign languages; other subjects do not have tiers. Resit opportunities will only be available each November in English language and maths, and then only for students who have turned 16 by the 31st of August in the year of the November assessment.

New GCSEs taught from September 2017: ancient history, astronomy, business, classical civilisation, design and technology, economics, electronics, engineering, film studies, geology, media studies, psychology, sociology, statistics, other (minority) foreign languages e.g. Italian, Polish.

New GCSEs taught from September 2018: ancient languages (biblical Hebrew) and modern foreign languages (Gujarati, Persian, Portuguese, Turkish).

Grading

The basic principle that exam boards follow when setting grade boundaries is that if the group of students (the cohort) taking a qualification in one year is of similar ability to the cohort in the previous year then the overall results (outcomes) should be comparable.

The reformed exams taken in summer 2017 were the first to show a new grading system, with the A* to G grades being phased out.

The new grading system is 9 to 1, with 9 being the top grade. Ofqual says this allows greater differentiation between students. It expects that broadly the same proportion of students will achieve a grade 4 and above as currently achieve a grade C and above, that broadly the same proportion of students will achieve a grade 7 and above as currently achieve a grade A and above. There are three anchor points between the new grading system and the old one: the bottom of the new 1 grade is the same as the bottom of the old G grade, the bottom of the new 4 grade is the bottom of the old C grade, and the bottom of the 7 grade is the same as the bottom of the old A grade. Grade 9 will be set using the tailored approach formula in the first award.

Grades 2, 3, 5 and 6 will be awarded arithmetically so that the grade boundaries are equally spaced in terms of marks from neighbouring grades.

The government's definition of a 'strong pass' will be set at grade 5 for reformed GCSEs. A grade 4 – or 'standard pass' – will continue to be a level 2 achievement. The DfE does not expect employers, colleges or universities to raise the bar to a grade 5 if a grade 4 would meet their requirements.

Can anyone take GCSE qualifications?

GCSEs are intended mainly for 16-year-old pupils, but are open to anyone of any age, whether studying full-time or part-time at a school, college or privately. There are no formal entry requirements.

Students normally study up to ten subjects over a

two-year period. Short course GCSEs are available in some subjects (including PE and religious studies) – these include half the content of a full GCSE, so two short course GCSEs are equivalent to one full GCSE.

The English Baccalaureate

The English Baccalaureate (EBacc) is a school performance measure. It allows people to see how many pupils get a grade C or above (current grading) in the core academic subjects at Key Stage 4 in any government-funded school.The DfE introduced the EBacc measure in 2010.

Progress 8 and Attainment 8

Progress 8 aims to capture the progress a pupil makes from the end of primary school to the end of secondary school. It is a type of value added measure, which means that pupils' results are compared to the actual achievements of other pupils with the same prior attainment.

The new performance measures are designed to encourage schools to offer a broad and balanced curriculum with a focus on an academic core at Key Stage 4, and reward schools for the teaching of all their pupils, measuring performance across 8 qualifications. Every increase in every grade a pupil achieves will attract additional points in the performance tables.

Progress 8 will be calculated for individual pupils solely in order to calculate a school's Progress 8 score, and there will be no need for schools to share individual Progress 8 scores with their pupils. Schools should continue to focus on which qualifications are most suitable for individual pupils, as the grades pupils achieve will help them reach their goals for the next stage of their education or training.

Attainment 8 will measure the achievement of a pupil across 8 qualifications including mathematics (double weighted) and English (double weighted), 3 further qualifications that count in the English Baccalaureate (EBacc) measure and 3 further qualifications that can be GCSE qualifications (including EBacc subjects) or any other non-GCSE qualification on the DfE approved list.

General Certificate of Education (GCE) Advanced level (A level)

Typically, A level qualifications are studied over a two-year period. There are no lower or upper age limits. Schools and colleges usually expect students aged 16-18 to have obtained grades A*-C (grade 5 in the new criteria) in five subjects at GCSE level before taking an advanced level course. This requirement may vary between centres and according to which specific subjects are to be studied. Mature students may be assessed on different criteria as to their suitability to embark on the course.

GCE Qualifications

Over the past few years, AS level and A level qualifications have been in a process of reform. New subjects have been introduced gradually, with the first wave taught from September 2015. Subjects that have not been reformed are no longer be available for teaching.

GCE qualifications are available at two levels: the Advanced Subsidiary (AS), which is generally delivered over one year and is seen as half an A level; and the A level (GCE). Nearly 70 titles are available, covering a wide range of subject areas, including humanities, sciences, language, business, arts, mathematics and technology.

One of the major reforms is that AS level results no longer count towards an A level (they previously counted for 50%). The two qualifications are linear, with AS assessments typically taking place after one year and A levels after two.

New-style AS and A levels were first taught from September 2015 for: art and design, biology, business studies, chemistry, computer studies, economics, English language, English language and literature, English literature, history, physics, psychology, and sociology.

Subjects first taught from September 2016 include: ancient languages such as Latin or Greek, dance, drama (theatre studies), geography, modern languages such as Spanish or French, music, physical education, religious studies.

Those introduced for first teaching from September 2017: accounting, design and technology, music technology, history of art, environmental science, philosophy, maths, further maths, archaeology, accounting, electronics, ancient history, law, classical civilisation, film studies, media studies, politics, geology, statistics, Chinese, Italian, Russian. In 2018 Biblical Hebrew, Modern Hebrew & languages such as Bengali, Polish and Urdu were available for first teaching.

Some GCE AS and A levels, particularly the practical ones, contain a proportion of coursework. All GCE A levels that contain one or more types of assessment will have an element of synoptic assessment that tests students' understanding of the whole specification. GCE AS are graded A-E and A levels are graded A*-E.

Overall the amount of coursework at A level has been reduced in the reforms. In some subjects, such as the sciences, practical work will not contribute to the final

A level but will be reported separately in a certificate of endorsement. In the sciences, students will do at least 12 practical activities, covering apparatus and techniques. Exam questions about practical work will make up at least 15% of the total marks for the qualification and students will be assessed on their knowledge, skills and understanding of practical work.

Cambridge International AS & A Level

Cambridge International AS & A Level is an internationally benchmarked qualification, taught in over 130 countries worldwide. It is typically for learners aged 16 to 19 years who need advanced study to prepare for university. It was created specifically for an international audience and the content has been devised to suit the wide variety of schools worldwide and avoid any cultural bias.

Cambridge International A Level is typically a two-year course, and Cambridge International AS Level is typically one year. Some subjects can be started as a Cambridge International AS Level and extended to a Cambridge International A Level. Students can either follow a broad course of study, or specialise in one particular subject area.

Learners use Cambridge International AS and A Levels to gain places at leading universities worldwide, including the UK, Ireland, USA, Canada, Australia, New Zealand, India, Singapore, Egypt, Jordan, South Africa, the Netherlands, Germany and Spain. In places such as the US and Canada, good grades in carefully chosen Cambridge International A Level subjects can result in up to one year of university course credit.

Assessment options:
Cambridge International AS & A Levels have a linear structure with exams at the end of the course. Students can choose from a range of assessment options:

Option 1: take Cambridge International AS Levels only. The Cambridge International syllabus content is half a Cambridge International A Level.

Option 2: staged assessment, which means taking the Cambridge International AS Level in one exam session and the Cambridge International A Level at a later session. However, this route is not possible in all subjects.

Option 3: take all Cambridge International A Level papers in the same examination session, usually at the end of the course.

Grades and subjects
Cambridge International A Levels are graded from A*-E. Cambridge International AS Levels are graded from A-E.

Subjects available: Afrikaans, Afrikaans – Language (AS only), Arabic, Arabic – Language (AS only), Art & Design, Biology, Business, Chemistry, Chinese – Language (AS only), Chinese (A Level only), Classical Studies, Computer Science, Design & Technology, Design & Textiles, Digital Media & Design, Divinity, Divinity (AS only), Drama, Economics, English – Language, English – Language and Literature (AS only), English – Literature, English General Paper (AS only), Environmental Management (AS only), Food Studies, French – Language (AS only), French – Literature (AS only), French (A Level only), General Paper (AS only), General Paper (AS only), Geography, German – Language (AS only), German (A Level only), Global Perspectives and Research, Hindi – Language (AS only), Hindi – Literature (AS only), Hindi (A Level only), Hinduism, Hinduism (AS only), History, Information Technology, Islamic Studies, Islamic Studies (AS only), Japanese Language (AS only), Law, Marathi – Language (AS only), Marathi (A Level only), Marine Science, Mathematics, Mathematics – Further, Media Studies, Music, Music (AS only), Nepal Studies (AS only), Physical Education, Physics, Portuguese – Language (AS only), Portuguese – Literature (AS only), Portuguese (A Level only), Psychology, Sociology, Spanish – First Language (AS only), Spanish – Language (AS only), Spanish – Literature (AS only), Spanish (A Level only), Tamil, Tamil – Language (AS only), Thinking Skills, Travel & Tourism, Urdu – Language (AS only), Urdu – Pakistan only (A Level only), Urdu (A Level only). Website: www.cambridgeinternational.org/alevel

Cambridge IGCSE

Cambridge IGCSE is the world's most popular international qualification for 14 to 16 year olds. It develops skills in creative thinking, enquiry and problem solving, in preparation for the next stage in a student's education. Cambridge IGCSE is taken in over 150 countries, and is widely recognised by employers and higher education institutions worldwide.

Cambridge IGCSE is graded from A*-G. In the UK, Cambridge IGCSE is accepted as equivalent to the GCSE. It can be used as preparation for Cambridge International A & AS Levels, UK A and AS levels, IB or AP and in some instances entry into university. Cambridge IGCSE First Language English and Cambridge IGCSE English Language qualifications are recognised by a significant number of UK universities as evidence of competence in the language for university entrance.

Subjects available: Accounting, Accounting (9-1), Afrikaans – First Language, Afrikaans – Second Language, Agriculture, Arabic – First Language, Arabic – First Language (9-1), Arabic – Foreign Language, Art & Design, Art & Design (9-1), Bahasa Indonesia, Bangladesh Studies, Biology, Biology (9-1), Business Studies, Business Studies (9-1), Chemistry, Chemistry (9-1), Child Development, Chinese - First Language, Chinese – Second Language, Computer Science, Computer Science (9-1), Czech – First Language, Design & Technology, Design & Technology (9-1), Development Studies, Drama, Drama (9-1), Dutch – First Language, Dutch – Foreign Language, Economics, Economics (9-1), English – First Language, English – First Language (9-1), English – First Language (9–1) (UK only), English – First Language (US), English – Literature (9-1) (UK only), English – Literature (English), English – Literature (US), English – Literature in English, English – Literature in English (9-1), English as a Second Language (Count-in speaking), English as a Second Language (Count-in Speaking) (9-1), English as a Second Language (Speaking endorsement), English Second Language (Speaking Endorsement) (9-1), Enterprise, Environmental Management, Food & Nutrition, French – First Language, French – Foreign Language, French (9-1), Geography, Geography (9-1), German – First Language, German – Foreign Language, German (9-1), Global Perspectives, Greek – Foreign Language, Hindi as a Second Language, History, History – American (US), History (9-1), India Studies, Indonesian – Foreign Language, Information & Communication Technology, Information & Communication Technology (9-1), IsiZulu as a Second Language, Islamiyat, Italian – Foreign Language, Italian (9-1), Japanese – Foreign Language, Kazakh as a Second Language, Korean (First Language), Latin, Malay – First Language, Malay – Foreign Language, Mandarin Chinese – Foreign Language, Marine Science (Maldives only), Mathematics, Mathematics – Additional, Mathematics – Additional (US), Mathematics – International, Mathematics (9-1), Mathematics (9-1) (UK only), Mathematics (US), Music – 0410, Music (9-1), Pakistan Studies, Physical Education, Physical Education (9-1, Physical Science, Physics, Physics (9-1), Portuguese – First Language, Portuguese – Foreign Language, Religious Studies, Russian – First Language, Sanskrit, Science – Combined, Sciences – Co-ordinated (9-1), Sciences – Co-ordinated (Double), Sociology, Spanish – First Language, Spanish – Foreign Language, Spanish – Literature, Spanish (9-1), Swahili, Thai – First Language, Travel & Tourism, Turkish – First Language, Urdu as a Second Language, World Literature.
Website: www.cambridgeinternational.org/igcse

Cambridge Pre-U

Cambridge Pre-U is a post-16 qualification that equips students with the skills they need to succeed at university, developed with universities.

Cambridge Pre-U is a linear course, with exams taken at the end of two years. It encourages the development of well-informed, open and independent-minded individuals; promotes deep understanding through subject specialisation, with a depth and rigour appropriate to progression to higher education; and develops skills in independent research valued by universities.

Assessment
Cambridge Pre-U Principal Subjects are examined at the end of two years. Cambridge Pre-U Short Courses are available in some subjects and are typically examined at the end of one year. Students can study a combination of A Levels and Principal Subjects.

In order to gain the Cambridge Pre-U Diploma, students must study at least three Cambridge Pre-U Principal Subjects (up to two A Levels can be substituted for Principal Subjects) and Cambridge Pre-U Global Perspectives & Research (GPR). Cambridge Pre-U GPR includes an extended project in the second year, developing skills in research and critical thinking.

Grades and subjects
Cambridge Pre-U reports achievement on a scale of nine grades, with Distinction 1 being the highest grade and Pass 3 the lowest grade.

Subjects available: Art & Design, Art History, Biology, Business & Management, Chemistry, Classical Greek, Economics, English, French, Further Mathematics, Geography, German, Global Perspectives & Independent Research (UK only), Global Perspectives (Short Course) (UK only), History, Italian, Latin, Mandarin Chinese, Mathematics, Music, Philosophy & Theology, Physics, Psychology, Russian, Spanish
Website: www.cambridgeinternational.org/cambridgepreu

Edexcel International GCSEs

Pearson's Edexcel International GCSEs are academic qualifications aimed at learners aged 14 to 16. They're equivalent to a UK General Certificate of Secondary Education (GCSE), and are the main requirement for Level 3 studies, including progression to GCE AS or A levels, BTECs or employment. International GCSEs are linear qualifications, meaning that students take all of the exams at the end of the course. They are available at Level 1 (grades 3-1) and Level 2 (grades 9-4). There are currently more than 100,000 learners studying Edexcel International GCSEs, in countries throughout Asia, Africa, Europe, the Middle East and Latin America. Developed by subject specialists and reviewed regularly, many of Pearson's Edexcel International GCSEs include specific international content to make them relevant to students worldwide.

Pearson's Edexcel International GCSEs were initially developed for international schools. They have since become popular among independent schools in the UK, but are not approved for use in UK state schools.

Free Standing Maths Qualifications (FSMQ)

Aimed at those students wishing to acquire further qualifications in maths, specifically additional mathematics and foundations of advanced mathematics (MEI). Further UCAS points can be earned upon completion of the advanced FSMQ in additional mathematics.

AQA Certificate in Mathematical Studies (Core Maths)

This Level 3 qualification has been available since September 2015. It is designed for students who achieved a Grade 4 or above at GCSE and want to continue studying Maths. The qualification carries UCAS points equivalent to an AS level qualification.

AQA Certificate in Further Maths

This level 2 qualification has been designed to provide stretch and challenge to the most able mathematicians. This will be best suited to students who either already have, or are expected to achieve the top grades in GCSE Mathematics and are likely to progress to A level Mathematics and Further Mathematics.

Additional and Alternative

Cambridge Primary

Cambridge Primary is typically for learners aged 5 to 11 years. It develops learner skills and understanding in 10 subjects: English as a first or second language, mathematics, science, art & design, digital literacy, music, physical education, Cambridge Global Perspectives and ICT. The flexible curriculum frameworks include optional assessment tools to help schools monitor learners' progress and give detailed feedback to parents. At the end of Cambridge Primary, schools can enter students for Cambridge Primary Checkpoint tests which are marked in Cambridge.
Website: www.cambridgeinternational.org/primary

Cambridge ICT Starters introduces learners, typically aged 5 to 14 years, to the key ICT applications they need to achieve computer literacy and to understand the impact of technology on our daily lives. It can be taught and assessed in English or Spanish.

Cambridge Lower Secondary

Cambridge Lower Secondary is typically for learners aged 11 to 14 years. It develops learner skills and understanding in 10 subjects: English, English as a second language, mathematics, science, art & design, digital literacy, music, physical education, Cambridge Global Perspectives and ICT, and includes assessment tools. At the end of Cambridge Lower Secondary, schools can enter students for Cambridge Lower Secondary Checkpoint tests which are marked in Cambridge and provide an external international benchmark for student performance.
Website:
www.cambridgeinternational.org/lowersecondary

European Baccalaureate (EB)

Not to be confused with the International Baccalaureate (IB) or the French Baccalaureate, this certificate is available in European schools and recognised in all EU countries.

To obtain the baccalaureate, a student must obtain a minimum score of 60%, which is made up from: coursework, oral participation in class and tests (40%); five written examinations (36%) – mother-tongue, first foreign language and maths are compulsory for all candidates; four oral examinations (24%) – mother tongue and first foreign language are compulsory (history or geography may be compulsory here, dependant on whether the candidate has taken a written examination in these subjects).

Throughout the EU the syllabus and examinations necessary to achieve the EB are identical. The only exception to this rule is the syllabus for the mother tongue language. The EB has been specifically designed to meet, at the very least, the minimum qualification requirements of each member state.

Study for the EB begins at nursery stage (age four) and progresses through primary (age six) and on into secondary school (age 12).

Syllabus
Languages: Bulgarian, Czech, Danish, Dutch, English, Estonian, Finnish, Finnish as a second national language, French, German, Greek, Hungarian, Irish, Italian, Latvian, Lithuanian, Maltese, Polish, Portuguese, Romanian, Slovak, Slovenian, Spanish, Swedish, Swedish for Finnish pupils.
Literary: art education, non-confessional ethics, geography, ancient Greek, history, human sciences, Latin, music, philosophy, physical education.
Sciences: biology, chemistry, economics, ICT, integrated science, mathematics, physics.
For more information, contact:
Office of the Secretary-General of the European Schools, rue de la Science 23 – 2nd floor, B-1040 Bruxelles, Belgique
Tel: +32 (0)2 895 26 11
Website: www.eursc.eu

The International Baccalaureate (IB)

The International Baccalaureate (IB) offers four challenging and high quality educational programmes for a worldwide community of schools, aiming to develop internationally minded people who, recognizing their common humanity and shared guardianship of the planet, help to create a better, more peaceful world.

The IB works with schools around the world (both state and privately funded) that share the commitment to international education to deliver these programmes.

Schools that have achieved the high standards required for authorization to offer one or more of the IB programmes are known as IB World Schools. There are over half a million students attending almost 5000 IB World Schools in over 150 countries and this number is growing annually.

The Primary Years, Middle Years and Diploma Programmes share a common philosophy and common characteristics. They develop the whole student, helping students to grow intellectually, socially, aesthetically and culturally. They provide a broad and balanced education that includes science and the humanities, languages and mathematics, technology and the arts. The programmes teach students to think critically, and encourage them to draw connections between areas of knowledge and to use problem-solving techniques and concepts from many disciplines. They instil in students a sense of responsibility towards others and towards the environment. Lastly, and perhaps most importantly, the programmes give students an awareness and understanding of their own culture and of other cultures, values and ways of life.

A fourth programme called the IB Career-related Programme (CP) became available to IB World Schools from September 2012. All IB programmes include:

- A written curriculum or curriculum framework
- Student assessment appropriate to the age range
- Professional development and networking opportunities for teachers
- Support, authorization and programme evaluation for the school

The IB Primary Years Programme

The IB Primary Years Programme (PYP), for students aged three to 12, focuses on the development of the whole child as an inquirer, both in the classroom and in the world outside. It is a framework consisting of five essential elements (concepts, knowledge, skills, attitude, action) and guided by six trans-disciplinary themes of global significance, explored using knowledge and skills derived from six subject areas (language, social studies, mathematics, science and technology, arts, and personal, social and physical education) with a powerful emphasis on inquiry-based learning.

The most significant and distinctive feature of the PYP is the six trans-disciplinary themes. These themes are about issues that have meaning for, and are important to, all of us. The programme offers a balance between learning about or through the subject areas, and learning beyond them. The six themes of global significance create a trans-disciplinary framework that allows students to 'step up' beyond the confines of learning within subject areas:

- Who we are
- Where we are in place and time
- How we express ourselves
- How the world works
- How we organize ourselves
- Sharing the planet

The PYP exhibition is the culminating activity of the programme. It requires students to analyse and propose solutions to real-world issues, drawing on what they have learned through the programme. Evidence of student development and records of PYP exhibitions are reviewed by the IB as part of the programme evaluation process.

Assessment is an important part of each unit of inquiry as it both enhances learning and provides opportunities for students to reflect on what they know, understand and can do. The teacher's feedback to the students provides the guidance, the tools and the incentive for them to become more competent, more skilful and better at understanding how to learn.

The IB Middle Years Programme (MYP)

The Middle Years Programme (MYP), for students aged 11 to 16, comprises eight subject groups:

- Language acquisition
- Language and literature
- Individuals and societies
- Sciences
- Mathematics
- Arts

- Physical and health education

- Design

The MYP requires at least 50 hours of teaching time for each subject group in each year of the programme. In years 4 and 5, students have the option to take courses from six of the eight subject groups within certain limits, to provide greater flexibility in meeting local requirements and individual student learning needs.

Each year, students in the MYP also engage in at least one collaboratively planned interdisciplinary unit that involves at least two subject groups.

MYP students also complete a long-term project, where they decide what they want to learn about, identify what they already know, discovering what they will need to know to complete the project, and create a proposal or criteria for completing it

The MYP aims to help students develop their personal understanding, their emerging sense of self and their responsibility in their community.

The MYP allows schools to continue to meet state, provincial or national legal requirements for students with access needs. Schools must develop an inclusion/special educational needs (SEN) policy that explains assessment access arrangements, classroom accommodations and curriculum modification that meet individual student learning needs.

The IB Diploma Programme (IBDP)

The IB Diploma Programme, for students aged 16 to 19, is an academically challenging and motivating curriculum of international education that prepares students for success at university and in life beyond studies.

DP students choose at least one course from six subject groups, thus ensuring depth and breadth of knowledge and experience in languages, social studies, the experimental sciences, mathematics, and the arts. With more than 35 courses to choose from, students have the flexibility to further explore and learn subjects that meet their interest. Out of the six courses required, at least three and not more than four must be taken at higher level (240 teaching hours), the others at standard level (150 teaching hours). Students can take examinations in English, French or Spanish.

In addition, three unique components of the programme – the DP core – aim to broaden students' educational experience and challenge them to apply their knowledge and skills. The DP core – the extended essay (EE), theory of knowledge (TOK) and creativity, activity, service (CAS) – are compulsory and central to the philosophy of the programme.

The IB uses both external and internal assessment to measure student performance in the DP. Student results are determined by performance against set standards, not by each student's position in the overall rank order. DP assessment is unique in the way that it measures the extent to which students have mastered advanced academic skills not what they have memorized. DP assessment also encourages an international outlook and intercultural skills, wherever appropriate.

The IB diploma is awarded to students who gain at least 24 points out of a possible 45 points, subject to certain minimum levels of performance across the whole programme and to satisfactory participation in the creativity, activity, and service requirement.

Recognized and respected by leading universities globally, the DP encourages students to be knowledgeable, inquiring, caring and compassionate, and to develop intercultural understanding, open-mindedness and the attitudes necessary to respect and evaluate a range of viewpoints.

The IB Career Related Programme (IBCP)

The IB Career-related Programme, for students aged 16 to 19, offers an innovative educational framework that combines academic studies with career-related learning. Through the CP, students develop the competencies they need to succeed in the 21st century. More importantly, they have the opportunity to engage with a rigorous study programme that genuinely interests them while gaining transferable and lifelong skills that prepares them to pursue higher education, apprenticeships or direct employment.

CP students complete four core components – language development, personal and professional skills, service learning and a reflective project – in order to receive the International Baccalaureate Career-related Programme Certificate. Designed to enhance critical thinking and intercultural understanding, the CP core helps students develop the communication and personal skills, as well as intellectual habits required for lifelong learning.

Schools that choose to offer the CP can create their own distinctive version of the programme and select career pathways that suit their students and local community needs. The IB works with a variety of CRS providers around the world and schools seeking to develop career pathways with professional communities can benefit from our existing collaborations. All CRS providers undergo a rigorous curriculum evaluation to ensure that their courses align with the CP pedagogy and meet IB quality standards. The flexibility to meet the needs, backgrounds and contexts of learners allows

CP schools to offer an education that is relevant and meaningful to their students.

Launched in 2012, there are 250 CP schools. Many schools with the IB Diploma Programme (DP) and the Middle Years Programme (MYP) have chosen the CP as an alternative IB pathway to offer students. CP schools often report that the programme has helped them raise student aspiration, increase student engagement and retention and encouraged learners to take responsibility for their own actions, helping them foster high levels of self-esteem through meaningful achievements.

For more information on IB programmes, visit: www.ibo.org

Africa, Europe, Middle East IB Global Centre,
Churchillplein 6, The Hague, 2517JW, The Netherlands
Tel: +31 (0)70 352 6000
Email: support@ibo.org

Pearson Edexcel Mathematics Awards

Pearson's Edexcel Mathematics Awards are small, stand-alone qualifications designed to help students to develop and demonstrate proficiency in different areas of mathematics. These Awards enable students to focus on understanding key concepts and techniques, and are available across three subjects, including: Number and Measure (Levels 1 and 2), Algebra (Levels 2 and 3) and Statistical Methods (Levels 1, 2 and 3).

Designed to build students' confidence and fluency; the Awards can fit into the existing programme of delivery for mathematics in schools and colleges, prepare students for GCSE and/or GCE Mathematics, and to support further study in other subjects, training or the workplace. They offer a choice of levels to match students' abilities, with clear progression between the levels. These small, 60-70 guided learning hour qualifications are assessed through one written paper per level. Each qualification is funded and approved for pre-16 and 16-18 year old students in England and in schools and colleges in Wales.

Projects

Extended Project Qualification (EPQ)

AQA, OCR, Pearson and WJEC offer the Extended Project Qualification, which is a qualification aimed at developing a student's research and independent learning skills. The EPQ can be taken as a stand-alone qualification, and it is equivalent to half an A level in UCAS points (but only a third of performance points).

Students complete a research based written report and may produce an artefact or a practical science experiment as part of their project.

Cambridge International Project Qualification (IPQ)

Cambridge International is offering a new standalone project-based qualification, which can be taken alongside Cambridge International AS & A levels. Students complete a 5000-word research project on a topic of their choice. The qualification is assessed by Cambridge International.

For more information, go to www.cambridgeinternational.org/advanced

Entry level and basic skills

Entry Level Qualifications

If you want to take GCSE or NVQ Level 1 but have not yet reached the standard required, then entry level qualifications are for you as they are designed to get you started on the qualifications ladder.

Entry level qualifications are available in a wide range of areas. You can take an entry level certificate in most subjects where a similar GCSE exists. There are also vocational entry level qualifications – some in specific areas like retail or catering and others where you can take units in different work-related subjects to get a taster of a number of career areas. Also available are entry level certificates in life skills and the basic skills of literacy and numeracy.

Anyone can take an entry level qualification – your school or college will help you decide which qualification is right for you.

Entry level qualifications are flexible programmes so the time it takes to complete will vary according to where you study and how long you need to take the qualification.

Subjects available include: Art and Design, Computer Science, English, Geography, History, Latin, Mathematics, Physical Education and Science.

Functional Skills

Functional Skills are qualifications in English and maths that equip learners with the basic practical skills required in everyday life, education and the workplace. They are available at Entry Level, Level 1 and Level 2. Functional Skills are identified as funded 'stepping stone' qualifications to English and maths GCSE for post-16 learners who haven't previously achieved a grade D in these subjects. There are part of apprenticeship completion requirements.

Vocational qualifications

Applied Generals/Level 3 Certificates

Applied General qualifications are available in Business and Science and are a practical introduction to these subjects, they are a real alternative to A level support progression to further study or employment aimed at students aged 16-18.

Developed together with teachers, schools, colleges and higher education institutions, they help learners to develop knowledge and skills.

A mixture of assessment types means learners can apply their knowledge in a practical way. An integrated approach creates a realistic and relevant qualification for learners.

AQA Technical Award

AQA's Technical Award is a practical, vocational Level 1/2 qualification for 14- to 16-year-olds to take alongside GCSEs.

The Technical Award in Performing Arts provides an introduction to life and work, equipping learners with the practical, transferable skills and core knowledge needed to progress to further general or vocational study, including Level 3 qualifications, employment or apprenticeships.

Learners are assessed on doing rather than knowing through the project-based internal assessments, where they can apply their knowledge to practical tasks. There are two internally assessed units worth 30% each, and an externally assessed exam worth 40%.

AQA Tech-levels

Level 3 technical qualifications have been designed in collaboration with employers and professional bodies. They're aimed at learners aged over 16 wanting to progress into a specific sector through apprenticeships, further study or employment. There are 16 individual qualifications within IT, Engineering, Business and Entertainment Technology. These vary in size of qualification.

Transferable skills have been contextualised explicitly within each qualification and are a mandatory part of the qualification outcome.

Learners are assessed through a combination of examinations, internally and externally assessed assignments.

The last time schools could enter Tech-level Business: Marketing was summer 2020.

June 2021 will be the final internally assessed unit certification opportunity, and January 2022 will be the last external exam resit and certification opportunity

BTECs

BTEC Level 2 First qualifications
ie BTEC Level 2 Diplomas, BTEC Level 2 Extended Certificates, BTEC Level 2 Certificates and BTEC Level 2 Award.

BTEC Firsts are Level 2 introductory work-related programmes covering a wide range of vocational areas including business, engineering, information technology, health and social care, media, travel and tourism, and public services.

Programmes may be taken full or part-time. They are practical programmes that provide a foundation for the knowledge and skills you will need in work. Alternatively, you can progress onto a BTEC National qualification, Applied GCE A level or equivalent.

There are no formal entry requirements and they can be studied alongside GCSEs. Subjects available include: Agriculture, Animal Care, Applied Science, Art and Design, Business, Children's Care, Learning and Development, Construction, Countryside and the Environment, Engineering, Fish Husbandry, Floristry, Health and Social care, Horse Care, Horticulture, Hospitality, IT, Land-based Technology, Business, Creative Media Production, Music, Performing Arts, Public Services, Sport, Travel and Tourism, and Vehicle Technology.

BTEC Foundation Diploma in Art and Design (QCF)
For those students preparing to go on to higher education within the field of art and design. This diploma is recognised as one of the best courses of its type in the UK, and is used in preparation for degree programmes. Units offered include researching, recording and responding in art and design, media experimentation, personal experimental studies, and a final major project.

BTEC Nationals
ie BTEC Level 3 Extended Diplomas (QCF), BTEC Level 3 Diplomas (QCF), BTEC Level 3 Subsidiary Diplomas (QCF), BTEC Level 3 Certificates (QCF)

BTEC National programmes are long-established vocational programmes. They are practical programmes that are highly valued by employers. They enable you to gain the knowledge and skills that you will need in work, or give you the choice to progress on to a BTEC Higher National, a Foundation Degree or a degree programme.

BTEC Nationals, which hold UCAS points cover a range of vocationally specialist sectors including child care, children's play, learning and development, construction, art and design, aeronautical engineering, electrical/electronic engineering, IT, business, creative and media production, performing arts, public services, sport, sport and exercise sciences and applied science. The programmes may be taken full- or part-time, and can be taken in conjunction with NVQs and/or functional skills units at an appropriate level.

There are no formal entry requirements, but if you have any of the following you are likely to be at the right level to study a BTEC national qualification.

- a BTEC Level 2 First qualification

- GCSEs – at grades A*-C in several subjects

- Relevant work experience

There are also very specialist BTEC Nationals, such as Pharmaceutical Science and Blacksmithing and Metalworking.

BTEC Higher Nationals
Known as HNDs and HNCs – ie BTEC Level 5 HND Diplomas (QCF) and BTEC Level 4 HNC Diplomas (QCF)

BTEC HNDs and HNCs are further and higher education qualifications that offer a balance of education and vocational training. They are available in over 40 work-related subjects such as Graphic Design, Business, Health and Social Care, Computing and Systems Development, Manufacturing Engineering, Hospitality Management, and Public Services.

BTEC higher national courses combine study with hands-on work experience during your course. Once completed, you can use the skills you learn to begin your career, or continue on to a related degree course.

HNDs are often taken as a full-time course over two years but can also be followed part-time in some cases.

HNCs are often for people who are working and take two years to complete on a part-time study basis by day release, evenings, or a combination of the two. Some HNC courses are done on a full-time basis.

There are no formal entry requirements, but if you have any of the following you are likely to be at the right academic level:

- at least one A level
- a BTEC Level 3 National qualification
- level 3 NVQ

BTEC specialist and professional qualifications

These qualifications are designed to prepare students for specific and specialist work activities. These are split into two distinct groups:

- Specialist qualifications (entry to Level 3)
- Professional qualifications (Levels 4-7)

Cambridge Nationals

Cambridge Nationals are vocationally-related qualifications that take an engaging, practical and inspiring approach to learning and assessment.

They are industry-relevant, geared to key sector requirements and very popular with schools and colleges because they suit such a broad range of learning styles and abilities.

Cambridge Nationals are available in: Child Development, Creative iMedia, Engineering Design, Engineering Manufacture, Enterprise and Marketing, Health and Social Care, ICT, Information Technologies, Principles in Engineering and Engineering Business, Sport Science, Sport Studies, Systems Control in Engineering. They are joint Level 1 and 2 qualifications aimed at students aged 14-16 in full-time study.

Cambridge Technicals

OCR's Cambridge Technicals are practical and flexible vocationally-related qualifications, offering students in-depth study in a wide range of subjects, including business, health and social care, IT, sport, art and design, digital media, science, performing arts and engineering.

Cambridge Technicals are aimed at young people aged 16-19 who have completed Key Stage 4 of their education and want to study in a more practical, work-related way.

Cambridge Technicals are available at Level 2 and Level 3, and carry UCAS points at Level 3.

NVQs

NVQs reward those who demonstrate skills gained at work. They relate to particular jobs and are usefully taken while you are working. Within reason, NVQs do not have to be completed in a specified amount of time. They can be taken by full-time employees or by school and college students with a work placement or part-time job that enables them to develop the appropriate skills. There are no age limits and no special entry requirements.

NVQs are organised into levels, based on the competencies required. Levels 1-3 are the levels most applicable to learners within the 14-19 phase. Achievement of Level 4 within this age group will be rare. See the OCR website for further information.

OCR Vocational Qualifications

These are available at different levels and different sizes. Levels 1-3 are the levels most applicable to learners within the 14-19 phase. The different sizes are indicated with the use of Award, Certificate and Diploma in the qualification title and indicate the number of hours it typically takes to complete the qualification.

Vocational qualifications are assessed according to each individual specification, but may include practical assessments and/or marked assessments. They are designed to provide evidence of a student's relevant skills and knowledge in their chosen subject. These qualifications can be used for employment or as a path towards further education. See the OCR website for further details.

Awarding organisations and examination dates

Awarding organisations

In England there are four awarding organisations, each offering GCSEs, AS and A levels (Eduqas offers only reformed qualifications in England, whereas WJEC offers in England, Wales, Northern Ireland and independent regions). There are separate awarding organisations in Wales (WJEC) and Northern Ireland (CCEA). The awarding organisation in Scotland (SQA) offers equivalent qualifications.

This information was supplied by the awarding bodies and was accurate at the time of going to press. It is intended as a general guide only for candidates in the United Kingdom. Dates are subject to variation and should be confirmed with the awarding organisation concerned.

AQA

Qualifications offered:
GCSE
AS and A level
Technical levels
Foundation Certificate of Secondary Education (FCSE)
Entry Level Certificate (ELC)
Foundation and Higher Projects
Extended Project Qualification (EPQ)
Applied Generals/AQA Level 3 Certificates and Extended Certificates
Functional Skills
AQA Certificate
Technical Award

Other assessment schemes:
Unit Award Scheme (UAS)

Contact:
Email: eos@aqa.org.uk
Website: www.aqa.org.uk
Tel: 0800 197 7162 (8am–5pm Monday to Friday)
+44 161 696 5995 (Outside the UK)

Devas Street, Manchester M15 6EX
Stag Hill House, Guildford, Surrey GU2 7XJ
Windsor House, Cornwall Road, Harrogate, HG1 2PW
2nd Floor, Lynton House, 7–12 Tavistock Square, London, WC1H 9LT

CCEA – Council for the Curriculum, Examinations and Assessment

Qualifications offered:
GCSE
GCE AS/A level
Key Skills (Levels 1-4)
Entry Level Qualifications
Occupational Studies (Levels 1 & 2)
QCF Qualifications
Applied GCSE and GCE

Contact:
Email: info@ccea.org.uk
Website: www.ccea.org.uk

29 Clarendon Road, Clarendon Dock, Belfast, BT1 3BG
Tel: (028) 9026 1200

Eduqas

Eduqas, part of WJEC, offers Ofqual reformed GCSEs, AS and A levels to secondary schools and colleges. Our qualifications are available in England, Channel Islands, Isle of Man, Northern Ireland and to the independent sector in Wales (restrictions may apply).

Qualifications offered:
GCSE (9-1)
AS
A level
Level 3

Contact:
Email: info@wjec.co.uk
Website: www.eduqas.co.uk

Eduqas (WJEC CBAC Ltd),
245 Western Avenue, Cardiff, CF5 2YX
Telephone: 029 2026 5000

IB – International Baccalaureate

Qualification offered:
IB Diploma
IB Career-related Certificate

Contact:
Email: support@ibo.org
Website: www.ibo.org

IB Global Centre, The Hague, Churchillplein 6, 2517 JW, The Hague, The Netherlands
Tel: +31 70 352 60 00
IB Global Centre, Washington DC, 7501 Wisconsin Avenue, Suite 200 West Bethesda, Maryland 20814, USA
Tel: +1 301 202 3000
IB Global Centre, Singapore, 600 North Bridge Road, #21-01 Parkview Square, Singapore 188778
Tel: +65 6 579 5000
IB Global Centre, Cardiff, Peterson House, Malthouse Avenue, Cardiff Gate, Cardiff, Wales, CF23 8GL, UK
Email: reception@ibo.org
Tel: +44 29 2054 7777
International Baccalaureate Foundation Office, Route des Morillons 15, Grand-Saconnex, Genève, CH-1218, Switzerland
Tel: +41 22 309 2540

OCR – Oxford Cambridge and RSA Examinations – and Cambridge International

Qualifications offered by OCR or sister awarding organisation Cambridge Assessment International Education (Cambridge International) include:
GCSE
GCE AS/A level
IGCSE
International AS/A level
Extended Project
Cambridge International Project Qualification
Cambridge Pre-U
Cambridge Nationals
Cambridge Technicals
Functional Skills
FSMQ – Free Standing Maths Qualification
NVQ

Contact:
OCR
OCR Head Office, The Triangle Building, Shaftesbury Road, Cambridge, CB2 8EA
Website: www.ocr.org.uk
Tel: +44 1223 553998

Cambridge International
Website: www.cambridgeinternational.org
Email: info@cambridgeinternational.org
Tel: +44 1223 553554

Pearson

Qualifications offered:
Pearson's qualifications are offered in the UK but are also available through their international centres across the world. They include:
DiDA, CiDA
GCE A levels
GCSEs
Functional Skills
International GCSEs and Edexcel Certificates
ESOL (Skills for Life)
BTEC Enterprise qualifications
BTEC Entry Level, Level 1 and Level 1 Introductory
BTEC Firsts
BTEC Foundation Diploma in Art and Design
BTEC Industry Skills
BTEC International Level 3
BTEC Level 2 Technicals
BTEC Level 3 Technical Levels in Hospitality
BTEC Nationals
BTEC Specialist and Professional qualifications
BTEC Tech Awards
Higher Nationals
T Levels

Contact:
190 High Holborn, London WC1V 7BH
See website for specific contact details:
qualifications.pearson.com

Educational organisations

Educational organisations

Artsmark

Arts Council England's Artsmark was set up in 2001, and rounds are held annually.

All schools in England can apply for an Artsmark – primary, middle, secondary, special and pupil referral units, maintained and independent – on a voluntary basis. An Artsmark award is made to schools showing commitment to the full range of arts – music, dance, drama and art and design.

Tel: 0161 934 4317
Email: artsmark@artscouncil.org.uk
Website: www.artsmark.org.uk

Association for the Education and Guardianship of International Students (AEGIS)

AEGIS brings together schools and guardianship organisations to ensure and promote the welfare of international students. AEGIS provides accreditation for all reputable guardianship organisations.

AEGIS, The Wheelhouse, Bond's Mill Estate, Bristol Road, Stonehouse, Gloucestershire GL10 3RF.
Tel: 01453 821293
Email: info@aegisuk.net
Website: www.aegisuk.net

The Association of American Study Abroad Programmes (AASAP)

Established in 1991 to represent American study abroad programmes in the UK.

Contact: Kalyn Franke, AASAP/UK,
University of Maryland in London, Connaught Hall,
36-45 Tavistock Square, London WC1H 9EX
Email: info@aasapuk.org
Website: www.aasapuk.org

The Association of British Riding Schools (ABRS)

An independent body of proprietors and principals of riding establishments, aiming to look after their interests and those of the riding public and to raise standards of management, instruction and animal welfare.

The Association of British Riding Schools, Unit 8, Bramble Hill Farm, Five Oaks Road, Slinfold, Horsham,
West Sussex RH13 0RL. Tel: 01403 790294
Email: office@abrs-info.org
Website: www.abrs-info.org

Association of Colleges (AOC)

Created in 1996 to promote the interest of further education colleges in England and Wales.

2-5 Stedham Place, London WC1A 1HU
Tel: 0207 034 9900
Email: enquiries@aoc.co.uk
Website: www.aoc.co.uk

Association of Governing Bodies of Independent Schools (AGBIS)

AGBIS supports and advises governing bodies of schools in the independent sector on all aspects of governance.

Registered charity No. 1108756
Association of Governing Bodies of Independent Schools,
3 Codicote Road, Welwyn, Hertfordshire AL6 9LY
Tel: 01438 840730
Email: office@agbis.org.uk
Website: www.agbis.org.uk

Association of Employment and Learning Providers (AELP)

AELP's purpose is to influence the education and training agenda. They are the voice of independent learning providers throughout England.
Association of Employment and Learning Providers,
2nd Floor, 9 Apex Court, Bradley Stoke, Bristol, BS32 4JT
Tel: 0117 986 5389
Email: enquiries@aelp.org.uk
Website: www.aelp.org.uk

The Association of School and College Leaders (ASCL)

Formerly the Secondary Heads Association, the ASCL is a professional association for secondary school and college leaders.
130 Regent Road, Leicester LE1 7PG
Tel: 0116 299 1122
Fax: 0116 299 1123
Email: info@ascl.org.uk
Website: www.ascl.org.uk

Boarding Schools' Association (BSA)

For information on the BSA see editorial on page 38

The British Accreditation Council (BAC)

The British Accreditation Council (BAC) has now been the principal accrediting body for the independent further and higher education and training sector for nearly 30 years. BAC-accredited institutions in the UK now number more than 300, offering everything from website design to yoga to equine dentistry, as well as more standard qualifications in subjects such as business, IT, management and law. As well as our accreditation of institutions offering traditional teaching, BAC has developed a new accreditation scheme for providers offering online, distance and blended learning. Some students may also look to study outside the UK at one of the institutions holding BAC international accreditation.
14 Devonshire Square, London, EC2M 4YT
Tel: 0300 330 1400
Email: info@the-bac.org
Website: www.the-bac.org

The British Association for Early Childhood Education (BAECE)

Promotes quality provision for all children from birth to eight in whatever setting they are placed. Publishes booklets and organises conferences for those interested in early years education and care. Registered charity Nos. 313082; SC039472
54 Clarendon Road, Watford, WD17 1DU
Tel: 01923 438 995
Email: office@early-education.org.uk
Website: www.early-education.org.uk

The Choir Schools' Association (CSA)

Represents 44 schools attached to cathedrals, churches and college chapels, which educate cathedral and collegiate choristers.
CSA Information Officer, Village Farm, The Street, Market Weston, Diss, Norfolk IP22 2NZ
Tel: 01359 221333
Email: info@choirschools.org.uk
Website: www.choirschools.org.uk

CIFE

CIFE is the professional association for independent sixth form and tutorial colleges accredited by the British Accreditation Council (BAC), the Independent Schools Council or the DfE (Ofsted). Member colleges specialise in preparing students for GCSE and A level (AS and A2) in particular and university entrance in general.

The aim of the association is to provide a forum for the exchange of information and ideas, and for the promotion of best practice, and to safeguard adherence to strict standards of professional conduct and ethical propriety. Further information can be obtained from CIFE:
Tel: 0208 767 8666
Email: enquiries@cife.org.uk
Website: www.cife.org.uk

Council of British International Schools (COBIS)

COBIS is a membership association of British schools of quality worldwide and is committed to a stringent process of quality assurance for all its member schools. COBIS is a member of the Independent Schools Council (ISC) of the United Kingdom.
COBIS, 55–56 Russell Square, Bloomsbury,
London WC1B 4HP
Tel: 020 3826 7190
Email: pa@cobis.org.uk
Website: www.cobis.org.uk

Council of International Schools (CIS)

CIS is a not-for-profit organisation committed to supporting its member schools and colleges in achieving and delivering the highest standards of international education. CIS provides accreditation to schools, teacher and leader recruitment and best practice development. CIS Higher Education assists member colleges and universities in recruiting a diverse profile of qualified international students.
Schipholweg 113, 2316 XC Leiden, The Netherlands.
Tel: +31 71 524 3300
Email: info@cois.org
Website: www.cois.org

Dyslexia Action (DA)

A registered, educational charity (No. 268502), which has established teaching and assessment centres and conducts teacher-training throughout the UK. The aim of the institute is to help people with dyslexia of all ages to overcome their difficulties in learning to read, write and spell and to achieve their potential.
Dyslexia Action Training and Guild, Centurion House,
London Road, Staines-upon-Thames TW18 4AX
Tel: 01784 222 304
Email: trainingcourses@dyslexiaaction.org.uk
Website: www.dyslexiaaction.org.uk

European Association for International Education (EAIE)

A not-for-profit organisation aiming for internationalisation in higher education in Europe. It has a membership of over 1800.
PO Box 11189, 1001 GD Amsterdam, The Netherlands
Tel: +31 20 344 5100
Fax: +31 20 344 5119
Email: info@eaie.org
Website: www.eaie.org

ECIS (European Collaborative for International Schools)

ECIS is a membership organisation which provides services to support professional development, good governance and leadership in international schools.
24 Greville Street,
London, EC1N 8SS
Tel: 020 7824 7040
Email: ecis@ecis.org
Website: www.ecis.org

The Girls' Day School Trust (GDST)

The Girls' Day School Trust (GDST) is one of the largest, longest-established and most successful groups of independent schools in the UK, with 4000 staff and over 20,000 students between the ages of 3 and 18. As a charity that owns and runs a family of 26 schools in England and Wales, it reinvests all its income into its schools for the benefit of the pupils. With a long history of pioneering innovation in the education of girls, the GDST now also educates boys in some of its schools, and has two coeducational sixth form colleges. Registered charity No. 306983
10 Bressenden Place, London, SW1E 5DH
Tel: 020 7393 6666
Email: info@wes.gdst.net
Website: www.gdst.net

Girls' Schools Association (GSA)

For information on the GSA see editorial on page 39

The Headmasters' and Headmistresses' Conference (HMC)

For information on the HMC see editorial on page 40

Human Scale Education (HSE)

An educational reform movement aiming for small education communities based on democracy, fairness and respect. Registered charity No. 1000400
Email: contact@hse.org.uk
Website: www.hse.org.uk

The Independent Association of Prep Schools (IAPS)

For further information about IAPS see editorial on page 41

The Independent Schools Association (ISA)

For further information about ISA see editorial on page 42

The Independent Schools' Bursars Association (ISBA)

Exists to support and advance financial and operational performance in independent schools. The ISBA is a charitable company limited by guarantee.
Company No. 6410037; registered charity No. 1121757
Bluett House, Unit 11–12 Manor Farm, Cliddesden, nr Basingstoke, Hampshire RG25 2JB
Tel: 01256 330369
Email: office@theisba.org.uk
Website: www.theisba.org.uk

The Independent Schools Council (ISC)

The Independent Schools Council exists to promote choice, diversity and excellence in education; the development of talent at all levels of ability; and the widening of opportunity for children from all backgrounds to achieve their potential. Its 1280 member schools educate more than 500,000 children at all levels of ability and from all socioeconomic classes. Nearly a third of children in ISC schools receive help with fees. The Governing Council of ISC contains representatives from each of the eight ISC constituent associations listed below.
See also page 44.

Members:
Association of Governing Bodies of Independent Schools (AGBIS)
Girls' Schools Association (GSA)
Headmasters' and Headmistresses' Conference (HMC)
Independent Association of Prep Schools (IAPS)
Independent Schools Association (ISA)
Independent Schools Bursars' Association (ISBA)
The Society of Heads
The council also has close relations with the BSA, COBIS, SCIS and WISC.

First Floor, 27 Queen Anne's Gate, London, SW1H 9BU
Tel: 020 7766 7070
Fax: 020 7766 7071
Email: research@isc.co.uk
Website: www.isc.co.uk

The Independent Schools Examinations Board (ISEB)

Details of the Common Entrance examinations are obtainable from:
Independent Schools Examinations Board,
Endeavour House, Crow Arch Lane, Ringwood BH24 1HP
Tel: 01425 470555
Email: enquiries@iseb.co.uk
Website: www.iseb.co.uk
Copies of past papers can be purchased from Galore Park: www.galorepark.co.uk

The Inspiring Futures Foundation (IFF)

The IFF provides careers education and guidance to schools and students. Professional support and training is available to school staff and our Futurewise programme provides individual, web-based, support for students and their parents. Career/subject insight courses, gap-year fairs and an information service are additional elements of the service.
Tel: 01491 820381
Email: helpline@inspiringfutures.org.uk
Website: www.inspiringfutures.org.uk

International Baccalaureate (IB)

For full information about the IB see full entry on page 194.

International Schools Theatre Association (ISTA)

International body of teachers and students of theatre, run by teachers for teachers. Registered charity No. 1050103
3 Omega Offices, 14 Coinagehall St,
Helston, Cornwall TR13 8EB
Tel: 01326 560398
Email: office@ista.co.uk
Website: www.ista.co.uk

Maria Montessori Institute (MMI)

Authorised by the Association Montessori Internationale (AMI) to run their training course in the UK. Further information is available from:
26 Lyndhurst Gardens, Hampstead, London NW3 5NW
Tel: 020 7435 3646
Email: schools@mariamontessori.org
Website: www.mariamontessori.org

The National Association of Independent Schools & Non-Maintained Schools (NASS)

A membership organisation working with and for special schools in the voluntary and private sectors within the UK.
Registered charity No. 1083632
PO Box 705, York YO30 6WW
Tel/Fax: 01904 624446
Email: krippon@nasschools.org.uk
Website: www.nasschools.org.uk

National Day Nurseries Association (NDNA)

A national charity that aims to promote quality in early years. Registered charity No. 1078275
NDNA, National Early Years Enterprise Centre,
Longbow Close, Huddersfield, West Yorkshire HD2 1GQ
Tel: 01484 407070
Fax: 01484 407060
Email: info@ndna.org.uk
Website: www.ndna.org.uk

NDNA Cymru, Office 3, Crown House, 11 Well Street,
Ruthin, Denbighshire LL15 1AE
Tel: 01824 707823
Email: wales@ndna.org.uk

NDNA Scotland, The Mansfield Traquair Centre,
15 Mansfield Place, Edinburgh EH3 6BB
Tel: 0131 516 6967
Email: scot@ndna.org.uk

National Foundation for Educational Research (NFER)

NFER is the UK's largest independent provider of research, assessment and information services for education, training and children's services. Its clients include UK government departments and agencies at both national and local levels. NFER is a not-for-profit organisation and a registered charity No. 313392
Head Office, The Mere, Upton Park,
Slough, Berkshire SL1 2DQ
Tel: 01753 574123
Fax: 01753 691632
Email: enquiries@nfer.ac.uk
Website: www.nfer.ac.uk

Potential Plus UK

Potential Plus UK is an independent charity that supports the social, emotional and learning needs of children with high learning potential of all ages and backgrounds. Registered charity No. 313182
Room 5 The Mansion, Sherwood Drive, Bletchley, Milton Keynes, Buckinghamshire MK3 6EB
Tel: 01908 646433
Email: amazingchildren@potentialplusuk.org
Website: www.potentialplusuk.org

Round Square

An international group of schools formed in 1967 following the principles of Dr Kurt Hahn, the founder of Salem School in Germany, and Gordonstoun in Scotland. The Round Square, named after Gordonstoun's 17th century circular building in the centre of the school, now has more than 100 member schools. Registered charity No. 327117
Round Square, First Floor, Morgan House, Madeira Walk, Windsor SL4 1EP
Tel: 01474 709843
Website: www.roundsquare.org

Royal National Children's SpringBoard Foundation

On 1 July 2017 the Royal National Children's Foundation (RNCF) merged with The SpringBoard Bursary Foundation to create the Royal National Children's SpringBoard Foundation ('Royal SpringBoard'). The newly merged charity gives life-transforming bursaries to disadvantaged and vulnerable children from across the UK.
Buckingham Suite, 7 Grosvenor Gardens,
London SW1W 0BD
Tel: 020 3405 3630
Email: admin@royalspringboard.org.uk
Website: www.royalspringboard.org.uk

School Fees Independent Advice (SFIA)

For further information about SFIA, see editorial page 46

Schools Music Association of Great Britain (SMA)

The SMA is a national 'voice' for music in education. It is now part of the Incorporated Society of Musicians Registered charity No. 313646
Website: www.ism.org/sma

Scottish Council of Independent Schools (SCIS)

Representing more than 70 independent, fee-paying schools in Scotland, the Scottish Council of Independent Schools (SCIS) is the foremost authority on independent schools in Scotland and offers impartial information, advice and guidance to parents. Registered charity No. SC018033
61 Dublin Street, Edinburgh EH3 6NL
Tel: 0131 556 2316
Email: info@scis.org.uk
Website: www.scis.org.uk

Society of Education Consultants (SEC)

The Society is a professional membership organisation that supports management consultants who specialise in education and children's services. The society's membership includes consultants who work as individuals, in partnerships or in association with larger consultancies.
SEC, Bellamy House, 13 West Street, Cromer NR27 9HZ
Tel: 0330 323 0457
Email: administration@sec.org.uk
Website: www.sec.org.uk

The Society of Heads

For full information see editorial on page 43

State Boarding Forum (SBF)

For full information about the SBF see editorial on page 38

Steiner Waldorf Schools Fellowship (SWSF)

Representing Steiner education in the UK and Ireland, the SWSF has member schools and early years centres in addition to interest groups and other affiliated organisations. Member schools offer education for children within the normal range of ability, aged 3 to 18.
Registered charity No. 295104
Steiner Waldorf Schools Fellowship® Ltd, Suite 1, 3rd Floor, Copthall House, 1 New Road, Stourbridge, West Midlands, DY8 1PH
Tel: 01384 374116
Email: admin@steinerwaldorf.org
Website: www.steinerwaldorf.org

Support and Training in Prep Schools (SATIPS)

SATIPS aims to support teachers in the independent and maintained sectors of education. Registered charity No. 313688
West Routengill, Walden, West Burton, Leyburn, North Yorkshire, DL8 4LF
Website: www.satips.org

The Tutors' Association

The Tutors' Association is the professional body for tutoring and wider supplementary education sector in the UK. Launched in 2013, they have over 850 members, including Individual and Corporate Members representing some 30,000 tutors throughout the UK.
Tel: 01628 306108
Email: info@thetutorsassociation.org.uk
Website: www.thetutorsassociation.org.uk

UCAS (Universities and Colleges Admissions Service)

UCAS is the organisation responsible for managing applications to higher education courses in England, Scotland, Wales and Northern Ireland. Registered charity Nos. 1024741 and SC038598
Rosehill, New Barn Lane, Cheltenham, Gloucestershire GL52 3LZ
Tel: 0371 468 0 468
Website: www.ucas.com

UKCISA – The Council for International Student Affairs

UKCISA is the UK's national advisory body serving the interests of international students and those who work with them. Registered charity No. 1095294
Website: www.ukcisa.org.uk

United World Colleges (UWC)

UWC was founded in 1962 and their philosophy is based on the ideas of Dr Kurt Hahn (see Round Square Schools). Registered charity No. 313690.
UWC International, Third Floor, 55 New Oxford Street, London, WC1A 1BS, UK
Tel: 020 7269 7800
Fax: 020 7405 4374
Email: info@uwcio.uwc.org
Website: www.uwc.org

World-Wide Education Service of CfBT Education Trust (WES)

A leading independent service which provides home education courses worldwide.
Waverley House, Penton,
Carlisle, Cumbria CA6 5QU
Tel: 01228 577123
Email: office@weshome.com
Website: www.weshome.com

Glossary

Glossary

ACETS	Awards and Certificates in Education
AEA	Advanced Extension Award
AEB	Associated Examining Board for the General Certificate of Education
AEGIS	Association for the Education and Guardianship of International Students
AGBIS	Association of Governing Bodies of Independent Schools
AHIS	Association of Heads of Independent Schools
AJIS	Association of Junior Independent Schools
ALP	Association of Learning Providers
ANTC	The Association of Nursery Training Colleges
AOC	Association of Colleges
AP	Advanced Placement
ASCL	Association of School & College Leaders
ASL	Additional and Specialist Learning
ATI	The Association of Tutors Incorporated
AQA	Assessment and Qualification Alliance/ Northern Examinations and Assessment Board
BA	Bachelor of Arts
BAC	British Accreditation Council for Independent Further and Higher Education
BAECE	The British Association for Early Childhood Education
BD	Bachelor of Divinity
BEA	Boarding Educational Alliance
BEd	Bachelor of Education
BLitt	Bachelor of Letters
BPrimEd	Bachelor of Primary Education
BSA	Boarding Schools' Association
BSc	Bachelor of Science
BTEC	Range of work-related, practical programmes leading to qualifications equivalent to GCSEs and A levels awarded by Edexcel
Cantab	Cambridge University
CATSC	Catholic Association of Teachers in Schools and Colleges
CCEA	Council for the Curriculum, Examination and Assessment
CDT	Craft, Design and Technology
CE	Common Entrance Examination
CEAS	Children's Education Advisory Service
CertEd	Certificate of Education
CIE	Cambridge International Examinations
CIFE	Conference for Independent Education
CIS	Council of International Schools
CISC	Catholic Independent Schools' Conference
CLAIT	Computer Literacy and Information Technology
CNED	Centre National d'enseignement (National Centre of long distance learning)

COBIS	Council of British International)
CSA	The Choir Schools' Association
CST	The Christian Schools' Trust
DfE	Department for Education (formerly DfES and DCFS)
DipEd	Diploma of Education
DipTchng	Diploma of Teaching
EAIE	European Association for International Education
ECIS	European Council of International Schools
EdD	Doctor of Education
Edexcel	GCSE Examining group, incorporating Business and Technology Education Council (BTEC) and University of London Examinations and Assessment Council (ULEAC)
EFL	English as a Foreign Language
ELAS	Educational Law Association
EPQ	Extended Project qualification
ESL	English as a Second Language
FCoT	Fellow of the College of Teachers (TESOL)
FEFC	Further Education Funding Council
FRSA	Fellow of the Royal Society of Arts
FSMQ	Free-Standing Mathematics Qualification
GCE	General Certificate of Education
GCSE	General Certificate of Secondary Education
GDST	Girls' Day School Trust
GNVQ	General National Vocational Qualifications
GOML	Graded Objectives in Modern Languages
GSA	Girls' Schools Association
GSVQ	General Scottish Vocational Qualifications
HMC	Headmasters' and Headmistresses' Conference
HMCJ	Headmasters' and Headmistresses' Conference Junior Schools
HNC	Higher National Certificate
HND	Higher National Diploma
IAPS	Independent Association of Prep Schools
IB	International Baccalaureate
ICT	Information and Communication Technology
IFF	Inspiring Futures Foundation (formerly ISCO)
IGCSE	International General Certificate of Secondary Education
INSET	In service training
ISA	Independent Schools Association
ISBA	Independent Schools' Bursars' Association
ISCis	Independent Schools Council information service
ISC	Independent Schools Council
ISEB	Independent Schools Examination Board
ISST	International Schools Sports Tournament
ISTA	International Schools Theatre Association

ITEC	International Examination Council
JET	Joint Educational Trust
LA	Local Authority
LISA	London International Schools Association
MA	Master of Arts
MCIL	Member of the Chartered Institute of Linguists
MEd	Master of Education
MIoD	Member of the Institute of Directors
MLitt	Master of Letters
MSc	Master of Science
MusD	Doctor of Music
MYP	Middle Years Programme
NABSS	National Association of British Schools in Spain
NAGC	National Association for Gifted Children
NAHT	National Association of Head Teachers
NAIS	National Association of Independent Schools
NASS	National Association of Independent Schools & Non-maintained Special Schools
NDNA	National Day Nurseries Association
NEASC	New England Association of Schools and Colleges
NFER	National Federation of Educational Research
NPA	National Progression Award
NQ	National Qualification
NQF	National Qualifications Framework
NQT	Newly Qualified Teacher
NVQ	National Vocational Qualifications
OCR	Oxford, Cambridge and RSA Examinations
OLA	Online Language Assessment for Modern Languages
Oxon	Oxford
PGCE	Post Graduate Certificate in Education
PhD	Doctor of Philosophy
PL	Principal Learning
PNEU	Parents' National Education Union
PYP	Primary Years Programme
QCA	Qualifications and Curriculum Authority
QCF	Qualifications and Credit Framework
RSIS	The Round Square Schools
SAT	Scholastic Aptitude Test
SATIPS	Support & Training in Prep Schools/Society of Assistant Teachers in Prep Schools
SBSA	State Boarding Schools Association
SCE	Service Children's Education
SCIS	Scottish Council of Independent Schools
SCQF	Scottish Credit and Qualifications Framework
SEC	The Society of Educational Consultants
SEN	Special Educational Needs
SFCF	Sixth Form Colleges' Forum
SFIA	School Fees Insurance Agency Limited
SFIAET	SFIA Educational Trust

SMA	Schools Music Association
SoH	The Society of Heads
SQA	Scottish Qualifications Authority
STEP	Second Term Entrance Paper (Cambridge)
SVQ	Scottish Vocational Qualifications
SWSF	Steiner Waldorf Schools Fellowship
TABS	The Association of Boarding Schools
TISCA	The Independent Schools Christian Alliance
TOEFL	Test of English as a Foreign Language
UCAS	Universities and Colleges Admissions Service for the UK
UCST	United Church Schools Trust
UKLA	UK Literacy Association
UKCISA	The UK Council for International Education
UWC	United World Colleges
WISC	World International Studies Committee
WJEC	Welsh Joint Education Committee
WSSA	Welsh Secondary Schools Association

Index

Index